# PRESERVED RAILWAY

# PRESERVED RAILWAY CARRIAGES

The complete stock-book of all known standard gauge carriages and passenger-rated vans preserved in Great Britain and Ireland

## John Lloyd & Murray Brown

Silver Link Publishing Ltd

This book is respectfully dedicated to those involved in preserving or restoring rolling stock, whether it be for commercial purposes or for the furtherance of a preserved railway. All of us owe so much for their selfless and often inadequately acknowledged efforts, and if it were not for them the generations that follow would not be able to savour the joys of travel in an historical vehicle behind a steam or diesel locomotive.

First published in March 1992
Reprinted August 1992

A catalogue record for this book is available from the British Library.

ISBN 0 947971 75 0

Silver Link Publishing Ltd
Unit 5, Home Farm Close
Church Street
Wadenhoe
Peterborough PE8 5NT

Typeset by G&M, Raunds, Northamptonshire
Printed and bound in Great Britain by
Woolnough Bookbinding Ltd,
Irthlingborough, Northamptonshire

Andy Hamper measures up the end of Thompson BG No E110 ready for its new panelling at Pickering on 31 December 1991. Progress on LNER-designed coaches has been transformed on the North Yorkshire Moors Railway following the completion of the carriage shed and the willingness of the C&W Engineer, Brian Crouch, to permit volunteers to restore their coaches in the railway's carriage shed. *Murray Brown*

# CONTENTS

# ACKNOWLEDGEMENTS

This record would not be so extensive were it not for helping hands extended over many years. The number of people who have contributed makes for a 'Roll of Honour' far too extensive to be listed herein, but we are duty bound to extend heartfelt personal thanks to the foremost few amongst these stalwarts.

To David Rouse, that 'founding father' of preservation. His foresight nearly 30 years ago resulted in the survival of what is now a unique centenarian and his extensive notes from that era contributed so much.

To Philip Millard and David Jenkinson, authors of note themselves and without whom the LMS section would have been appreciably less accurate.

To Colin Holliday and W. Sullivan-Boomer, whose invaluable help resulted in an Irish section that no longer looked totally insignificant.

To Roger Butcher, whose devotion to BR's departmental stock has rewarded the entire railway fraternity and who checked so much on our behalf.

To Peter Hall, whose Lineside lists first itemised BR's less salubrious stock and who set standards of accuracy for us all to attempt to follow.

To Roger Crombleholme, who with Terry Kirtland produced the 'Steam Yearbook' that led the field — they started a ball rolling, in more ways than one.

And finally we must not forget the 'home team', especially the distaff side. To Helen and to Sonia, who smilingly tolerated the hours their men spent distracted by railway enthusiasm!

# PREFACE

What started more than a decade ago as a hobby became, with the passage of time and the intervention of fate, a collective project. Many thousands of hours of research (and as many miles!) have been devoted to it, the intention being that all information within should be as accurate as possible, but six months' enforced abstention from the task in 1990 — encompassing a mad dash across the Atlantic in a marine feline! — meant that the reins briefly slipped through my fingers at a somewhat crucial stage.

Quite apart from the on-going task of accumulating and improving the wealth of data, keeping it all up to date was a headache of Topsy-like proportions. Most of those contacted extended every assistance, but I must express severe disappointment at the number of requests for information that produced a less than satisfactory response, despite the mandatory SAE and a donation. Surprisingly, the small-fry were usually most conscientious correspondents; even more so, it was amongst the largest and most respected organisations that a lack of any response whatsoever was found. I do recognise the problems of overstretched human resources, which seem to proliferate as the square (or is it the cube?) of the number of items in a group's charge, but that one of the most noteworthy societies having a large collection of coaching stock failed to reply to four out of five letters (each with a donation) did little to foster my support! Let us hope that this criticism goes some way towards improving their efforts regarding correspondence in future.

One of the unexpected facts to emerge from our research was the number of owning groups or societies turning to the market place for income. Using the woodworking skills developed during their formative years they are now able to contract their services out, thereby earning the funds needed to rejuvenate a growing collection of decrepit vehicles in their charge. Praiseworthy indeed, and more power to their elbows!

Collating so much information, from what was often a wealth of insignificant observations, had undoubted problems. Mistaken number reporting, be it caused by imperfect research or typographical error, was a not uncommon problem. If not resolved it can lead to accidental duplication, so our deep gratitude to correspondents was tempered somewhat by the number of ambiguities that arose, some of which remain unsolved. We can also anticipate the occasional omission resulting from lack of observation and/or publicity. Since the upsurge of interest in what trails behind a locomotive is a relatively recent phenomenon this is inevitable, so although it was always my wish that our final product should be error-free it would be unrealistic not to expect some inadvertent mistakes. For these the blame must be mine alone, as researcher and compiler, and I extend heartfelt apologies to those affected.

Over the last decade we have seen a proliferation in 'private owner' coaches on the main line, amongst them some exquisitely restored antiques. Whilst the vintage coaches formerly operated by the Great Western Society, Severn Valley and Scottish RPS are now confined to home base, others have taken their place. Most prominent in this area are undoubtedly the vehicles running within the 'Orient Express' and 'Royal Scotsman' luxury trains, but there are others too. British Rail's sympathetic stance to the presence of wooden vehicles on their tracks was of major importance, though their insistence on a cladding of steel sheet for the expensively rebuilt Gresley Full Brake in the 'Orient Express' was the progenitor of a hardening attitude. In recent years grounded bodies were purchased with the intention of adding to these trains after restoration, but once it became clear that British Rail would not countenance indefinitely the regular operation of wooden stock these plans had rapidly to be shelved. What the fates hold is unclear: their sale for restoration to original form as a labour of love is possible, but the idea of transplanting intact interiors into the empty shells of all-steel British Rail vehicles has been mooted as the only realistic alternative! In a few cases we may see unique carriages, emerging from the workshops with 'old wine in new bottles' — if that enables the likes of the 'Orient Express' to continue we may not really be the worse for all that.

Already, at the time of writing, a number of former main-line runners are destined for long-term storage and a load more alterations are in the offing. I would love to wait for them all, just to 'get it right', but unfortunately perfection is merely a dream that comes tantalisingly close to being within one's grasp. Even an artist as eminent as David Shepherd admits that there comes a time when one must lay the brushes aside, so the decision had finally to be taken to publish as

was. Hopefully this will help cultivate the growing enthusiasm for rolling stock, but it might also stimulate you, the devotees at large, into supplying those snippets of personal knowledge that are needed to remove the remaining errors. Should enough interest be shown, it may prove viable to publish a Supplement listing any corrections and additions. If you wish to assist in this aim, please write via the publishers; all contributors would of course be individually credited.

I felt that to omit the Emerald Isle was impossible in view of the former Midland coaches there, let alone that it would somewhat decry the magnificent efforts of the RPSI, but to my regret it is somewhat less fulsome than the others. Information was rather difficult to glean at this range, though the destruction of many items became apparent when, literally at the 11th hour, a wealth of data arrived. The 'bare bones' have been included, but the data may not be as accurate as in other sections.

Finally I must thank my co-author Murray, a preservationist himself, who has done so much for carriage buffs in the periodical press — without the wealth of his data, his contacts and his support, a once less worthy manuscript might never have seen the light of day.

John Lloyd
Ramsgate, September 1991

# INTRODUCTION

The Locomotive has always been the centre of attraction. T'was ever thus; t'will always be. However, behind the bunker, tender, or in a few cases the diesel's rear cab, is another world. It is a world not widely appreciated, but one which holds a fascination for a growing number of enthusiasts and the general public. The latter may surprise you, but when Barry Cogar, General Manager of the Paignton & Dartmouth Steam Railway, advises that the public makes a bee-line for a historic coach in preference to the standard Mk 1, then the proof is there!

When you consider the plethora of publications on traction, be it steam or diesel, and the

multitudes of books on individual classes, it puts things in perspective when this publication you are holding may well be the first attempt at actually cataloguing the thousands of extant vehicles around the country.

Note the word extant! Indeed, the title of the book was itself a problem, for the authors readily acknowledge that many 'preserved' coaches are in fact destined to remain derelict and, in some cases, be scrapped. It may seem sacrilege, but some vehicles are now being bought so as to be scrapped, yet by so doing yield spares to restore sister vehicles. Already some Hawksworth and Gresley coaches have met their end in this way.

They gave their lives so that others may live.

An elderly gentleman was looking at some young men restoring the battered hulk of Gresley Buffet Car No 641 at Pickering station. He was shown around and told the young restorers that he helped build the coach. Not only that, he marked and laid out the LNER Coronation Beavertail Observation Cars. This was how 82-year-old Les Browning became President of the LNER Coach Association, and he hopes to live long enough to ride in the Buffet on its inaugural run after restoration. All over the country the same thing is happening.

It is a thankless task being a coach preservationist. It is not long after a vehicle has arrived on a private line that the complaints and criticisms start. Vehicles are classed as 'eyesores' and their owners are castigated for making what appears to be negligible progress. Transformation of a derelict coach can take place almost in one week for, following the time-consuming and exhaustive frame repairs which can literally take several years, when the panelling is applied a former 'hen-hut' suddenly becomes a coach. Throw in an overhauled roof and the external body is something to behold. Then the hypocrisy starts from those same critics who now change their tune!

Around the country there can now be found on practically all private railways a thriving Carriage & Wagon (C&W) Department. Invariably it is under-resourced from a railway's management, which prefers to throw money at the Locomotive Department, completely forgetting that it is the actual coaches that are used by the public, who then judge that railway on the state of their journey. Even the 'First Division' private lines in Britain could still do more to provide their C&W men with the tools for the job. It is a salutary thought that some vehicles of Britain's ever-growing private scene are running astonishing mileages — for instance, on one notable concern, carriages in 1991 were rostered to run 269,000 miles! This raises the question of preservation or conservation, for coaches running hundreds of miles every year soon degenerate and the battle for their upkeep starts again.

Let us not forget the humble British Rail Mk 1 coach. Whilst the wooden-bodied coaches are lovingly restored, their stablemate Mk 1s are invariably the 'bread and butter' vehicles of so many private railways. Nevertheless, they come in numerous types and liveries which all contribute to the carriage world. Dating from 1951, these coaches are themselves venerable and should not be dismissed lightly. Nor should BR's blue and grey livery, which itself is now history! The major overhauls now being undertaken on Mk 1s, involving extensive body rebuilding, are an eye-opener to anyone who has the chance to see such expertise in action. Perhaps the strangest irony of coach restoration is that, in so many instances, the people restoring the vehicles are not old enough to remember them running in as-built condition. What is it that drives them ever on? Besides the hard graft, there is a social world which is a vital ingredient of the coach preservationist. Here the benefits of a Gresley over a Bulleid design are disected and the verdict reached.

It is thanks to British Rail that so much of railway carriage history has survived long enough for it to pass into private hands. With so many gems surviving as Departmental vehicles (although in most cases much altered from their original form), the engineering fleets continue to provide 50-year-old coaches full of challenge to the growing band of preservationists.

Look out for the body hunters too! These intrepid heroes decide to boldly go where no coach hunter has been before, and in the process split the infinitive! However, can you imagine their unadulterated joy when they stumble upon one half of a Stanier non-corridor Third with all its compartment fittings still intact?

History starts yesterday, and it is hard to believe that already a number of Mk 2 coaches are now in private hands. What we all thought in 1966 were plastic soulless vehicles are gradually becoming interesting. Can you imagine anyone ever wanting to buy and restore a present-day Mk 4, with its all-pervading depressing grey plastic environment?

It is to be hoped that this publication provides you not only with hours of pleasure but also some surprise at just how much rolling stock has been saved for future generations. With the many van types which are classified as coaching stock, notwithstanding the growing number of multiple-unit coaches saved from BR, the total number of coaching stock vehicles extant now runs to several thousand. If this book has given you some insight and pleasure, then why not join in the fun and become a part or whole owner of a coach? Not only is it an investment, but to ride in your own vehicle makes you a man, or woman, of distinction! Meanwhile, the authors have found their own Forth Bridge in this book and so we must move on — just as so many coaches are doing right now.

Murray Brown
Peterborough, September 1991

# NOTES ON THE DATA

The book is divided into sections. Vehicles from the 'Big Four' created by the 1923 Grouping are followed by those of British Rail, Pullman, Minor and Irish Companies, and finally the few Replicas. At the end there are lists of all Departmental and Plated numbers appearing in the main text, the latter borne by private owner coaches running on the main line, and together they offer other means of accessing information.

For convenience, the order in which the 'Big Four' appear is per Ian Allan's ABC of Locomotives, with which so many of us grew up, ie GWR, SR, LMS, then LNER. Within each section the pre-Grouping vehicles appear first, by owning company in alphabetical order, then the post-Grouping vehicles. Normally the determining factor in some borderline cases is the first number painted on, so (for example) a coach built by the Southern to a Brighton design will appear in the LBSCR list unless its first painted number was in the SR series. This leaves only those vehicles which underwent a major rebuild (often with a new underframe) which are generally listed in their later guise with a reference to their original form appearing in the Remarks.

## Entries
The most difficult question of all is how on earth does one assess whether a coach is 'preserved'! Generally speaking, the following policy was adopted on what should be included.

Vehicles sold to a railway preservation organisation or individual supporter are all included, whatever the purpose, even if they have been subsequently scrapped, whereas those sold for non-railway use only appear if intended for use by the public or for display after restoration. Needless to say this still left some puzzles, so for completeness the 'Heritage' stock retained by British Rail for special use had to go in (ie the '4-SUB', Class 303 'Blue Train' and Class 306) and the 'Travelling College' vehicles crept in too.

Part-bodies obtained merely for spares are included only if another part of the same body remains extant.

## Numbers and Dates
Each vehicle is listed by its original number, or its first known number if prior ones are unidentified. Parentheses enclose a number allocated but never painted on. Where the date that a change of number was painted on is uncertain, the date of the re-numbering scheme is shown (eg 1933 for the LMS). A small 'c' (for circa) before a number or date indicates that the figure is approximate, and an 'x' is used in place of an uncertain figure (eg 195x is used where a date is known only to lie between 1950 and 1959). Vehicles for which no known identity is available, those reported preserved but which remain unconfirmed, and those whose underframe alone has been preserved will all be found grouped together at the end of each company subsection.

In the British Rail section alone, where the 1983 renumbering scheme led to a number change this has been left undated. Instead, since the new numbers are derived from the old, an oblique line has been placed between the old and new numbers, the date of the change being left implicit in the style adopted. As an example, *Duke of Gloucester*'s Support coach appears as '14041 / 17041' since the renumbering added 3000 to the original numbers of BFKs.

Pullman Cars are listed by their Schedule Number, according to the 1960 list. Since most of Pullman's own records on the earlier cars were destroyed by fire during the War, the original authoritative work (George Behrend's *Pullman in Europe*) included a table of the Cars painstakingly recreated on the author's behalf. Subsequent research has revealed doubts about the accuracy of the Schedule Numbers in some areas of this list, but since it forms a most worthy standard reference (also utilised by more recent authors in the field) I have chosen to adhere strictly to it herein.

## Names

Apart from the Pullman Cars these are relatively scarce. Those allocated, but not painted on, are bracketed as per the numbers, and names only borne since preservation appear within inverted commas. An example of this is the Pullman Car on the Worth Valley which appears as: Car No 84 originally, then 'Lorna' and 'Mary'.

## Vehicle Type

The BR (ex-LNER) coding system has been used. Most of those in full capitals are official, the rest abbreviations (eg Insp – Inspection Saloon, Inv – Invalid Saloon, Spec – Specified in Remarks column). Those who wish to be further enlightened (or mystified?) on the BR Coaching Stock Codes can do no better than read the layman's guide written by Steve Huson in the Spring 1983 issue of 'The Wyvern' (Journal No 53 of the Midland Railway Trust) entitled 'TO B or not TO B? That is the Question'.

Some suffix letters have been used which may not normally appear in Official Stock Lists, such as 'Y' for a four-wheeled vehicle (eg the Southern PMV appears as PMVY), 'Z' for a six-wheeled vehicle or, right up to date, 'D' with a coach converted for the Disabled. No suffix is used for those few having 12 wheels (ie six-wheeled bogies) so this fact is noted in the Remarks. One word of warning — 'ROY' is a Royal Saloon, but not necessarily four-wheeled.

## Builder

Where the body and underframe were built at separate locations only the body builder is shown, thus: Location of works if built by a railway company, or firm's name if built by a contractor.

## Diagram and Lot Numbers

This was the way that the GWR, LMS and BR differentiated between their various designs, and the idea has been extended throughout.

The Diagrams quoted are, for convenience, taken from the published work on each company (for which see the Bibliography) except where otherwise shown. In some cases where Lot numbers were not used this column contains that Company's realistic alternative (eg 'Code' for GCR or 'Drawing' for LSWR, though this is not so specified on their respective pages).

## Location

Impending changes of location have been included only where firm information exists. Location alone should not be assumed to imply ownership.

Immobilised vehicles are often listed by actual location rather than by preserved railway.

Names of most preserved railways are self-explanatory, though items shown at 'Midland' are those on the Midland Railway Trust's line through Butterley in Derbyshire or in their museum at Swanwick. One possible source of ambiguity was in the Dart Valley stock, since until recent times they were allocated to either the Buckfastleigh or Kingswear lines. The situation at September 1991 is shown, vehicles being listed at either 'S Devon' or 'Torbay', though where the situation is unclear 'Dart Valley' has been retained.

Vehicles regularly operated on BR tracks are listed by their home base, but to signify that appearance there may be irregular the name of that base has been enclosed within brackets.

An asterisk appears first against the items that are part of the National Collection.

A hyphen has been used where the coach body no longer exists, though its chassis may still be around.

Tracing a few of the entries has proved impossible, especially in the case of bodies that have been sold and relocated whilst dismantled for restoration. Where no other recourse is available, a question mark has been placed against the location and further information would naturally be welcomed, via the publishers please.

## Remarks

Initially, where applicable, this shows those vehicles having a longitudinal raised centre section to their roof, this feature being broadly categorised as 'Clerestory' (pronounced 'clear-storey').

Historical details follow, in the order in which they took place.

W'.. is year of withdrawal and P'.. is year of preservation. Since some purchases fall through, while others spend a considerable time awaiting transportation, the latter is most often the year of delivery to a preserved railway unless otherwise noted herein.

## Abbreviations

AERPS – Altrincham Electric RPS; A-FRPS – Appleby-Frodingham RPS (British Steel staff & premises); B&CDRT – Belfast and County Down Railway Trust; CIWL – Compagnie Internationale des Wagons Lit; D+EG – Diesel and Electric Group; D&ARS – Downpatrick and Ardglas Railway Society (N Ireland based); EMF – Erlestoke Manor Fund; F&DRS – Fakenham and Dereham Railway Society; FSE/S – Flying Scotsman Enterprises/Services; GCRCG – Great Central Railway Coach Group; GS&WR – Great Scottish and Western Railway (operators of 'Royal Scotsman' train); GSRPS – Great Southern RPS (Eire based); GWS – Great Western Society; HIRS – Hayling Island Railway Society; HDG – Hastings Diesel Group; HLPG – Humberside Locomotive Preservation Group; HRSG   Historic Rolling Stock Group; IoWSR – Isle of Wight Steam Railway; K&ESR – Kent and East Sussex Railway; LMSSPG – LMS Steam Preservation Group; LNERCA – LNER Coach Association (based at N Yorks Moors); LURS – London Underground Railway Society; M&GNJRS – Midland and Great Northern Joint Railway Society (based at N Norfolk); MLST – Main Line Steam Trust (Great Central); MNLPS – Merchant Navy Locomotive Preservation Society (owners of 'Clan Line'); MRT – Midland Railway Trust; NRM – National Railway Museum (at York); OOU – out of use; RPS – Railway Preservation Society; RPSI – RPS of Ireland; SEG – Southern Electric Group; SLOA – Steam Locomotive Operators Association; SRPS – Scottish RPS; SST – Southern Steam Trust; TFP – Trains for Pleasure (intended train operator, since defunct); TWERPS – Tunbridge Wells and Eridge RPS; VCT – Vintage Carriages Trust; VSOE – Venice Simplon-Orient Express; WISRA – West of Ireland Steam Railway Association.

**Note** The information has been updated to 8 January 1992.

# THE GREAT WESTERN RAILWAY GROUP

| Numbers | Year | Type | Built | Diag | Lot | Location |
|---------|------|------|-------|------|-----|----------|

## ALEXANDRA (NEWPORT) DOCK & RAILWAY

| Numbers | Year | Type | Built | Diag | Lot | Location |
|---------|------|------|-------|------|-----|----------|
| 3 | 1908 | DTT | | | | Cardiff |
| 64 | 1923 | | | | | |

*Remarks:* Originally a Sleeper (No.50-57) built by Renshaw of Stoke on Trent for the 1898 season of Barnum & Bailey's 'Greatest Show on Earth'; used till end of 1906 season. Sold to ADR 1908 & converted to Autotrailer, then in use 1909-26. Body grounded as holiday chalet at Totnes till P'85 at Welsh Ind Mus

## BARRY RAILWAY

| Numbers | Year | Type | Built | Diag | Lot | Location |
|---------|------|------|-------|------|-----|----------|
| 45 | 1896 | TZ | Ashbury | 2 | | W Somerset |
| 465 | 1923 | | | | | |

*Remarks:* W'28, body grounded at Starcross. P'85

## BRISTOL & EXETER RAILWAY

| Numbers | Year | Type | Built | Diag | Lot | Location |
|---------|------|------|-------|------|-----|----------|
| ? | 1862 | ? | Metro C&W | | | Leighton Buzzard |

*Remarks:* Broad gauge body grounded at Stud Farm, Myton (Warks). P'80

## CAMBRIAN RAILWAYS

| Numbers | Year | Type | Built | Diag | Lot | Location |
|---------|------|------|-------|------|-----|----------|
| 238 | 1895 | BC | Metro C&W | S | | * NRM |
| 6277 | 1925 | | | | | |
| 40576 | 1939 | | | | | |
| 80945 | 1946 | | | | | |

*Remarks:* Became Diag 7 tri-compo before grouping. Condemned '69, P'70 & loaned to GWS till owner's death in 1982. Bequeathed to the National Collection, but remained at Didcot till moved to York in '84

| Numbers | Year | Type | Built | Diag | Lot | Location |
|---------|------|------|-------|------|-----|----------|
| 250 | 1895 | TZ | Metro C&W | | | Wallingford |
| 4109 | 1924 | | | | | |

*Remarks:* W'34, body grounded at Lambourn Downs. P'89 ?

*Others:*
Body of an unidentified 4-wheel coach is at Welsh I&M Museum, Cardiff

| Numbers | Year | Type | Built | | Diag | Lot | Location |
|---------|------|------|-------|---|------|-----|----------|

## CORNWALL RAILWAY

| 5 | 186? | TZ | | | | | * NRM |

*Remarks:* Broad gauge coach; grounded at Grampound Road as a gangers' hut after 1892. P'77, only a section (of two compartments) being restored for museum display.

## SHREWSBURY & HEREFORD RAILWAY

| ? | 1852 | FY | Wrights | | | | Llangollen |

*Remarks:* Derailed 1874 & one end damaged; body grounded nearby at Dorrington Grove. P'86

## SWINDON, MARLBOROUGH & ANDOVER RAILWAY

| ? | 188? | ?Z | | | | | Blunsdon |

*Remarks:* Body grounded at Swindon c1935. P'85

## TAFF VALE RAILWAY

37M – see Metropolitan District Railway

| 153 | ? | ? | ? | | | | Caerphilly |

*Remarks:* Body only reported here

| 203 | 1912 | BT | Gloucester | | | | Cardiff |
| 1775 | 1926 | | | | | | |

*Remarks:* Body built onto underframe of an 1889 built Third destroyed in the 1911 Hopkinstown Coke Ovens accident. Body grounded in 1928 as a farm store, the underframe presumed scrapped. P'72 by S&DR Trust, at Radstock 1974- , then sold to Welsh I&M Museum & mounted on ex-GER underframe (MOD No. 82667) in ' ?

| 220 | 1891 | BTY | Cathays | | | | Gwili |
| 3846 | 1925 | | | | | | |
| | 1990 | BTDY | Bridgend | | | | |

*Remarks:* W'26, body grounded as garden shed in Herefordshire. P'77, mounted on LNER Brake van u'frame '86 & under restoration by school children at Bridgend as Obs'n Saloon for the disabled till '90

*Others:*
Bodies of 2 unidentified bogie Compos are at Welsh I&M Museum, Cardiff

## GREAT WESTERN RAILWAY

| 4 | 1934 | DMBT | Park Royal | V | 1522 | | * Swindon Mus |

*Remarks:* P'60 as part of the National Collection & placed on loan to GWS at Didcot 196?-79. Restored by Resco 1981-4 & replaced *City of Truro* in the GWR Museum

7 – see 790

| Numbers | Year | Type | Built | Diag | Lot | Location |
|---------|------|------|-------|------|-----|----------|
| 8 | 1900 | CY | Swindon | U4 | 944 | W Somerset |
| 6008 | 1907 | | | | | |
| 747 | 1938 | TY | | | | |
| DW215 | 1946 | | | | | |

*Remarks:* Used in workmen's trains from '38, then became Mess & Tool van in '46. P'68, on Dart Valley (where known as 'Liza') till '86, then sold to GWR 813 Fund & at Bitton till '89

| | | | | | | |
|---------|------|------|-------|------|-----|----------|
| 20 | 1940 | DMBT | Swindon | A1 | 1635 | K&ESR |

*Remarks:* P'66

| | | | | | | |
|---------|------|------|-------|------|-----|----------|
| 22 | 1940 | DMBT | Swindon | A1 | 1635 | Didcot |

*Remarks:* P'63 by GWS, placed on loan to Severn Valley 1967-78

| | | | | | | |
|---------|------|------|-------|------|-----|----------|
| 38 | 1907 | DTT | Swindon | N | 1126 | Telford |

*Remarks:* P between '72 & '76

| | | | | | | |
|---------|------|------|-------|------|-----|----------|
| 64 | 1941 | BG | Swindon | K44 | 1667 | Quainton |

*Remarks:* P'78

| | | | | | | |
|---------|------|------|-------|------|-----|----------|
| 92 | 1912 | DTT | Swindon | U | 1198 | Didcot |

*Remarks:* P'71? by GWS, at Taunton till after '77

There is a veritable treasure trove of GWR-designed coaches based at the Great Western Society at Didcot depot. This is 1912-built Driving Trailer Third No 92 which was initially preserved at Taunton. The photo is dated 5 May 1990. *John Stretton*

| Numbers | Year | Type | Built | Diag | Lot | Location |
|---------|------|------|-------|------|-----|----------|
| 93 | 1908 | Spec | Swindon | R | 1142 | Didcot |
| 212 | 1936 | DTT | Swindon | A26 | 1542 | |

*Remarks:* Steam Railmotor, converted to Auto-Trailer in 1936. P pre'72 by GWS

| | | | | | | |
|---------|------|------|-------|------|-----|----------|
| 98 | 1945 | BG | Swindon | K42 | 1665 | Kidderminster |

*Remarks:* P'78 on SVR by GWR 813 Preservation Fund

| | | | | | | |
|---------|------|------|-------|------|-----|----------|
| 111 | 1934 | BG | Swindon | K41 | 1512 | Didcot |

*Remarks:* P'? by GWS

| | | | | | | |
|---------|------|------|-------|------|-----|----------|
| 160 | 1928 | DTT | Swindon | A27 | 1394 | |
| DW150342 | 1962 | | | | | |

*Remarks:* P'69 on Severn Valley, but broken up for spares the same year

| | | | | | | |
|---------|------|------|-------|------|-----|----------|
| 163 | 1928 | DTT | Swindon | A27 | 1394 | Oswestry |
| DW150315 | | | | | | |

*Remarks:* P'75 by Cambrian R S

| | | | | | | |
|---------|------|------|-------|------|-----|----------|
| 167 | 1929 | DTT | Swindon | A27 | 1394 | Dean Forest |
| 079050 | 1961 | | | | | |

*Remarks:* P'71

| | | | | | | |
|---------|------|------|-------|------|-----|----------|
| 169 | 1929 | DTT | Swindon | A27 | 1394 | Gloucs-Warks |
| 064749 | | | | | | |

*Remarks:* P'81

| | | | | | | |
|---------|------|------|-------|------|-----|----------|
| 174 | 1930 | DTT | Swindon | A28 | 1410 | Wallingford |
| DW150313 | | | | | | |

*Remarks:* P'83

| | | | | | | |
|---------|------|------|-------|------|-----|----------|
| 178 | 1930 | DTT | Swindon | A28 | 1410 | Llangollen |
| Dep'tl No ? | | | | | | |

*Remarks:* P'68 on Severn Valley, sold '75 (but there till '79), at Dean Forest till c'89

| | | | | | | |
|---------|------|------|-------|------|-----|----------|
| 184 | 1935 | BG | Swindon | K41 | 1535 | Wallingford |
| DB975157 | 1971 | | | | | |

*Remarks:* P'87 by Active Force (Swindon Ry Eng Ltd), resold '90 (to be DTBSO)

| | | | | | | |
|---------|------|------|-------|------|-----|----------|
| 185 | 1935 | BG | Swindon | K41 | 1535 | Gloucs-Warks |
| DB975158 | 1971 | | | | | |

*Remarks:* P'87 by Active Force (Swindon Ry Eng Ltd), resold '90

| | | | | | | |
|---------|------|------|-------|------|-----|----------|
| 190 | 1933 | DTT | Swindon | A30 | 1480 | Didcot |
| 079052 | 1968 | | | | | |

*Remarks:* P pre'72 by GWS

212 – see 93

| Numbers | Year | Type | Built | Diag | Lot | Location |
|---------|------|------|-------|------|-----|----------|
| 225 | 1951 | DTT | Swindon | A38 | 1736 | Torbay |

*Remarks:* P pre'72

| 228 | 1951 | DTT | Swindon | A38 | 1736 | S Devon |

*Remarks:* P pre'72

| 229 (i) 9001 | 1874 1907 | ROY | Swindon | | | |

*Remarks:* Queen Victoria's Saloon, rebuilt 1897. Scrapped 1912, but a small interior section claimed to be preserved at NRM York.

| 229 (ii) 9033 | 1899 1907 | BFO | Swindon | G32 | 924 | Shropshire |

*Remarks:* Clerestory; body later grounded. P'79 & '80 in two halves at Blunsdon, but left there Sept '88

| 231 (i) 9035 80971 | 1896 1907 1941 | BFO | Swindon | G31 | 804 | S Devon |

*Remarks:* Clerestory. P'67

| 231 (ii) | 1951 | DTT | Swindon | A38 | 1736 | Didcot |

*Remarks:* P pre'72 by GWS

| 232 | 1951 | DTT | Swindon | A38 | 1736 | Torbay |

*Remarks:* P pre'72

| 233 9002 | 1897 1907 | ROY | Swindon | G4 | 840 | Windsor |

*Remarks:* Clerestory Saloon from Diamond Jubilee Royal Train. Body grounded as a holiday chalet at Aberporth in '??. P'82 by Madame Tussauds, then restored by Resco using shortened underframe from BR Mk.1 BSK 34626 (qv)

| 235 | 1904 | BG | Swindon | K15 | 1075 | Blunsdon |

*Remarks:* Body P'86

| 238 | 1954 | DTT | Swindon | A43 | 1766 | Torbay |

*Remarks:* P pre'72

| 240 | 1954 | DTT | Swindon | A43 | 1766 | S Devon |

*Remarks:* P pre'72

| 242 9038 | 1897 1907 | SLF | Swindon | J5 | 787 | W Somerset |

*Remarks:* Clerestory. Body grounded at Burton (nr Stogursey & Williton) in 1933. P'85 & removed from within bungalow; moved to WSR '86 & mounted on u'frame ex 6912 (qv)

| Numbers | Year | Type | Built | Diag | Lot | Location |
|---------|------|------|-------|------|-----|----------|
| 243 | 1897 | SLF | Swindon | J5 | 787 | |
| 9039 | 1907 | | | | | |

*Remarks:* Clerestory. Body grounded as a holiday chalet at Aberporth in 192?. P'83, taken to Didcot by GWS but found to be in worse condition than originally thought; dismantled '84-6, providing spares for 242 above.

| 248 | 1881 | BFO | Swindon | G2 | | Swindon |
|------|------|------|---------|------|------|---------|
| 9044 | 1907 | | | | | |
| 80973 | 1936 | Insp | | | | |

*Remarks:* Clerestory. P'64 by David Rouse & Dowty RPS; at Ashchurch till '83, then Toddington till '89

| 249 | 1894 | BFO | Swindon | G3 | 745 | S Devon |
|------|------|------|---------|------|------|---------|
| 9045 | 1907 | Spec | | | | |
| 80978 | 1940 | Insp | | | | |

*Remarks:* Clerestory Family Saloon, converted to Directors' Saloon pre-1907. Rebuilt as DE's Saloon in 1940. W'63, P'65

| 254 | c1870 | TZ | | | | E Somerset |
|------|-------|------|---|---|---|-----------|

*Remarks:* Body grounded as a store at Bradford-on-Avon c1905. P'8l, to be mounted onto underframe from a BR horsebox

| 261 | 1921 | BG | Swindon | K22 | 1288 | Blaenavon |
|------|------|------|---------|------|------|-----------|

*Remarks:* P'82, intended to be restored as a catering vehicle

| 276 | 1945 | BG | Swindon | K42 | 1665 | S Devon |
|------|------|------|---------|------|------|---------|
| DB975640 | 1977 | | | | | |

*Remarks:* P'91 by DVRA members, initially at Old Oak Common; to become store/shop at Littlehempston

| 290 | 1902 | CY | Swindon | U4 | 990 | Didcot |
|------|------|------|---------|------|------|--------|
| 6290 | 1907 | | | | | |
| DW29 | 1942 | | | | | |

*Remarks:* P'72? by GWS, on Severn Valley till '73

| 295 | 1949 | BG | Swindon | K45 | 1722 | Steamtown |
|------|------|------|---------|------|------|-----------|

*Remarks:* P' by Sea Containers

| 297 | 1949 | BG | Swindon | K45 | 1722 | Pitsford |
|------|------|------|---------|------|------|----------|
| DW150354 | 1963 | | | | | |

*Remarks:* P'??

| 316 | 1950 | BG | Swindon | K45 | 1740 | Nene Valley |
|------|------|------|---------|------|------|-------------|

*Remarks:* P'80?

| 333 | 1951 | BG | Swindon | K46 | 1752 | Severn Valley |
|------|------|------|---------|------|------|---------------|

*Remarks:* P'85 by EMF

| 334 | 1951 | BG | Swindon | K46 | 1752 | Brightlingsea |
|------|------|------|---------|------|------|---------------|

*Remarks:* P'??

| Numbers | Year | Type | Built | Diag | Lot | Location |
|---|---|---|---|---|---|---|
| 416 | 1891 | BTY | Swindon | T49 | 582 | Didcot |
| 9940 | c1935 | Camp | | | | |
| DW416 | 1938 | | | | | |

*Remarks:* Became Camper some time 1935-9. P pre'72, reportedly by Somerset Railway Museum, but kept at Didcot

| | | | | | | |
|---|---|---|---|---|---|---|
| 484 | 1911 | CCT | Swindon | P18 | 1223 | Didcot |

*Remarks:* 'Monster'. To BSC Port Talbot '58, given to GWS '80, but not moved till '86

| | | | | | | |
|---|---|---|---|---|---|---|
| 485 | 1913 | CCT | Swindon | P18 | 1223 | Port Talbot |

*Remarks:* 'Monster', seen in France '45 (SHAEF train used by Gen Eisenhower '44-5). Details per 484 above, but still not moved

| | | | | | | |
|---|---|---|---|---|---|---|
| 536 | 1940 | TK | Swindon | C77 | 1623 | Didcot |
| ? plated | | | | | | |

*Remarks:* P pre'72 by GWS

| | | | | | | |
|---|---|---|---|---|---|---|
| 542 | 1931 | HBY | Swindon | N15 | 1461 | Severn Valley |

*Remarks:* Body grounded on platform at Highley

| | | | | | | |
|---|---|---|---|---|---|---|
| 565 | 1914 | CCTY | Swindon | P19 | 1238 | Didcot |
| DW150265 | | | | | | |

*Remarks:* 'Python'. P'76 by GWS

| | | | | | | |
|---|---|---|---|---|---|---|
| 594 | 1920 | PMVG | Swindon | P18 | 1265 | Gwili |

*Remarks:* 'Giant'. P by '85 ex BSC Port Talbot

| | | | | | | |
|---|---|---|---|---|---|---|
| 600 | 1954 | CCT | Swindon | P24 | 1769 | Bluebell |

*Remarks:* 'Monster'. P'79

| | | | | | | |
|---|---|---|---|---|---|---|
| 650 | 1940 | BTO | Swindon | D130 | 1644 | Foley Park |

*Remarks:* W'65 & grounded at Kerne Bridge as Scout hut, still on its underframe but with the trussing removed. P'90, restored in Brit Sugar Corp's sidings area beside SVR

| | | | | | | |
|---|---|---|---|---|---|---|
| 701 | 1879 | | Swindon | U10 | 171 | ? |

*Remarks:* Clerestory, W'38. Body P pre'82 in two halves at Stogumber, but removed as a 'kit of parts' to Colchester area '89

| | | | | | | |
|---|---|---|---|---|---|---|
| 709 | 1937 | HBY | Swindon | N16 | 1577 | S Devon |
| DW150424 | | | | | | |

*Remarks:* P'81

| | | | | | | |
|---|---|---|---|---|---|---|
| 752 | 1952 | SCVZ | Ashford | W17 | 1774 | Didcot |
| DW150420 | | | | | | |

*Remarks:* 'Beetle', Special Cattle Van. P'71 by GWS

| | | | | | | |
|---|---|---|---|---|---|---|
| 765 | 1953 | SCVZ | Stratford | | | Chappel |

| Numbers | Year | Type | Built | Diag | Lot | Location |
|---------|------|------|-------|------|-----|----------|
| 790 | 1901 | Spec | Swindon | | Wagon | S Devon |
| 7 | 1907 | | | | 293 | |

*Remarks:* Dynamometer Car with Royal Clerestory. In use till P' ?, but stored at Swindon till '65. All equipment having been removed by Swindon, vehicle is now used as a catering coach

| 796 | 1947 | TK | Swindon | C82 | 1691 | (Didcot) |
| DW150192 | 1961 | Spec | Swindon | | | |
| Test Car No.4 | | | | | | |
| 99140 plated | | | | | | |

*Remarks:* Converted '61 to Dynamometer Car for RTC Derby. P'83 at Foxfield, moved to Wolverton '88 by 71000 Loco Trust & restored for main line use by '90

| 814 | 1940 | BPOT | Swindon | L23 | 1666 | Didcot |
| DB975156 | 1972 | | | | | |

*Remarks:* P'75 by GWS

| 820 | 1887 | CZ | Swindon | U29 | 370 | * Swindon |
| 6820 | 1907 | | | | | |
| 9962 | 1935 | Camp | Swindon | | | |

*Remarks:* Clerestory Tri-Compo, 2nd Class comp't to 3rd Class c1907. To Dept'l use c1952. P'??, at Bristol Mus till moved to Swindon for restoration '89 & display '90

| 824 | 1887 | CZ | Swindon | U29 | 370 | Didcot |
| 6824 | 1907 | | | | | |

*Remarks:* Clerestory, P post'75? by GWS

| 829 | 1948 | TK | Swindon | C82 | 1691 | Severn Valley |

*Remarks:* P'68

| 933 | 1898 | B | Swindon | K14 | 883 | Didcot |

*Remarks:* P'68 on Severn Valley, bequeathed to GWS & moved south in '76

| 975 | 1902 | TY | Swindon | S9 | 992 | Didcot |
| DW108 | 1939 | | | | | |

*Remarks:* P pre'72 by GWS

| 1009 | 1951 | PMVG | Swindon | O62 | 1751 | Pitsford |

*Remarks:* 'Siphon.G'. P'87

| 1019 | 1951 | PMVG | Swindon | O62 | 1751 | Llangollen |

*Remarks:* 'Siphon.G'. P'83 by GW Steam Locomotives Group, on Gloucs-Warks till '89

| 1025 | 1952 | PMVG | Swindon | O62 | 1751 | Great Central |
| DB975832 | 1979 | | | | | |

*Remarks:* 'Siphon.G'. P'86?

| Numbers | Year | Type | Built | Diag | Lot | Location |
|---|---|---|---|---|---|---|
| 1037 | 1955 | PMVG | Swindon | O62 | 1768 | Quainton |

*Remarks:* 'Siphon.G'. P'78, at Llangollen till '85

| 1043 | 1955 | PMVG | Swindon | O62 | 1768 | Wallingford |
|---|---|---|---|---|---|---|

*Remarks:* 'Siphon.G'. P'87 by Active Force (Swindon Ry Eng Ltd), resold '90

| 1046 | 1955 | PMVG | Swindon | O62 | 1768 | W Somerset |
|---|---|---|---|---|---|---|

*Remarks:* 'Siphon.G'. Condemned due end damage, C&W store at Swindon Works till closure. P'88?

| 1047 | 1955 | PMVG | Swindon | O62 | 1768 | Blunsdon |
|---|---|---|---|---|---|---|

*Remarks:* 'Siphon.G'. P'83

| 1086<br>99234 plated | 1938 | TK | Swindon | C77 | 1593 | Severn Valley |
|---|---|---|---|---|---|---|

*Remarks:* P'69

| 1087<br>99235? plated | 1938 | TK | Swindon | C77 | 1593 | Severn Valley |
|---|---|---|---|---|---|---|

*Remarks:* P'69

| 1111 | 1938 | TK | Swindon | C77 | 1593 | Didcot |
|---|---|---|---|---|---|---|

*Remarks:* P pre'72 by GWS

| 1116<br>992?? plated | 1938 | TK | Swindon | C77 | 1593 | Severn Valley |
|---|---|---|---|---|---|---|

*Remarks:* P'69

| 1145 | 1922 | BG | Swindon | K22 | 1301 | Arley |
|---|---|---|---|---|---|---|

*Remarks:* P'73, briefly at Didcot then to SVR

| 1146<br>? plated | 1938 | TK | Swindon | C77 | 1593 | Severn Valley |
|---|---|---|---|---|---|---|

*Remarks:* P'69 by GWR 813 Pres Fund

| 1150<br>DW150241 | 1922 | BG | Swindon | K22 | 1301 | Bewdley |
|---|---|---|---|---|---|---|

*Remarks:* P'81, now houses model railway

| 1159<br><br>DW150294 | 1925<br>1945 | BG<br>Spec | Swindon<br>Swindon | K36<br>M33 | 1344<br>1481 | Didcot |
|---|---|---|---|---|---|---|

*Remarks:* Toplight BG built from WW1 Ambulance coach, becoming the Medical Officer's Saloon in 1945. P'75 by GWS

| 1184 | 1930 | BG | Swindon | K40 | 1413 | Didcot |
|---|---|---|---|---|---|---|

*Remarks:* P pre'72, bought by GWS in '86

| Numbers | Year | Type | Built | Diag | Lot | Location |
|---|---|---|---|---|---|---|
| 1199<br>DW150322 | 1928<br>1962 | PMVG | Swindon | O22 | 1396 | Blunsdon |

Remarks: 'Siphon.G'. P'83

| 1257<br>079060 | 1927<br>1961 | PMVG | Swindon | O11 | 1378 | Arley |

Remarks: 'Siphon.G'. P'76 on SVR

| 1285 | 1937 | TO | Swindon | C74 | 1575 | S Devon |

Remarks: P pre'72

| 1289 | 1937 | TO | Swindon | C74 | 1575 | Didcot |

Remarks: P pre'72, bought by GWS in '86

| 1295 | 1937 | TO | Swindon | C74 | 1575 | S Devon |

Remarks: P pre'72

| 1316 | 1950 | PMVG | Swindon | O62 | 1721 | Bodmin |

Remarks: 'Siphon.G'. P'87 by 3802 Pres Grp members & on Plym Valley till '90

| 1357<br>14571 | 1903 | T | Swindon | C22 | 1038 | Didcot |

Remarks: Clerestory. P pre'72 by GWS

| 1399<br>079062 | 1921<br>1961 | BY | Swindon | O13 | 1299 | Bewdley |

Remarks: Milk Train Brake, but originally WW1 Pharmacy Car 39035. P'67 on SVR

| 1580<br>9518 | 1903<br>1907 | RC | Swindon | H7 | 1010 | Didcot |

Remarks: Clerestory. Body mounted on u/f ex-TK 3655 (rebuilt 1921 to C31 Lot 1292 from WW1 Ambulance coach itself once TK to C31 built c1912). P post'76 by GWS

| 1645<br>079170 | 1938<br>1967 | BTK | Swindon | D127 | 1594 | Dean Forest |

Remarks: P'73 by Forest Peckett Fund, but sold to DFR in '78

| 1941<br>DW14198 | 1901<br>1945 | T | Swindon | C10 | 962 | Didcot |

Remarks: Clerestory. P'66 by GWS members, at Cardiff Canton till '69

| 2009 | 1927<br>1936 | MTY<br>MTZ | Swindon | | | Burnham-on-Crouch |

Remarks: P'90 at Mangapps Farm

| Numbers | Year | Type | Built | Diag | Lot | Location |
|---|---|---|---|---|---|---|
| 2115 DW150111 | 1919 1956 | FVY | Swindon | S8 | 1259 | Quainton |

*Remarks: P'88*

| Numbers | Year | Type | Built | Diag | Lot | Location |
|---|---|---|---|---|---|---|
| 2119 992?? plated | 1949 | TK | Gloucester | C82 | 1720 | Severn Valley |

*Remarks: P'68*

| Numbers | Year | Type | Built | Diag | Lot | Location |
|---|---|---|---|---|---|---|
| 2148 DW150403 | 1950 1968 | BTK | Metro-Cammell Wolverton | D133 | 1732 | Severn Valley |

*Remarks: P'90, mainly for its bogies*

| Numbers | Year | Type | Built | Diag | Lot | Location |
|---|---|---|---|---|---|---|
| 2180 DW150405 | 1950 1968 | BTK | Metro-Cammell Wolverton | D133 | 1732 | W Somerset |

*Remarks: P'79*

| Numbers | Year | Type | Built | Diag | Lot | Location |
|---|---|---|---|---|---|---|
| 2202 | 1950 | BTK | Metro-Cammell | D133 | 1732 | Didcot |

*Remarks: P'69 on Severn Valley, bequeathed to GWS & moved south in '76*

| Numbers | Year | Type | Built | Diag | Lot | Location |
|---|---|---|---|---|---|---|
| 2214 DW150393 | 1950 1967 | BTK | Metro-Cammell Wolverton | D133 | 1732 | Severn Valley |

*Remarks: P'90, mainly for its bogies*

**Built the year Queen Victoria died, this is eight-compartment Third No 1941, pictured nearing the end of its restoration in 1990 and still devoid of its number.** *Murray Brown*

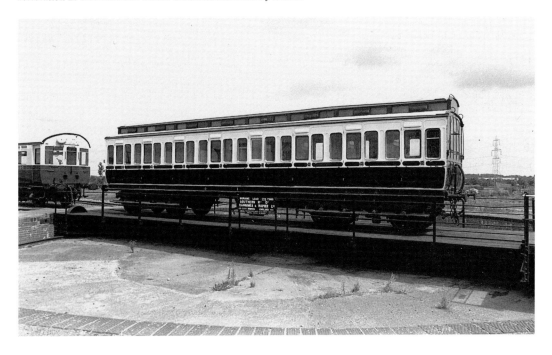

| Numbers | Year | Type | Built | Diag | Lot | Location |
|---|---|---|---|---|---|---|
| 2216<br>DW150402 | 1950<br>1968 | BTK | Metro-Cammell<br>Wolverton | D133 | 1732 | Llangollen |

Remarks: P'89, stored at Radyr till '90

| Numbers | Year | Type | Built | Diag | Lot | Location |
|---|---|---|---|---|---|---|
| 2218<br>DW150400 | 1950<br>1967 | BTK | Metro-Cammell<br>Wolverton | D133 | 1732 | Severn Valley |

Remarks: P'90, mainly for its bogies

| Numbers | Year | Type | Built | Diag | Lot | Location |
|---|---|---|---|---|---|---|
| 2225<br>DW150392 | 1950<br>1967 | BTK | Metro-Cammell<br>Wolverton | D133 | 1732 | Wallingford |

Remarks: P'87

| Numbers | Year | Type | Built | Diag | Lot | Location |
|---|---|---|---|---|---|---|
| 2232<br>DW150397 | 1950<br>1967 | BTK | Metro-Cammell<br>Wolverton | D133 | 1732 | Gloucs-Warks |

Remarks: P'86

| Numbers | Year | Type | Built | Diag | Lot | Location |
|---|---|---|---|---|---|---|
| 2233<br>DW150401 | 1950<br>1967 | BTK | Metro-Cammell<br>Wolverton | D133 | 1732 | Severn Valley |

Remarks: P'90, mainly for its bogies

| Numbers | Year | Type | Built | Diag | Lot | Location |
|---|---|---|---|---|---|---|
| 2240<br>DW150210 | 1921<br>1959 | FVY | Swindon | S9 | 1271 | Swindon |

Remarks: 'Bloater'. Pooley Van P'87

| Numbers | Year | Type | Built | Diag | Lot | Location |
|---|---|---|---|---|---|---|
| 2242<br>DW150391 | 1950<br>1970 | BTK | Metro-Cammell | D133 | 1744 | Quainton |

Remarks: P'83 by 9466 Group

| Numbers | Year | Type | Built | Diag | Lot | Location |
|---|---|---|---|---|---|---|
| 2249<br>DW150407 | 1950<br>1968 | BTK | Metro-Cammell<br>Wolverton | D133 | 1744 | |

Remarks: P'86 by Active Force (Swindon Ry Eng Ltd) but stored at Bristol Marsh Jn; fire damaged winter '89/90 & broken up mid'90 (nothing left by 18th June).

| Numbers | Year | Type | Built | Diag | Lot | Location |
|---|---|---|---|---|---|---|
| 2303<br>DW150063 | 1898 | PMVY | Swindon | Y2 | 230 | Severn Valley |

Remarks: 'Fruit.A'. P'73 by 813 Fund (orig No.47833 in freight series)

| Numbers | Year | Type | Built | Diag | Lot | Location |
|---|---|---|---|---|---|---|
| 2342 | 1892 | PMVY | Swindon | Y1 | 638 | Tyseley |

Remarks: 'Fruit.D'? (orig No.47872 in freight series)

| Numbers | Year | Type | Built | Diag | Lot | Location |
|---|---|---|---|---|---|---|
| 2356<br>DW150035 | 1892 | PMVY | Swindon | Y1 | 638 | Didcot |

Remarks: 'Fruit.B'. P'71 by GWS (orig No.47886 in freight series)

| Numbers | Year | Type | Built | Diag | Lot | Location |
|---------|------|------|-------|------|-----|----------|
| 2360 | 1911 | BTK | Swindon | D46 | 1174 | * NRM |
|  | 1932 | Spec | Swindon | D114 |  |  |
| DW139 | 1950 |  |  | Q21 |  |  |

*Remarks:* Taken over by Experimental Dept at Swindon in '28 & converted to the famous 'Whitewash Coach' in '30. P'89 by NRM, at Swindon till 5/91

| | | | | | | |
|---------|------|------|-------|------|-----|----------|
| 2370 | 1911 | BTK | Swindon | D47 | 1180 | Llangollen |
| DW309 | 1955 |  |  |  |  |  |

*Remarks:* P'81 by GW Steam Locomotives Group, on Gloucs-Warks till '89

| | | | | | | |
|---------|------|------|-------|------|-----|----------|
| 2391 | 1900 | PMVY | Swindon | Y2? | 311 | Blunsdon |
| DB975345 | 1973 |  |  |  |  |  |
| 060972 |  |  |  |  |  |  |

*Remarks:* 'Fruit.D'. P'84? (orig No.59821 in freight series)

| | | | | | | |
|---------|------|------|-------|------|-----|----------|
| 2424 | 1912 | PMVY | Swindon | Y3 | 668 | Severn Valley |
| DB975291 | 1973? |  |  |  |  |  |

*Remarks:* 'Fruit.C'. P'86 by 813 Fund

| | | | | | | |
|---------|------|------|-------|------|-----|----------|
| 2426 | 1910 | TK | Swindon | C30 | 1167 | Severn Valley |
| 9918 | 1952 | Camp | Swindon |  |  |  |

*Remarks:* P'72

| | | | | | | |
|---------|------|------|-------|------|-----|----------|
| 2434 | 1910 | TK | Swindon | C30 | 1167 | Bodmin |
| DW150038 | 1956 |  |  |  |  |  |

*Remarks:* P'71 by GWS, at Bodmin till '77 then at Bugle till '87

| | | | | | | |
|---------|------|------|-------|------|-----|----------|
| 2447 | 1911 | TK | Swindon | C31 | 1172 | Llangollen |
| DW150019 | 1956 |  |  |  |  |  |

*Remarks:* P'81 by GW Steam Locomotives Group, on Gloucs-Warks till '88

| | | | | | | |
|---------|------|------|-------|------|-----|----------|
| 2511 | 1894 | TOZ | Swindon | G20 | 740 | Didcot |
| 9317 | 1907 |  |  |  |  |  |

*Remarks:* Family Saloon. Body grounded 1936 as a dwelling at Purley? P'72 by GWS, later mounted on 6-wheel chassis from Tool Van DW109 (grounded as Antiquary Shop)

| | | | | | | |
|---------|------|------|-------|------|-----|----------|
| 2536 | 1934 | MTZ | Swindon | O39 | 1517 | Quainton |

*Remarks:* P'73 as donation from Unigate, owned by 6024 Pres Soc till '89

| | | | | | | |
|---------|------|------|-------|------|-----|----------|
| 2573 | 1914 | TK | Swindon | C32 | 1234 | W Somerset |
| 9879 | 1958 | Camp | Swindon |  |  |  |
| 'Carol' | 196? |  |  |  |  |  |

*Remarks:* P'80

| | | | | | | |
|---------|------|------|-------|------|-----|----------|
| 2578 | 1914 | TK | Swindon | C32 | 1234 | W Somerset |
| 9889 | 1957 | Camp | Swindon |  |  |  |

*Remarks:* P'71, sold to S&DR Trust circa 1980

| Numbers | Year | Type | Built | Diag | Lot | Location |
|---------|------|------|-------|------|-----|----------|
| 2617 DW150267 | 1922 | FVY | Swindon | S9 | 1307 | Dean Forest |

*Remarks:* 'Bloater'. P'81

| 2625 DW150236 | 1922 1960 | FVY | Swindon | S9 | 1307 1056 | Llangollen |

*Remarks:* 'Bloater'. Pooley Van P'89

| 2660 DW150169 | 1925 1958 | FVY | Swindon | S10 | 1356 | Llangollen |

*Remarks:* 'Bloater'. Pooley Van P'89 by GW Steam Loco Grp

| 2661 DW150289 | 1926 1961 | FVY | Swindon | S10 | 1356 1084 | W Somerset |

*Remarks:* 'Bloater'. P'86

| 2671 DW150160 | 1925 | FVY | Swindon | S10 | 1356 | Didcot |

*Remarks:* 'Bloater'. P'76 by GWS

| 2749 | 1895 | TY | Swindon | S11 | 737 | Rowden Mill |

*Remarks:* Body P'90

| 2775 4509 2775 DW150028 | 1936 1944 1946 1957 | PMVG Ward PMVG | Swindon | O33 M34 | 1578 | * NRM |

*Remarks:* 'Siphon.G'. Converted '39 for CasEvac Train use, & to Ambulance Train 45 in '44. Generator Van for 1st WR Control Train in '57. P'80

| 2790 3303 2790 DW150027 | 1936 1943 1946 1957 | PMVG Ward PMVG | Swindon | O33 M34 | 1578 | Dean Forest |

*Remarks:* 'Siphon.G'. Converted '39 for CasEvac Train use, & to Ambulance Train 33 in '43. Generator Van for 1st WR Control Train 1957-80. P'86

| 2796 | 1937 1945 | PMVG | Swindon | O33 O59 | 1578 | Didcot |

*Remarks:* 'Siphon.G', used in WW2 CasEvac Train. P'?? by GWS

| 2815 DW150343 070843 | 1937 1962 1978 | PMVY | Swindon | Y9 | 1606 | Rowden Mill |

*Remarks:* 'Fruit.C'. P'89

| Numbers | Year | Type | Built | Diag | Lot | Location |
|---------|------|------|-------|------|-----|----------|
| 2823 | 1937 | PMVY | Swindon | Y9 | 1606 | W Somerset |
| DW150346 | 1963 | | | | | |

*Remarks:* 'Fruit.C'. P'75

| 2826 | 1937 | PMVY | Swindon | Y9 | 1606 | Bristol |
|------|------|------|---------|----|------|---------|
| DW150312 | 1961 | | | | 1107 | |

*Remarks:* 'Fruit.C'. P'86 by Active Force (Swindon Ry Eng Ltd), stored at Marsh Jct ever since

| 2851 | 1938 | PMVY | Swindon | Y9 | 1634 | Blunsdon |
|------|------|------|---------|----|------|----------|
| DW150309 | | | | | | |

*Remarks:* 'Fruit.C'. P'81

| 2862 | 1938 | PMVY | Swindon | Y9 | 1634 | Bitton |
|------|------|------|---------|----|------|--------|
| DW150356 | | | | | | |

*Remarks:* 'Fruit.C'. P'81

| 2869 | 1939 | PMVY | Swindon | Y11 | 1649 | Gloucs-Warks |
|------|------|------|---------|-----|------|--------------|

*Remarks:* 'Fruit.D'. P'88?

| 2887 | 1939 | PMVY | Swindon | Y11 | 1649 | Swindon |
|------|------|------|---------|-----|------|---------|
| DW150351 | | | | | | |

*Remarks:* 'Fruit.D'. Pooley Van P'89?

| 2902 | 1940 | PMVY | Swindon | Y11 | 1649 | Dean Forest |
|------|------|------|---------|-----|------|-------------|
| DW150318 | 1961 | | | | 1111 | |

*Remarks:* 'Fruit.D'. P'81

| 2910 | 1941 | PMVY | Swindon | Y11 | 1649 | W Somerset |
|------|------|------|---------|-----|------|------------|
| DW150319 | 1961 | | | | 1111 | |

*Remarks:* 'Fruit.D'. P'86

| 2913 | 1941 | PMVY | Swindon | Y11 | 1649 | W Somerset |
|------|------|------|---------|-----|------|------------|
| DW150363 | 1963 | | | | | |

*Remarks:* P'88

| 2926 | 1940 | PMVG | Swindon | O33 | 1651 | Severn Valley |
|------|------|------|---------|-----|------|---------------|
| 7009? | 1943 | Ward | | | | |
| 2926 | 1946 | PMVG | | O59 | | |

*Remarks:* 'Siphon.G'. Converted '39 for CasEvac Train use, & to US Ambulance Train No 70 in '43. P'85

| 2943 | 1944 | PMVG | Swindon | O33 | 1664 | Preston Park |
|------|------|------|---------|-----|------|--------------|
| DB975841 | 1979 | | | | | |

| 2980 | 1945 | PMVG | Swindon | O59 | 1664 | W Somerset |
|------|------|------|---------|-----|------|------------|

*Remarks:* 'Siphon.G'. Maybe in US Ambulance Train No 69 till '46. P'79 by WSRA members, sold '87 to 813 Fund

| Numbers | Year | Type | Built | Diag | Lot | Location |
|---------|------|------|-------|------|-----|----------|
| 2983<br>DB975783 | 1945 | PMVG | Swindon | O59 | 1664 | Gloucs-Warks |

*Remarks:* 'Siphon.G'. Maybe in US Ambulance Train No 69 till '46. P'82 by Cotswold Steam Preservations

| | | | | | | |
|---------|------|------|-------|------|-----|----------|
| 2988<br>DB975789 | 1945 | PMVG | Swindon | O33 | 1664 | Dean Forest |

*Remarks:* 'Siphon.G'. P'82 by 813 Fund

| | | | | | | |
|---------|------|------|-------|------|-----|----------|
| 2994<br>DB975843<br>061057 | 1945<br>1979<br>1986 | PMVG | Swindon | O33 | 1664 | Bodmin |

*Remarks:* P'90

| | | | | | | |
|---------|------|------|-------|------|-----|----------|
| 3030 | 1947 | OCTZ | Swindon | O58 | 1715 | Didcot |

*Remarks:* 'Rotank'. P'?

| | | | | | | |
|---------|------|------|-------|------|-----|----------|
| 3052<br>DW3052 | | MTZ | Swindon | | | Steamtown |

*Remarks:* P'83

| | | | | | | |
|---------|------|------|-------|------|-----|----------|
| 3299<br>079002 | 1905<br>1951 | TK | B R C W | C24 | 1098 | Didcot |

*Remarks:* The only surviving 'Dreadnought', P'64 by GWS from Newquay, at Totnes till '?

| | | | | | | |
|---------|------|------|-------|------|-----|----------|
| 3403 | 1950 | PMVY | Swindon | Y11 | 1723 | Caerphilly |

*Remarks:* 'Fruit.D'.

| | | | | | | |
|---------|------|------|-------|------|-----|----------|
| 3411 | 1950 | PMVY | Swindon | Y11 | 1723 | Dean Forest |

*Remarks:* 'Fruit.D'. P'72

| | | | | | | |
|---------|------|------|-------|------|-----|----------|
| 3429 | 1950 | PMVY | Swindon | Y11 | | Severn Valley |

*Remarks:* 'Fruit.D'. P'73

| | | | | | | |
|---------|------|------|-------|------|-----|----------|
| 3436<br>DB975300<br>(068724) | 1950 | PMVY | Swindon | Y11 | 17xx | Wallingford |

*Remarks:* 'Fruit.D'. P'83

| | | | | | | |
|---------|------|------|-------|------|-----|----------|
| 3450<br>DB975212 | 1955 | PMVY | Swindon | Y14 | 1771 | W Somerset |

*Remarks:* 'Fruit.D'. P'76

| | | | | | | |
|---------|------|------|-------|------|-----|----------|
| 3461<br>DB975177 | 1955<br>1972 | PMVY | Swindon | Y11 | 1780 | Llangollen |

*Remarks:* 'Fruit.D'. P'85 by GW Stm Loco Grp, on Gloucs-Warks till '88

| Numbers | Year | Type | Built | Diag | Lot | Location |
|---|---|---|---|---|---|---|
| 3462 | 1955 | PMVY | Swindon | Y11 | 1780 | Blunsdon |
| DB975265 | 1973 | | | | | |

*Remarks:* 'Fruit.D'. P' ?

| 3467 | 1955 | PMVY | Swindon | Y11 | 1780 | Severn Valley |

*Remarks:* 'Fruit.D'. P'73

| 3631 | 1921 | TK | Swindon | C32 | 1286 | S Devon |
| 9880 | 1958 | Camp | Swindon | | | |
| 'Florence' | 1983 | | | | | |

*Remarks:* Rebuilt from TK 3939 (Diag C32 Lot 1246) built 1915 & converted for use in Ambulance Train 16 or 19 the same year, repurchased after the war. Converted to a Camping Coach in '58. P'81

| 3639 | 1921 | TK | Swindon | C31 | 1289 | W Somerset |
| 9887 | 1957 | Camp | Swindon | | | |

*Remarks:* Rebuilt from a TK to Diag C31 built 1910 & converted for Ambulance Train use in 1915. P'72 by WSRA member

3655 underframe – see 1580

| 3665 | 1921 | TK | Swindon | C35 | 1295 | Swindon |
| 9886 | 1957 | Camp | Swindon | | | |
| 'Beryl' | 196? | | | | | |

*Remarks:* Rebuilt from a TK to Diag C35 built 1917 & converted for Ambulance Train use in 1918. P'81, on Gloucs-Warks till '88

| 3668 | 1922 | TK | Swindon | C35 | 1313 | W Somerset |
| 9888 | 1957 | Camp | Swindon | | | |

*Remarks:* Rebuilt from a TK to Diag C35 built 1917 & converted for Ambulance Train use in 1918. P'81

| 3755 | 1921 | BT | Swindon | D62 | 1275 | Didcot |

*Remarks:* P'65, stored in Devon till '67, then on Severn Valley; bequeathed to GWS, moving south in '76

| 3756 | 1921 | BT | Swindon | D62 | 1275 | Didcot |

*Remarks:* P'65, stored in Devon till '67, then on Severn Valley; bequeathed to GWS, moving south in '76

| 3885 | 1920 | TK | Swindon | C32 | 1269 | W Somerset |
| 3385 | 1955 | | | | | |
| 9882 | 1958 | Camp | Swindon | | | |
| 'Hilda' | 196? | | | | | |

*Remarks:* Renumbered in 1955 to avoid confusion with new BR Mk.1 TSO's. P'80

| 3898 | 1920 | TK | Swindon | C32 | 1269 | Llangollen |
| 9884 | 1958 | Camp | Swindon | | | |
| 'Freda' | 196? | | | | | |

*Remarks:* P'81, on Gloucs-Warks till '88

| Numbers | Year | Type | Built | | Diag | Lot | Location |
|---------|------|------|-------|--|------|-----|----------|
| 3917 | 1915 | TK | Swindon | | C32 | 1246 | Llangollen |
| 9883 | 1958 | Camp | Swindon | | | | |
| 'Grace' | 196? | | | | | | |

Remarks: P'81, on Gloucs-Warks till '88

| 3930 | 1915 | TK | Swindon | | C32 | 1246 | Severn Valley |
|---------|------|------|-------|--|------|-----|----------|
| DW150011 | 1956 | | | | | | |

Remarks: P'67

3939 – see 3631

| 3950 | 1919 | TK | Swindon | | C35 | 1256 | Bodmin |
|---------|------|------|-------|--|------|-----|----------|
| 9876 | | Camp | | | | | |
| 060905 | 1979 | | | | | | |

Remarks: P'90

| 3951 | 1919 | TK | Swindon | | C35 | 1256 | Bodmin |
|---------|------|------|-------|--|------|-----|----------|
| 9875 | | Camp | | | | | |
| 060904 | 1979 | | | | | | |

Remarks: P'90

| 3963 | 1917 | TK | Swindon | | C35 | 1256 | Llangollen |
|---------|------|------|-------|--|------|-----|----------|
| 9885 | 1957 | Camp | Swindon | | | | |
| 'Alice' | 196? | | | | | | |

Remarks: P'81, on Gloucs-Warks till '88

| 3980 | 1917 | TK | Swindon | | C35 | 1256 | W Somerset |
|---------|------|------|-------|--|------|-----|----------|
| 9881 | 1958 | Camp | Swindon | | | | |
| 'Elsie' | 196? | | | | | | |

Remarks: P'72

| 4546 | 1925 | TK | Swindon | | C54 | 1352 | Severn Valley |
|---------|------|------|-------|--|------|-----|----------|
| DW150205 | 1959 | | | | | | |
| 060903 | | | | | | | |

Remarks: (May have a second-hand underframe from a WW1 Ambulance Train coach) P'82

| 4553 | 1925 | TK | Swindon | | C54 | 1352 | Didcot |
|---------|------|------|-------|--|------|-----|----------|
| DW150207 | 1959 | | | | | | |

Remarks: (May have a second-hand underframe from a WW1 Ambulance Train coach) P'74 by GWS

| 4777 | 1926 | TK | Swindon | | C54 | 1369 | Bodmin |
|---------|------|------|-------|--|------|-----|----------|
| DW150206 | 1959 | | | | | | 1030 |
| 060907 | 1979 | | | | | | |

Remarks: P'89

| 4786 | 1926 | TK | Swindon | | C54 | 1369 | Kidderminster |
|---------|------|------|-------|--|------|-----|----------|
| DW150208 | 1959 | | | | | | |

Remarks: P'84 on SVR

| Numbers | Year | Type | Built | Diag | Lot | Location |
|---------|------|------|-------|------|-----|----------|
| 4872 | 1926 | TK | Swindon | C54 | 1372 | Severn Valley |
| DW150209 | 1959 | | | | | |

*Remarks:* P'84

| 4886 | 1927 | TK | Swindon | C54 | 1374 | |
| DW150201 | 1959 | | | | | |

*Remarks:* P'73 on Severn Valley, but broken up for spares in '?, remains of body in 2 parts still in yard at Bewdley in '87.

| 5043 | 1928 | TK | Swindon | C54 | 1383 | Bewdley |
| DW150301 | | | | | | |

*Remarks:* P'81 on SVR

| 5085 | 1928 | TK | Swindon | C54 | 1383 | Didcot |
| DW150200 | 1959 | | | | | |

*Remarks:* P'74 by GWS

| 5102 | 1928 | BTK | Swindon | D95 | 1384 | Pitsford |
| DW150234 | 1959 | | | | 1051 | |

*Remarks:* P'??

| 5131 | 1928 | BTK | Swindon | D95 | 1384 | Bodmin |
| DW150246 | | | | | | |

*Remarks:* P'87 by GW 3802 Pres Grp members, at Plym Valley till '90 (to be restored as BSO?)

| 5136 | 1929 | BTK | Swindon | D104 | 1399 | |
| 079144 | | | | | | |

*Remarks:* P pre'72 on Severn Valley, broken up for spares in '75.

| 5240 | 1929 | BTK | Swindon | D104 | 1412 | Severn Valley |
| DW150272 | 1961 | | | | 1078 | |

*Remarks:* P'91 by GWR Assoc

| 5500 | 1934 | BT | Swindon | D117 | 1493 | Blaenavon |
| 071343 | 1962 | | | | | |

*Remarks:* P'90 ex Newport Docks

| 5539 | 1928 | BT | Swindon | D101 | 1392 | Southport |
| DW150328 | | | | | | |

*Remarks:* P'67, on Severn Valley till '73, stored till '76 then at Llangollen till c'86

| 5787 | 1933 | BTK | Swindon | D116 | 1490 | Didcot |

*Remarks:* P'67 on Severn Valley; bequeathed to GWS & moved south in '76

| Numbers | Year | Type | Built | Diag | Lot | Location |
|---------|------|------|-------|------|-----|----------|
| 5796<br>DW150341 | 1933 | BTK | Swindon | D116 | 1490 | |

*Remarks:* Latterly a Tunnel Inspection unit; P'81 on Severn Valley, mainly for its bogies. Broken up for spares in '83.

| Numbers | Year | Type | Built | Diag | Lot | Location |
|---------|------|------|-------|------|-----|----------|
| 5804<br>3406<br>5804<br>DW150304 | 1934<br>1943<br>1946 | BTK<br>Ward | Swindon | D118 | 1510 | Plym Valley |

*Remarks:* In Ambulance Train No 34 1943-6. P'83

| Numbers | Year | Type | Built | Diag | Lot | Location |
|---------|------|------|-------|------|-----|----------|
| 5813<br>DW150324 | 1934<br>1962 | TK | Swindon | C67 | 1509 | Dean Forest |

*Remarks:* Damaged by enemy action '41 & rebuilt with new body to original design. In second WR Control Train. P'80, sold to Forest Pannier Tank Fund c'85

| Numbers | Year | Type | Built | Diag | Lot | Location |
|---------|------|------|-------|------|-----|----------|
| 5848<br>DW150029 | 1934<br>1957 | TK | Swindon | C67 | 1509 | Dean Forest |

*Remarks:* In first WR Control Train. P'80

| Numbers | Year | Type | Built | Diag | Lot | Location |
|---------|------|------|-------|------|-----|----------|
| 5856<br>DW150031 | 1934<br>1957 | TK | Swindon | C67 | 1509 | Blunsdon |

*Remarks:* In first WR Control Train. P'80, at Bitton till '86

| Numbers | Year | Type | Built | Diag | Lot | Location |
|---------|------|------|-------|------|-----|----------|
| 5863<br>DW150325 | 1934<br>1962 | TK | Swindon | C67 | 1509 | Dean Forest |

*Remarks:* In second WR Control Train. P'80, conv'd to volunteers' dormitory/mess in '91

| Numbers | Year | Type | Built | Diag | Lot | Location |
|---------|------|------|-------|------|-----|----------|
| 5883<br>? plated | 1934 | BTK | Swindon | D118 | 1514 | Severn Valley |

*Remarks:* P'73

| Numbers | Year | Type | Built | Diag | Lot | Location |
|---------|------|------|-------|------|-----|----------|
| 5929<br>DW150030 | 1935<br>1957 | TK | Swindon | C67 | 1527 | Dean Forest |

*Remarks:* In first WR Control Train. P'80 (to be restored as SO?)

| Numbers | Year | Type | Built | Diag | Lot | Location |
|---------|------|------|-------|------|-----|----------|
| 5952 | 1935 | TK | Swindon | C67 | 1527 | Didcot |

*Remarks:* P pre'72 by GWS

| Numbers | Year | Type | Built | Diag | Lot | Location |
|---------|------|------|-------|------|-----|----------|
| 6045<br>DW150293 | 1928 | CK | Swindon | E132 | 1382 | Severn Valley |

*Remarks:* P'73

| Numbers | Year | Type | Built | Diag | Lot | Location |
|---|---|---|---|---|---|---|
| 6479<br>80977 | 1910 | Spec | Swindon | Q1 | 1170 | S Devon |

*Remarks:* Engineer's Saloon built using underframe from Manchester & Milford Railway Composite No.14 (listed as No.149 sometimes) built Ashbury 1895, becoming GWR No.7900 in 1906 & withdrawn 1908. P pre'72

| | | | | | | |
|---|---|---|---|---|---|---|
| 6515<br>DW150270 | 1926 | BCK | Swindon | E128 | 1350 | Tyseley |

*Remarks:* P'76

| | | | | | | |
|---|---|---|---|---|---|---|
| 6562<br>99238 plated | 1938 | BCK | Swindon | E159 | 1589 | Severn Valley |

*Remarks:* P'67, resold '75

| | | | | | | |
|---|---|---|---|---|---|---|
| 6705 | 1938 | BCK | Swindon | E159 | 1589 | Vermont, USA |

*Remarks:* P'67 & exported to American 'Steamtown'

| | | | | | | |
|---|---|---|---|---|---|---|
| 6912<br>079133 | 1934 | BCK | Swindon | E148 | 1508 | |

*Remarks:* P'74 on Severn Valley; broken up '86, its u'frame then sold off to carry 242 (qv).

| | | | | | | |
|---|---|---|---|---|---|---|
| 6913<br>079134<br>99240 plated | 1934 | BCK | Swindon | E148 | 1508 | Severn Valley |

*Remarks:* P'74

| | | | | | | |
|---|---|---|---|---|---|---|
| 7284<br>? plated | 1941 | CK | Swindon | E162 | 1639 | Severn Valley |

*Remarks:* P'69

| | | | | | | |
|---|---|---|---|---|---|---|
| 7285 | 1941 | CK | Swindon | E162 | 1639 | Didcot |

*Remarks:* P'67 on Severn Valley; bequeathed to GWS & moved south in '76

| | | | | | | |
|---|---|---|---|---|---|---|
| 7313 | 1940 | CK | Swindon | E158 | 1621 | Didcot |

*Remarks:* P pre'72 by GWS

| | | | | | | |
|---|---|---|---|---|---|---|
| 7362 | 1941 | BCK | Swindon | E159 | 1640 | Blunsdon |

*Remarks:* P pre'72, at Didcot till '84

| | | | | | | |
|---|---|---|---|---|---|---|
| 7371 | 1941 | BCK | Swindon | E159 | 1640 | Didcot |

*Remarks:* P pre'72, bought by GWS in '86

| | | | | | | |
|---|---|---|---|---|---|---|
| 7372<br>? plated | 1948 | BCK | Swindon | E164 | 1690 | Didcot |

*Remarks:* Used in WR Royal duties. P pre'72 by GWS & at Bodmin till '77.

| Numbers | Year | Type | Built | Diag | Lot | Location |
|---------|------|------|-------|------|-----|----------|
| 7377<br>? plated | 1948 | BCK | Swindon | E164 | 1690 | S Devon |

*Remarks:* Used in WR Royal duties. P pre'72

| Numbers | Year | Type | Built | Diag | Lot | Location |
|---------|------|------|-------|------|-----|----------|
| 7538<br>DW150020 | 1907 | BCK | Swindon | E83 | 1138 | Wallingford |

*Remarks:* P'74 by W McAlpine, but stored by GWS at Didcot till '85

| Numbers | Year | Type | Built | Diag | Lot | Location |
|---------|------|------|-------|------|-----|----------|
| 7545<br>079076 | 1907<br>1957 | BCK | Swindon | E83 | 1138 | Blunsdon |

*Remarks:* P'81

| Numbers | Year | Type | Built | Diag | Lot | Location |
|---------|------|------|-------|------|-----|----------|
| 7740<br>DW317 | 1911<br>1955 | CK | Swindon | E88 | 1171 | W Somerset |

*Remarks:* P'77 by WSRA member

| Numbers | Year | Type | Built | Diag | Lot | Location |
|---------|------|------|-------|------|-----|----------|
| 7976 | 1923 | BCK | Swindon | E114 | 1323 | Didcot |

*Remarks:* P post'72 on Severn Valley; bequeathed to GWS & moved south in '76 (intended to be restored as kitchen/bar & lounge)

| Numbers | Year | Type | Built | Diag | Lot | Location |
|---------|------|------|-------|------|-----|----------|
| 9001<br>99106 plated | 1940 | Spec | Swindon | G62 | 1626 | Tyseley |

*Remarks:* 12-wheel VIP Saloon. P'68, on Severn Valley till '76

9002 (i) – see 233

| Numbers | Year | Type | Built | Diag | Lot | Location |
|---------|------|------|-------|------|-----|----------|
| 9002 (ii) | 1940 | Spec | Swindon | G62 | 1626 | Didcot |

*Remarks:* 12-wheel VIP Saloon. P'69, bought by GWS in '86

| Numbers | Year | Type | Built | Diag | Lot | Location |
|---------|------|------|-------|------|-----|----------|
| 9004<br>DE321011<br>99053 plated | 1930<br>1963 | BFO | Swindon | G59 | 1431 | Steamtown |

*Remarks:* Latterly NE Region CCE's Saloon. P'72 by W H McAlpine, named 'Stapleford Park' for a time

| Numbers | Year | Type | Built | Diag | Lot | Location |
|---------|------|------|-------|------|-----|----------|
| 9005 | 1930<br>1961 | BFO<br>Spec | Swindon<br>Swindon | G59<br>G66 | 1431 | Didcot |

*Remarks:* Latterly W Region General Manager's Saloon mounted on B4 bogies. P'74 by GWS with B1 bogies, re-shod with GWR 9ft bogies in '83

| Numbers | Year | Type | Built | Diag | Lot | Location |
|---------|------|------|-------|------|-----|----------|
| 9006 | 1945<br>1948 | Spec<br>ROY | Swindon<br>Swindon | G64 | 1673 | * NRM |

*Remarks:* Special Saloon, built on underframe of war damaged TK No.1133 built 1938. P'84, at York till '90 then 'NRM On Tour' exhibition at Swindon till 5/91

| Numbers | Year | Type | Built | Diag | Lot | Location |
|---------|------|------|-------|------|-----|----------|
| 9007 | 1945 | Spec | Swindon | G65 | 1673 | * NRM |
|  | 1948 | ROY | Swindon |  |  |  |

*Remarks:* Special Saloon, built on underframe of war damaged BTK No.1598 built 1937. P'84, at York till '90 then 'NRM On Tour' exhibition at Swindon till 5/91

9033/5/44/5 – see 229/31/48/9 respectively

| Numbers | Year | Type | Built | Diag | Lot | Location |
|---------|------|------|-------|------|-----|----------|
| 9055 DW150127 | 1912 | BTO | Swindon | G43 | 1209 | Severn Valley |

*Remarks:* P'72

| 9082 | 1951 | SLF | Swindon | J18 | 1702 | Bewdley |

*Remarks:* 12-wheel. P'71 on SVR

| 9083 | 1951 | SLF | Swindon | J18 | 1702 | Didcot |

*Remarks:* 12-wheel. P'70? by GWS

| 9084 | 1951 | SLF | Swindon | J18 | 1702 | Bewdley |

*Remarks:* 12-wheel. P'70 on SVR

| 9085 | 1951 | SLF | Swindon | J18 | 1702 | Arley |

*Remarks:* 12-wheel. P'71, at Bridgnorth till '87

| 9103 079124 | 1929 196? | BTO | Swindon | G58 | 1400 | Severn Valley |

*Remarks:* P'72

| 9111 King George | 1931 | RFO | Swindon | G60 | 1471 | S Devon |

*Remarks:* P'?? by DVR Association

| 9112 Queen Mary | 1932 | RFO | Swindon | G60 | 1471 | Didcot |

*Remarks:* P'?? by GWS

| 9113 Prince of Wales | 1932 | RFO | Swindon | G61 | 1471 | Didcot |

*Remarks:* P'67 on Severn Valley; bequeathed to GWS & moved south in '76

| 9116 Duchess of York | 1932 | RFO | Swindon | G61 | 1471 | Torbay |

| 9118 Princess Elizabeth | 1932 | RFO | Swindon | G61 | 1471 | Didcot |
|  | 1935 | RF | Swindon | H46 |  |  |

*Remarks:* P'?? by GWS

| Numbers | Year | Type | Built | Diag | Lot | Location |
|---------|------|------|-------|------|-----|----------|
| 9369<br>DW150128 | 1923 | BTO | Swindon | G56 | 1250 | Severn Valley |

*Remarks:* P'72

9518 – see 1580

| 9580<br><br>DW150266 | 1925<br>1953<br>1960 | RCO<br>RB<br>Spec | Swindon | H33<br><br> | 1349<br><br>1073 | E Lancs |

*Remarks:* Latterly S&T Manager's Saloon. P'90

| 9605<br>DW150330 | 1930 | RC | Swindon | H38 | 1451 | * Wroughton |

*Remarks:* P'76, but kept in store by NRM. Restored by Resco '83-6, then to Science Mus outstation

| 9615<br>DW150336<br>992?? plated | 1932 | RF | Swindon | H39 | 1468 | Severn Valley |

*Remarks:* P'73

| 9627<br>079112<br>99237 plated | 1932 | RTO | Swindon | H40 | 1469 | Severn Valley |

*Remarks:* P'72

| 9631<br>992?? plated | 1934 | RB | Swindon | H41 | 1518 | * Severn Valley |

*Remarks:* P'62, at Clapham till '73

| 9635 | 1935 | RF | Swindon | H43 | 1540 | Didcot |

*Remarks:* Only surviving 'Centenary' coach. P'63 by Dowty RPS at Ashchurch, moved to Toddington '83 then sold to GWS '88 & taken to Didcot

| 10020<br>9653<br>DW150032 | 1925<br>1937<br>1957 | RTO<br>RTO | Swindon<br>Swindon | H32<br>H51 | 1359 | * Severn Valley |

*Remarks:* Originally one end of a three-car articulated dining set rebuilt as three single units in 1937. In first WR Control Train. P'80 but in store till '81

| 10036<br>9654<br>DW150326 | 1925<br>1937<br>1962 | RTO<br>RTO | Swindon<br>Swindon | H32<br>H51 | 1359 | * Severn Valley |

*Remarks:* Originally one end of a three-car articulated dining set rebuilt as three single units in 1937. In second WR Control Train. P'80 but in store till '81

| 80943 | 1948 | Insp | Swindon | Q13 | 1701 | Dean Forest |

*Remarks:* P post'75, stored on Severn Valley till '79

| Numbers | Year | Type | Built | Diag | Lot | Location |
|---------|------|------|-------|------|-----|----------|
| 80945 – see Cambrian 238 | | | | | | |
| 80969 | 1948 | Insp | Swindon | Q13 | 1701 | Severn Valley |
| *Remarks:* P'73 | | | | | | |
| 80970 | 1948 | Insp | Swindon | Q13 | 1701 | * NRM |
| *Remarks:* P'84 | | | | | | |
| 80971 – see 231 | | | | | | |
| 80972 99103 plated | 1948 | Insp | Swindon | Q13 | 1701 | Tyseley |
| *Remarks:* P'73 | | | | | | |
| 80973 – see 248 | | | | | | |
| 80974 | 1948 | Insp | Swindon | Q13 | 1701 | N Yorks Moors |
| *Remarks:* P'72?, at Tyseley till '73 | | | | | | |
| 80976 | 1948 | Insp | Swindon | Q13 | 1701 | Colne Valley |
| *Remarks:* P'88 | | | | | | |

**The Severn Valley Railway operates an excellent dining train — The Severn Valley Limited — and one of the vehicles used in the consist is Restaurant Third Open No 9653, seen at Kidderminster in 1991. Whilst dining in the beautifully restored vehicle, one can reflect on its use from 1962 until withdrawal when it was one of BR's most secret coaches — used for a mobile Control Train in case of hostilities.** *Murray Brown*

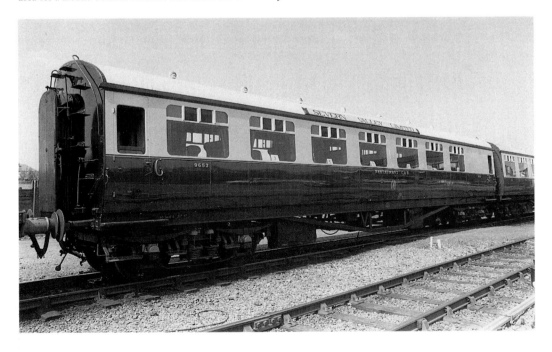

| Numbers | Year | Type | Built | Diag | Lot | Location |
|---------|------|------|-------|------|-----|----------|

80977 – see 6479

80978 – see 249

*Others:*
Body of TY built c1845 – P post'76 for Buckfastleigh museum
Body of unidentified 4-wheel coach – Welsh I&M Museum, Cardiff
2 bodies from c1880's – Bodmin, at Bugle till '87
Body of TY built c1882 – Grounded c1936, P'82 at Zelah, but may be GWR constituent?
Another body, ex 4-wheel – Zelah
Broad gauge body sections – Bristol Ind Mus

# THE SOUTHERN RAILWAY GROUP

| Numbers | Year | Type | Built | | Diag | Lot | Location |
|---------|------|------|-------|---|------|-----|----------|

## BODMIN & WADEBRIDGE RAILWAY

| | c1840 | FY | L&SR/LSWR? | | - | - | * NRM |
| | | CY | | | | | |

*Remarks:* Possibly L&SR/LSWR, to B&WR in 1855; out of use from c1886. P'95 by LSWR, displayed on a plinth at Waterloo till 1940, then stored at ? till '60. Restored at Eastleigh, then at Clapham till '73

| | ? | SY | ? | | - | - | * NRM |

*Remarks:* Origins rather uncertain; out of use from c1886. P'95 by LSWR, on display at Kingston-on-Thames till about early 1930's, then at York museum and NRM

| | c1834 | TY | Locally? | | - | - | * NRM |

*Remarks:* Origins completely obscure; out of use from c1886. P'95 by LSWR, to York Railway Museum in 1926

## ISLE OF WIGHT RAILWAY

| 10 | 1864 | ÇY | Oldbury | | | | IoWSR |

*Remarks:* W'20, body grounded at Bembridge. P'83

| 21 | 1864 | FY | Oldbury | | | | IoWSR |

*Remarks:* W'13, body grounded as workshop & garage at Cranmore (IoW). P'77

| 38 | 1882 | CY | Oldbury | | | | IoWSR |
| 6335 | 1924 | | | | | | |

*Remarks:* W'27, body grounded on Hayling Island. P'75

| 39 | 1882 | SY | Oldbury | | | | IoWSR |
| 2421 | 1924 | | | | | | |

*Remarks:* W'27, body grounded on Hayling Island. P'77, but stored in Portsmouth till '78

46 – see North London Ry (LMS Section)

| Numbers | Year | Type | Built | Diag | Lot | Location |
|---------|------|------|-------|------|-----|----------|

# LONDON, BRIGHTON & SOUTH COAST RAILWAY

7 – see SR 6164

| Numbers | Year | Type | Built | Diag | Lot | Location |
|---------|------|------|-------|------|-----|----------|
| 20 | 1896 | SY | Brighton | 57 | | IoWSR |
| 1520 | 1911 | TY | | 154 | | |
| 1840 | 1924 | | | | | |
| 2343 | 1925 | | | 60 | | |

Remarks: To IoW 1925. W'31 & body grounded at Gurnard. P'84 with twin sister No.21 (1521/2344), though the latter was broken up to provide parts

| Numbers | Year | Type | Built | Diag | Lot | Location |
|---------|------|------|-------|------|-----|----------|
| 60 | 1914 | Spec | Lancing | 67 | | Bluebell |
| 291S | c1924 | | | 1851 | | |
| DS291 | 1948 | | | | | |

Remarks: 12-wheel Directors' Saloon, later an Inspection Saloon & used for Driver training from 1962. P'65

| Numbers | Year | Type | Built | Diag | Lot | Location |
|---------|------|------|-------|------|-----|----------|
| 93 | 1922 | BT | Lancing | 202 | | IoWSR |
| 3870 | 1924 | | | 198 | | |
| 4168 | 1938 | | | 230 | | |

Remarks: Built on chassis from 1905-built 'Balloon' that was WW1 Ambulance coach. P'67, at Newport till '71 (reportedly to get new u/frame from SR 752)

| Numbers | Year | Type | Built | Diag | Lot | Location |
|---------|------|------|-------|------|-----|----------|
| 142 | 1902 | F | Brighton | 64 | | Bluebell |
| | 1911 | | | 49 | | |
| 7598 | 1924 | | | 514 | | |

Remarks: W'29, body grounded '31 at W Chiltington as dwelling, later an aviary. P'89, temporarily mounted on 1949 Bulleid u/f (ex 1433?), parts for its restoration found by stripping FZ No 106 (SR No 7527) & Balloon SL No 233 (SR No 7768). To be given shortened LNWR u/f ex Steamtown (Army 80.081)

| Numbers | Year | Type | Built | Diag | Lot | Location |
|---------|------|------|-------|------|-----|----------|
| 270 | 1908 | PMVZ | Brighton | 232 | | Bluebell |
| 2178 | 1927 | | | 975 | | |
| 1525S | 1939 | | | | | |
| DS1525 | 1948 | | | | | |

Remarks: Milk Van. P'64

| Numbers | Year | Type | Built | Diag | Lot | Location |
|---------|------|------|-------|------|-----|----------|
| 521 | 1878 | FZ | Brighton | 37 | | Hayling Is Stn |
| 98 | 1908 | CZ | | 37c | | |

Remarks: W'21, body grounded on Hayling Is as a dwelling. P'86 by HIRS

| Numbers | Year | Type | Built | Diag | Lot | Location |
|---------|------|------|-------|------|-----|----------|
| 641 | 1916 | BT | Lancing | 201 | | IoWSR |
| 4019 | 1927 | | | 203 | | |
| 2416 | 1936 | T | | 90 | | |

Remarks: Brake area converted to 3 comp'ts before shipped to Isle of Wight. P'67, at Newport till '71

| Numbers | Year | Type | Built | Diag | Lot | Location |
|---------|------|------|-------|------|-----|----------|
| 660 | 1880 | FZ | Brown Marshall | 37 | | Hayling Is Stn |
| 261 | 1908 | BSZ | | 37d | | |
| 1646 | 1911 | BTZ | | 149 | | |

Remarks: W'21, body grounded on Hayling Is as a dwelling. P'86 by HIRS

| Numbers | Year | Type | Built | Diag | Lot | Location |
|---------|------|------|-------|------|-----|----------|
| 667 | 1880 | FZ | Brown Marshall | 37 | | Bluebell |
| 194 | 1908 | BSZ | | 37d | | |
| 1648 | 1912 | BTZ | | 149 | | |

*Remarks:* W'20 as B1 from Set 54, body grounded at Wittering as centre part of a bungalow. P'83

*Others:*
Body believed LBSCR P'86 on Plym Valley
Body P'90 from Shelley Beach, Exmouth

# LONDON, CHATHAM & DOVER RAILWAY

| Numbers | Year | Type | Built | Diag | Lot | Location |
|---------|------|------|-------|------|-----|----------|
| 9 | c1880 | FY | Longhedge | | | Quainton |
| 2405 | 1900 | | | | | |

*Remarks:* Sold to Woolwich Arsenal 1915, out of use from c1924! P'62, stored at Bishops Stortford till '69

| Numbers | Year | Type | Built | Diag | Lot | Location |
|---------|------|------|-------|------|-----|----------|
| 20 | 1887 | SOZ | Longhedge | | | IoWSR |
| 2938 | 1901 | | | | | |
| | 190x | TOZ | | | | |
| 7909 | 1924 | | | | | |
| 6369 | 1924 | COY | Lancing | | | |

*Remarks:* To IoW '24, W'38. Body P'90

| Numbers | Year | Type | Built | Diag | Lot | Location |
|---------|------|------|-------|------|-----|----------|
| 45 | 1894 | BSZ | Longhedge | | | IoWSR |
| (279) | 1897 | BTZ | | | | |
| 3357 | 1901 | | | | | |
| | 1916 | BTY | | | | |
| 3585 | 1930 | | | 92 | | |
| 2515 | 1930 | TY | | | | |

*Remarks:* Downgraded c1899 then lost centre wheelset c1916. Converted to 5-comp't Third & shipped to IoW 1930, grounded as chalet at Colwell Bay 1937. P'81

| Numbers | Year | Type | Built | Diag | Lot | Location |
|---------|------|------|-------|------|-----|----------|
| 48 | 1894 | BSZ | Longhedge | | | Bluebell |
| 2781 | 1907 | BTZ | | | | |
| 3630 | 1927 | | | | | |
| 873S | 1935 | | | | | |
| DS873 | 1948 | | | | | |

*Remarks:* Latterly a Mess & Tool van, the last Chatham coach in any form with BR. P'62

| Numbers | Year | Type | Built | Diag | Lot | Location |
|---------|------|------|-------|------|-----|----------|
| 49 | 1889 | BSY | Longhedge | | | K&ESR |
| 105 | 1894 | BTY | | | | |
| 3059 | 1901 | | | | | |
| K&ESR 70 | 1976 | | | | | |

*Remarks:* W'c1918, body grounded 1921 at Kingsnorth (nr Ashford). P'76, placed on shortened u/f from SR PMVY in '80

| Numbers | Year | Type | Built | Diag | Lot | Location |
|---------|------|------|-------|------|-----|----------|
| 52 | 1890 | BSY | Longhedge | | | |
| 3361 | 1903 | BTY | | | | |

*Remarks:* Body grounded 1921 as part of a bungalow at Ashford (with 68, 108 & SECR 2947), but with most of one side cut away. P'86 but dismantled for parts.

| Numbers | Year | Type | Built | Diag | Lot | Location |
|---------|------|------|-------|------|-----|----------|
| 68 | 1879 | TY | Longhedge | | | K&ESR |
| 502 | 1899 | | | | | |
| 3022 | 1906 | | | | | |

*Remarks:* Body grounded 1921 as part of a bungalow at Ashford, but with most of one side cut away. P'86, mostly dismantled during recovery, but the one intact compartment to be restored for museum display.

| Numbers | Year | Type | Built | Diag | Lot | Location |
|---------|------|------|-------|------|-----|----------|
| 108 | 1888 | BSY | Longhedge | | | K&ESR |
| | 1891 | BTY | | | | |
| 3062 | 1903 | | | | | |

*Remarks:* Body grounded 1921 as part of a bungalow at Ashford. P'86

| Numbers | Year | Type | Built | Diag | Lot | Location |
|---------|------|------|-------|------|-----|----------|
| 114 | c1888 | BTY | | | | Bluebell |
| 3068 | | | | | | |

*Remarks:* Body grounded pre-Grouping? P'77

| Numbers | Year | Type | Built | Diag | Lot | Location |
|---------|------|------|-------|------|-----|----------|
| 233 | 1886 | FZ | Longhedge | | | IoWSR |
| 2623 | c1903 | | | | | |
| | 1920 | FY | | | | |
| 6378 | 1927 | | | 363 | | |

*Remarks:* To IoW 1930, W'37. Body P'84 from Rookley (tentative identity only)

| Numbers | Year | Type | Built | Diag | Lot | Location |
|---------|------|------|-------|------|-----|----------|
| 348 | 1895 | T | Longhedge | | | IoWSR |
| 3302 | 1900 | | | | | |
| 850 | 1924 | | | 37 | | |
| 2418 | 1933 | | | | | |

*Remarks:* W'48, body grounded '49 at Newport cut in two. One half P'78, other half P'90 (to be restored using u'frame from SR CCT 4605?)

| Numbers | Year | Type | Built | Diag | Lot | Location |
|---------|------|------|-------|------|-----|----------|
| 653 | 1898 | BTZ | | | | IoWSR |
| 3173 | 1904 | | | | | |
| | c1919 | BTOZ | | | | |
| (7932) | 1924 | | | | | |
| 4112 | 1924 | BTOY | | | | |

*Remarks:* Converted to Saloon after WW1, losing its centre wheelset in '24. W'38, body grounded at ? till P'81. Mounted on u/f from PMV 1134 or 1720, though which is uncertain

| Numbers | Year | Type | Built | Diag | Lot | Location |
|---------|------|------|-------|------|-----|----------|
| 1075 | 1897 | T | Gloucester | | | |
| 3394 | 1907 | | | | | |
| 905 | 1924 | | | 45 | | |
| 2426 | 1931 | | | | | |

*Remarks:* To IoW 1931. Half-body grounded at Gurnard Marsh '??. P'81 by IoWSR, but dismantled for spares in '84/5? (The other half of this body was still extant at Leechmore in '85)

| Numbers | Year | Type | Built | Diag | Lot | Location |
|---------|------|------|-------|------|-----|----------|
| 1185 | 1898 | BT | Brown Marshall | | | IoWSR |
| 3411 | 1902 | | | | | |
| 3247 | 1924 | | | 144 | | |
| 4115 | 1933 | | | | | |

*Remarks:* W'48, body grounded at Atherfield in '49 as a henhouse and store. P'75

| Numbers | Year | Type | Built | Diag | Lot | Location |
|---------|------|------|-------|------|-----|----------|

*Others:*
Unidentified body of SY or TY built c1875, grounded as farm store at Cliffe, P'82 by N Downs Rly at Chatham, now Dartford
see also SECR 2947

# LONDON & SOUTH WESTERN RAILWAY

[Diags per Carriage Register]

| Numbers | Year | Type | Built | Diag | Lot | Location |
|---------|------|------|-------|------|-----|----------|
| 11 | 1910 | Spec | Eastleigh | 43 | 1906 | K&ESR |
| 4105 | 1919 | | | | | |
| 7803 | 1927 | | | 581 | | |
| Army119 | 1938 | | | | | |
| Army 3007 | | | | | | |
| K&ESR 83 | 1985 | | | | | |

*Remarks:* Invalid Saloon. Sold to the Army in 1938 for use in Longmoor Military Railway Officers' Train. P'70, a gift to the Transport Trust, & remained on LMR till moved to the Severn Valley in 1971. Sold by the Transport Trust & moved south in '85

| | | | | | | |
|---------|------|------|-------|------|-----|----------|
| 17 | 1885 | FO | | | | Burnham-on-Crouch |
| | 1887 | ROY | | | | |
| 4107 | 1913 | Sal | | | | |
| 7805 | 1923 | | | | | |

*Remarks:* Built with Arc roof, but rebuilt as Royal Saloon with Clerestory; rebuilt again as Picnic Saloon 1913. W'31 & grounded at W Chiltington as part of bungalow. Body P'89 by Sail & Steam, loaned to Mangapps Farm from 6/9/89

| | | | | | | |
|---------|------|------|-------|------|-----|----------|
| 49 | 1891 | CZ | Nine Elms | 55 | | Swanage |
| 2296 | 1912 | CY | | | | |

*Remarks:* W'22, body grounded at Worth Matravers as part of a holiday chalet with another body (1512 qv). P'83 by Swanage RPS, initially at Corfe Castle Station site

| | | | | | | |
|---------|------|------|-------|------|-----|----------|
| 70 | 1907 | RC | Eastleigh | 42 | 1601 | Mid-Hants |
| 4132 | 1919 | | | | | |
| 7832 | 1925 | | | 590 | | |
| WD1641 | 1943 | | | | | |
| Army 3321 | 1955 | | | | | |

*Remarks:* Clerestory roof removed when converted to a Nondescript Saloon in 1931. Converted to Ambulance coach in '43, based at Netley till moved to Longmoor pre-'55, then to Marchwood in '67. P'78

| | | | | | | |
|---------|------|------|-------|------|-----|----------|
| 74 | 1923 | TK | Eastleigh | 24c | 3709 | Swanage |
| 728 | 1928 | | | 24 | | |
| DS70011 | 1960 | | | | | |

*Remarks:* Built by SR to LSWR design. P'88 by SST, at Hoo Jct Yard till '91

| | | | | | | |
|---------|------|------|-------|------|-----|----------|
| 75 | 1881 | TY | | | | Hele |
| 075 | 1903 | | | | | |

*Remarks:* Sold '05, grounded at Exmouth Docks & bungalow built round it. Body P'91 at 'Fagin's Antiques'

| Numbers | Year | Type | Built | Diag | Lot | Location |
|---------|------|------|-------|------|-----|----------|
| 76 | 1908 | RC | Eastleigh | 42 | 1601 | Mid-Hants |
| 4138 | 1913 | | | | | |
| 7838 | c1924 | | | 590 | | |
| USTC 202 | 1943 | | | | | |
| Army 3019 | | | | | | |

*Remarks:* As per 70 above till leaving Netley for Longmoor in '54. Converted to Breakdown coach '61, moving to Bicester '69. P'77 by Urie Soc. member

| Numbers | Year | Type | Built | Diag | Lot | Location |
|---------|------|------|-------|------|-----|----------|
| 126 | 1876 | FOY | | | | Hele |

*Remarks:* Sold '05 with 75 (above). Part body P'91 at 'Fagin's Antiques'

| Numbers | Year | Type | Built | Diag | Lot | Location |
|---------|------|------|-------|------|-----|----------|
| 494 | 1911 | TK | Eastleigh | 14 | 1872 | Bluebell |
| 673 | 1924 | | | 21 | | |
| 39 | 1954 | Camp | | | | |

*Remarks:* To departmental stock in 1964 at St. Blazey, then at Westbury till P'75

| Numbers | Year | Type | Built | Diag | Lot | Location |
|---------|------|------|-------|------|-----|----------|
| 773 | 1921 | TK | Eastleigh | 24b | 3251 | Horsebridge |
| 717 | 1924 | | | 24 | | |
| ADS226 | 1958 | | | | | |

*Remarks:* W'57. P'86

| Numbers | Year | Type | Built | Diag | Lot | Location |
|---------|------|------|-------|------|-----|----------|
| 847 | 1903 | BCL | Eastleigh | 69 | 1190 | * NRM |
| 3598 | 1914 | | | | | |
| 6474 | 1926 | | | 407 | | |

*Remarks:* Tri-composite. P'48 & refurbished at Eastleigh for exhibition at Waterloo centenary. Stored at Farnham, Clay Cross & Preston Park till moved to NRM Annexe in '77

| Numbers | Year | Type | Built | Diag | Lot | Location |
|---------|------|------|-------|------|-----|----------|
| 911 | 1890 | CZ | Nine Elms | 9 | | Swanage |
| 695 | | | | | | |
| 0695 | | | | | | |

*Remarks:* W'21, body sold to Miss Cathcart, Ashbury, & grounded as a chalet at Highcliffe. P'76 by SST member, at Corfe Castle Station site till '80

| Numbers | Year | Type | Built | Diag | Lot | Location |
|---------|------|------|-------|------|-----|----------|
| 959 | 1907 | CL | Eastleigh | 69 | 1298 | K&ESR |
| 3078 | 1919 | | | | | |
| 5065 | 1925 | | | 274 | | |
| 31 | 1953 | Camp | | | | |
| K&ESR 62 | 1968 | | | | | |

*Remarks:* 1/3 Composite, latterly a Camping coach at Amberley, Combpyne & Bere Ferrers till c'65, then dept'l stock at Southall till P'68

| Numbers | Year | Type | Built | Diag | Lot | Location |
|---------|------|------|-------|------|-----|----------|
| 1228 | 1900 | T | Eastleigh | 19 | 772 | Bluebell |
| 288 | 1916 | | | | | |
| 320 | 1923 | | | 12 | | |
| | 1935 | TL | Eastleigh | 31 | 801 | |

*Remarks:* 48ft Third rebuilt on new 58ft u/f in '35, with one compartment and two toilets inserted; W'59. P'60 & in service till c'71

| Numbers | Year | Type | Built | Diag | Lot | Location |
|---------|------|------|-------|------|-----|----------|
| 1282 | 1921 | BTK | Eastleigh | 24c | 3252 | Burnham on Crouch |
| 3187 | 1925 | | | 135 | | |
| DS179 | 1957 | | | | | |

*Remarks:* P'79, at Mid-Hants '80-5 then Knebworth till moved to Mangapps Farm '89

| 1353 | 1923 | BTK | Eastleigh | 24c | 3710 | Mid-Hants |
| 3190 | 1928 | | | 135 | | |
| DS70016 | 1959 | | | | | |

*Remarks:* Built by SR to LSWR design. Relegated to secondary duties 1937, converted to Mess coach '59. P'78 & arrived Mid-Hants '79

| 1512 | 1891 | SZ | Eastleigh | 7 | | Swanage |
| 56 | 1915 | | | | | |
| 5440 | ? | Fruit | | | | |

*Remarks:* Probably built on second-hand u'frame from c1857. W'22, body grounded at Worth Matravers as part of a holiday chalet with another body (49 qv). P'83 by Swanage RPS, initially at Corfe Castle Station site

| 1520 | 1910 | BTL | Eastleigh | 16 | 1446 | Bluebell |
| 2975 | 1928 | | | 124 | | |
| DS1119 | 1949 | | | | | |

*Remarks:* W'69. P'70 by MNLPS & at Longmoor till '71, then at Ashford till abandoned there '77. Removed by Southern Coach Group? & since used as Staff/Equipment Van in the Fire-fighting Train

One of the National Railway Museum's most recent restorations is Brake Composite Lavatory No 6474, restored to its London & South Western Railway livery of salmon pink and brown. The NRM authorities actively encourage visitors to sit inside and sample the outstanding restoration work, not to mention the ambience. *Murray Brown*

| Numbers | Year | Type | Built | Diag | Lot | Location |
|---------|------|------|-------|------|-----|----------|
| 4151 | 1923 | RT | Eastleigh | | 3854 | Mid-Hants |
| 7851 | 1923 | | | 592 | | |
| 625S | 1948 | | | | | |
| DS625 | 1960 | | | | | |

Remarks: W'47, converted to Mess & Tool van. P'80

| | | | | | | |
|---------|------|------|-------|------|-----|----------|
| 5025 | 1917 | PMVY | Eastleigh | 88 | 2104 | Quainton |
| 1451 | 1929 | | | 929 | | |

Remarks: Luggage Van. W'40, grounded at Tisbury. P'71 by RVP & moved to Quainton; sold to them in '83

| | | | | | | |
|---------|------|------|-------|------|-----|----------|
| 5498 | 1920 | PMVY | Eastleigh | 88 | 2104 | Bluebell |
| 1584 | 1927 | | | 929 | | |
| 1686S | 1941 | | | | | |
| DS1686 | 1948 | | | | | |

Remarks: Luggage Van. W'41, converted to Battery-charging van & in use till '69. P'70 by Southern Loco Pres Co & at Longmoor till '71

| | | | | | | |
|---------|------|------|-------|------|-----|----------|
| ? | 1921 | PMVY | | | | Bluebell |
| ? | | | | | | |
| DS1309 | | | | | | |

Remarks: Latterly Generator Van for BR(S) Cinema coach. P'??, body grounded as a store at Horsted Keynes

Others:
U'frame of a CL (48ft, built c1900, extended to 58ft in '35, SR No.4668) P'82 on K&ESR as crane runner DS70003 (K&ESR 134)
U'frame of a CL (built 1904) P'82 at Midland as crane runner DS3104
see also SR 3204

## SOMERSET & DORSET JOINT RAILWAY

| | | | | | | |
|---------|------|------|-------|------|-----|----------|
| 4 | 1886 | FZ | Highbridge | | | W Somerset |
| | 1905 | TZ | | | | |
| (1405) | SR | | | | | |

Remarks: W'30, body grounded as sports pavilion at Templecombe. P'86 by S&DR Trust

## SOUTH EASTERN RAILWAY

| | | | | | | |
|---------|------|------|-------|------|-----|----------|
| 585 | 1897 | TZ | Cravens | | | |
| 792 | 1899 | SZ | Brown Marshall | | | |

Remarks: Part of 585, whole of 792 & part of another used by SR to build a new bogie Composite in 1927, SR 5546 (qv)

| Numbers | Year | Type | Built | Diag | Lot | Location |
|---------|------|------|-------|------|-----|----------|

# SOUTH EASTERN & CHATHAM RAILWAY

| 152 | 1922 | PMVY | Ashford | | | Cymmer, W Glamorgan |
| 1993 | 1928 | | | 960 | | |
| DS747 | 1947 | | | | | |

*Remarks:* P'84 by W Glamorgan CC, initially on BSC's sidings (Port Talbot) before moving to Afon Argoed country park

| 153 | 1922 | PMVY | Bristol C&W | | | Bluebell |
| 1994 | 1930 | | | 960 | | |
| DS/DW70031 | | | | | | |

*Remarks:* P'73

| 154 | 1922 | PMVY | Ashford | | | Mid-Hants |
| 1995 | 1929 | | | 960 | | |
| DS792 | | | | | | |

| 177 (i) | 1900 | FO | Ashford | 4330 | | K&ESR |
| | 1908 | Spec | | | | |
| 7913 | 1927 | | | 613 | | |
| Army 118 | 1936 | | | | | |
| Army 3006 | | | | | | |
| K&ESR 84 | 1985 | | | | | |

*Remarks:* Converted to Invalid Saloon in 1908; sold to Army in '36 for LMR Officers' Train. P'70, a gift to the Transport Trust, remaining at Longmoor till moved to Severn Valley in '71. Sold to K&ESR Loco Trust & came south '85

| 177 (ii) | 1922 | PMVY | Ashford | | | K&ESR |
| 2012 | 1928 | | | 960 | | |
| DS1035 | 1948 | | | | | |
| K&ESR 89 | 1990 | | | | | |

*Remarks:* P'90

| 267 | | CCTZ | Ashford | | | ? |
| 4670 | 1929 | | | 1156 | | |
| 1450S | 1939 | | | | | |
| DS1450 | 1948 | | | | | |

*Remarks:* P'?? at Ashford (not seen since, but may still be extant)

| 719 | 1905 | BZ | Metro C&W | 1542A | | Bluebell |
| 616 | 192x | | | | | |
| 1601S | 1941 | | | | | |

*Remarks:* 'Birdcage' lookout. Became Mess/Tool van in 1941, to Derwent Valley Railway in '47. P'67 by Southern Loco Pres Co, stored first at Wheldrake, then at Chasewater from 1968-72

| 950 | 1907 | BS | Metro C&W | | | ? |
| 3582 | 1928 | BT | | 168 | | |
| DS27 | 1954 | | | | | |

*Remarks:* 'Birdcage' lookout. P' ?, at Ashford till '83 (not seen since, but believed extant)

| Numbers | Year | Type | Built | Diag | Lot | Location |
|---------|------|------|-------|------|-----|----------|
| 1061 | 1909 | BC | Ashford | | | Bluebell |
| 3334 | 1929 | BT | | 155 | | |
| DS3208 | 1952 | | | | | |

Remarks: 'Birdcage' lookout. P'62.

| Numbers | Year | Type | Built | Diag | Lot | Location |
|---------|------|------|-------|------|-----|----------|
| 1084 | 1910 | BCL | Metro C&W | | | K&ESR |
| 3363 | 1928 | BTL | | 157 | | |
| DS22 | 1954 | | | | | |
| K&ESR 68 | 1978 | | | | | |

Remarks: 'Birdcage' lookout. Converted to Gauge Template Unit in 1954. P'78.

| Numbers | Year | Type | Built | Diag | Lot | Location |
|---------|------|------|-------|------|-----|----------|
| 1100 | 1910 | BCL | Ashford | 3185A | | K&ESR |
| 3368 | 1924 | BTL | | 158 | | |
| AD 13582 | 1943 | | | | | |
| Army 5311 | | | | | | |
| K&ESR 61 | 1970 | | | | | |

Remarks: 'Birdcage' lookout. Sold to Army in 1943 for Longmoor Military Railway. P'70

| Numbers | Year | Type | Built | Diag | Lot | Location |
|---------|------|------|-------|------|-----|----------|
| 1106 | 1910 | BC | Ashford | 3186A | | K&ESR |
| 3388 | 1924 | BT | | 159 | | |
| AD 13583 | 1943 | | | | | |
| Army 5312 | | | | | | |
| K&ESR 60 | 1970 | | | | | |

Remarks: 'Birdcage' lookout. Sold to Army with 1100 above in Set 552. P'70

| Numbers | Year | Type | Built | Diag | Lot | Location |
|---------|------|------|-------|------|-----|----------|
| 1122 | 1911 | BC | Ashford | 3186A | | IoWSR |
| 3390 | 1924 | BT | | 159 | | |
| 4145 | 1949 | | | 235 | | |

Remarks: 'Birdcage' lookout, removed before shipped to Isle of Wight '49. P'66, at Newport till '71

| Numbers | Year | Type | Built | Diag | Lot | Location |
|---------|------|------|-------|------|-----|----------|
| 1133 | 1911 | CL | Ashford | 3184A | | IoWSR |
| 5412 | 1927 | | | 313 | | |
| 6375 | 1949 | | | 378 | | |

Remarks: To IoW '49. P'66, at Newport till '71

| Numbers | Year | Type | Built | Diag | Lot | Location |
|---------|------|------|-------|------|-----|----------|
| 1148 | 1911 | BC | Ashford | 3186A | | IoWSR |
| 3402 | 1926 | BT | | 159 | | |
| 4149 | 1949 | | | 235 | | |

Remarks: 'Birdcage' lookout, removed before shipped to Isle of Wight '49. P'66, at Newport till '71

| Numbers | Year | Type | Built | Diag | Lot | Location |
|---------|------|------|-------|------|-----|----------|
| 1170 | 1912 | BT | Ashford | | | Bluebell |
| 3410 | 1928 | | | 160 | | |
| 33S | 195? | | | | | |
| DS33 | | | | | | |
| 083180 | | | | | | |

Remarks: 'Birdcage' lookout. P'82

| Numbers | Year | Type | Built | Diag | Lot | Location |
|---------|------|------|-------|------|-----|----------|
| 1416 | 1922 | T | Ashford | | | Bluebell |
| 1098 | 1929 | | | 52 | | |

*Remarks:* P'63

| | | | | | | |
|---------|------|------|-------|------|-----|----------|
| 1434 | 1923 | T | Ashford | | | Bluebell |
| 971 | 1929 | | | 52 | | |

*Remarks:* P'63

| | | | | | | |
|---------|------|------|-------|------|-----|----------|
| 23xx | c1900 | C | Metro or Cravens? | 1253 | | K&ESR |
| 72xx | | | | | | |

*Remarks:* Body on platform at Tenterden. (Orig 23xx/72xx from Metro or 34xx/52xx from Cravens; probably 2329/7287 or 2338/7296, but maybe 3445/5237)

| | | | | | | |
|---------|------|------|-------|------|-----|----------|
| 2947 | 1901 | SY | Ashford | | | K&ESR |

*Remarks:* LCDR design. Body grounded '21 as part of a bungalow at Ashford (with LCDR's 52, 68 & 108). P'86, a gift to Ashford Area Group by the site developers

**Dating from 1912, this 'Birdcage' Brake Third ended its BR days as an internal user vehicle (No 083180) stabled at Clapham Junction. In such obvious good condition, it was small wonder that preservationists were panting at the thought of its survival and, indeed, this took place in 1982. The coach can now be seen at the Bluebell Railway.** *Martin Allen*

| Numbers | Year | Type | Built | Diag | Lot | Location |
|---------|------|------|-------|------|-----|----------|

*Others:*
Body P'?? by N Downs at Dartford
Body P'90 from Shelley Beach, Exmouth
Body section (one end comp't) of No.436 (SY built Cravens 1897 & W'26 ?) at Horsted Keynes
U'frame of 2351 (C built Metro 1900, SR F 7258, stores van 1696S till '48) P'90 on K&ESR as crane runner
DS3141 (K&ESR 162)
see also SR 3554

# SOUTHERN RAILWAY

| Numbers | Year | Type | Built | Diag | Lot | Location |
|---------|------|------|-------|------|-----|----------|
| 13 | 1941 | BY | Eastleigh | | | Swanage |

*Remarks:* P'79

| Numbers | Year | Type | Built | Diag | Lot | Location |
|---------|------|------|-------|------|-----|----------|
| 201 | 1939 | B | Eastleigh | 3093 | 1029 | Dartford |

*Remarks:* P'86 by N Downs Stm Ry

| Numbers | Year | Type | Built | Diag | Lot | Location |
|---------|------|------|-------|------|-----|----------|
| 205 083571 | 1939 1984 | B | Eastleigh | 3093 | 1029 | Tonbridge |

*Remarks:* Former 'Golden Arrow' brake, P'89 by Tonbridge Model Eng Soc at Brightfriars Meadow

| Numbers | Year | Type | Built | Diag | Lot | Location |
|---------|------|------|-------|------|-----|----------|
| 207 | 1939 | B | Eastleigh | 3093 | 1029 | Steamtown |

*Remarks:* P'82?

| Numbers | Year | Type | Built | Diag | Lot | Location |
|---------|------|------|-------|------|-----|----------|
| 219 | 1939 | B | Eastleigh | 3093 | 1029 | Burnham-on-Crouch |

*Remarks:* P'91 at Mangapps Farm

| Numbers | Year | Type | Built | Diag | Lot | Location |
|---------|------|------|-------|------|-----|----------|
| 227 | 1939 | B | Eastleigh | 3093 | 1029 | Dean Forest |

*Remarks:* P'82?

| Numbers | Year | Type | Built | Diag | Lot | Location |
|---------|------|------|-------|------|-----|----------|
| 232 DB977065 | 1939 1982 | B | Eastleigh | 3093 | 1029 | Swanage |

*Remarks:* P'91

| Numbers | Year | Type | Built | Diag | Lot | Location |
|---------|------|------|-------|------|-----|----------|
| 256 | 1952 | B | Lancing | 3093 | 3227 | Preston Park |

*Remarks:* P'87

| Numbers | Year | Type | Built | Diag | Lot | Location |
|---------|------|------|-------|------|-----|----------|
| 273 | 1953 | B | Lancing | 3093 | 3227 | Burnham-on-Crouch |

*Remarks:* P'87 at Mangapps Farm ex Mayer Newman

320 – see LSWR 1228

| Numbers | Year | Type | Built | Diag | Lot | Location |
|---------|------|------|-------|------|-----|----------|
| 385 | 1938 | B | Eastleigh | 3093 | 927 | Swanage |

*Remarks:* P'82

| Numbers | Year | Type | Built | Diag | Lot | Location |
|---------|------|------|-------|------|-----|----------|
| 404 | 1936 | BY | Eastleigh | 3092 | 928 | Bluebell |

*Remarks:* P'71 by SCPG, at Ashford till '78.

| Numbers | Year | Type | Built | Diag | Lot | Location |
|---------|------|------|-------|------|-----|----------|
| 407 | 1937 | BY | Eastleigh | 3092 | 928 | Betws-y-Coed |

Remarks: P pre'74 by Conwy Valley Railway Museum

| Numbers | Year | Type | Built | Diag | Lot | Location |
|---------|------|------|-------|------|-----|----------|
| 440 | 1937 | BY | Eastleigh | 3092 | 928 | K&ESR |
| K&ESR 66 | 1977 | | | | | |

Remarks: P'77

| Numbers | Year | Type | Built | Diag | Lot | Location |
|---------|------|------|-------|------|-----|----------|
| 442 | 1937 | BY | Eastleigh | 3092 | 928 | Bluebell |

Remarks: P'70

| Numbers | Year | Type | Built | Diag | Lot | Location |
|---------|------|------|-------|------|-----|----------|
| 653 | 1938 | BY | Ashford | 3092 | 974 | Bluebell |

Remarks: P'73

717/28 – see LSWR 773/4

There are numerous vans classed as coaching stock and many earn their keep in preservationists' hands as store vehicles. The Southern Railway's bogied Brake (B) is represented by nine in private hands to date. Of these four (Nos S270, S263, S201 and S273), photographed at Tunbridge West yard on 10 February 1985, two are still extant — No 273 at Mangapps Farm Museum at Burnham-on-Crouch and S201 at Dartford by the North Downs Steam Railway. *Rodney Lissenden*

| Numbers | Year | Type | Built | Diag | Lot | Location |
|---------|------|------|-------|------|-----|----------|
| 730 | 1923 | TK | Eastleigh | 24 | | K&ESR |
| DS228 | 1959 | | | | | |
| K&ESR 90 | 1990 | | | | | |

*Remarks:* 'Ironclad' P'90

| 748 | 1924 | TK | Eastleigh | 24 | | K&ESR |
| DS229 | 1959 | | | | | |

*Remarks:* 'Ironclad' P'91

| 752 | 1924 | TK | Eastleigh | 24 | | IoWSR |
| DS70014 | 1960 | | | | | |

*Remarks:* 'Ironclad' P'90 (underframe reportedly intended for LBSCR No.93)

| 765 | 1939 | BY | Eastleigh | 3092 | 1030 | Mid-Hants |

*Remarks:* P'76

| 798 | 1939 | BY | Eastleigh | 3092 | 1030 | Embsay |
| YDR 20 | | | | | | |

*Remarks:* P'79?

| 931 | 1941 | BY | Eastleigh | 3092 | 1090 | Llangollen |

*Remarks:* P'78

| 1020 | 1934 | TK | Eastleigh | 2004 | 709 | K&ESR |
| DS70134 | 1961 | | | | | |
| K&ESR 59 | 1971 | | | | | |

*Remarks:* P'71

1050 – see 5546

| 1070 | 1936 | PMVY | Ashford | 3103 | 855 | Betws-y-Coed |

*Remarks:* P'74 by Conwy Valley Railway Museum

| 1074 | 1936 | PMVY | Ashford | 3103 | 855 | Middleton |

*Remarks:* P'87?

| 1108 | 1936 | PMVY | Ashford | 3103 | 855 | Quainton |

*Remarks:* P'73 by 6024 Preservation Soc

| 1125 | 1936 | PMVY | Ashford | 3103 | 855 | Worth Valley |
| KWVR 107 | | | | | | |

*Remarks:* P pre'74

| Numbers | Year | Type | Built | Diag | Lot | Location |
|---------|------|------|-------|------|-----|----------|
| 1134 | 1936 | PMVY | Ashford | 3103 | 855 | IoWSR |
| 1046 | 1950 | | | | | |
| DS70256 | 1966 | | | | | |
| 082055 | | | | | | |

Remarks: P'85 (the underframe of either this or 1720 has been used under LCDR BT 653, the body grounded as C&W Dept. store)

| 1137 | 1936 | PMVY | Ashford | 3103 | 855 | E Somerset |

Remarks: P'73

| 1145 | 1936 | PMVY | Ashford | 3103 | 855 | K&ESR |
| DS70217 | 1966 | | | | | |
| KESR 79 | 1985 | | | | | |

Remarks: P'84

| 1152 | 1936 | PMVY | Ashford | 3103 | 855 | Chappel |

Remarks: P'75

| 1153 | 1936 | PMVY | Ashford | 3103 | 855 | Great Central |

Remarks: P'87

| 1162 | 1936 | PMVY | Ashford | 3103 | 824 | Swanage |
| DS149 | 1954 | | | | | |

Remarks: P'88? by Port Line Project

| 1168 | 1936 | PMVY | Ashford | 3103 | 824 | Caerphilly |
| DS8 | 1953 | | | | | |

Remarks: P'?

| 1174 | 1936 | PMVY | Ashford | 3103 | 824 | Severn Valley |
| DS70004 | 1958 | | | | | |

Remarks: P'88, ex Cohen's scrapyard

| 1176 | 1936 | PMVY | Ashford | 3103 | 824 | Midland |
| DS70056 | 1959 | | | | | |

Remarks: P'89

| 1184 | 1936 | PMVY | Ashford | 3103 | 824 | Bluebell |
| DS164 | 1957 | | | | | |

Remarks: P'86

| 1213 | 1936 | PMVY | Ashford | 3103 | 824 | K&ESR |
| DS70006 | 1958 | | | | | |

Remarks: P'91

| 1218 | 1936 | PMVY | Ashford | 3103 | 824 | Nene Valley |

Remarks: P'75 & at Chappel till pre'87

| Numbers | Year | Type | Built | Diag | Lot | Location |
|---------|------|------|-------|------|-----|----------|
| 1225 | 1936 | PMVY | Ashford | 3103 | 824 | K&ESR |

Remarks: P' ?, body grounded at Wittersham Road ' ?

| Numbers | Year | Type | Built | Diag | Lot | Location |
|---------|------|------|-------|------|-----|----------|
| 1227 | 1936 | PMVY | Ashford | 3103 | 824 | Dean Forest |

Remarks: P'81

| Numbers | Year | Type | Built | Diag | Lot | Location |
|---------|------|------|-------|------|-----|----------|
| 1228 | 1936 | PMVY | Ashford | 3103 | 824 | K&ESR |
| DS800 | 1950 | | | | | |

Remarks: P'90 with fire-damaged body, u'frame to be used for one of the SECR bodies ex-Ashford

| Numbers | Year | Type | Built | Diag | Lot | Location |
|---------|------|------|-------|------|-----|----------|
| 1234 | 1936 | PMVY | Ashford | 3103 | 824 | Swanage |
| DS3065 | 1950 | | | | | |

Remarks: P'76 by SST members

| Numbers | Year | Type | Built | Diag | Lot | Location |
|---------|------|------|-------|------|-----|----------|
| 1240 | 1936 | PMVY | Ashford | 3103 | 824 | K&ESR |
| DS154 | 1956 | | | | | |

Remarks: P'89 by M James, stored at Hoo Jct Yard till '91

| Numbers | Year | Type | Built | Diag | Lot | Location |
|---------|------|------|-------|------|-----|----------|
| 1248 | 1936 | PMVY | Ashford | 3103 | 824 | K&ESR |
| DS161 | 1957 | | | | | |
| KESR 80 | 1984 | | | | | |

Remarks: P'84

| Numbers | Year | Type | Built | Diag | Lot | Location |
|---------|------|------|-------|------|-----|----------|
| 1258 | 1939 | PMVY | Ashford | 3103 | 1031 | Market Bosworth |

Remarks: P'81?

| Numbers | Year | Type | Built | Diag | Lot | Location |
|---------|------|------|-------|------|-----|----------|
| 1283 | 1939 | PMVY | Ashford | 3103 | 1031 | IoWSR |
| 1047 | 1950 | | | | | |
| 082756 | 1967 | | | | | |

Remarks: P'86 as a store

| Numbers | Year | Type | Built | Diag | Lot | Location |
|---------|------|------|-------|------|-----|----------|
| 1304 | 1939 | PMVY | Ashford | 3103 | 1031 | Worth Valley |
| KWVR 113 | 1982 | | | | | |

Remarks: P'81? for filming 'The Wall', then reconstructed as a Store van.

| Numbers | Year | Type | Built | Diag | Lot | Location |
|---------|------|------|-------|------|-----|----------|
| 1309 | 1935 | TO | Eastleigh | 2007 | 761 | Bluebell |
| 081642 | 1963 | | | | | |

Remarks: P'73 by Southern Loco Preservation Group

| Numbers | Year | Type | Built | Diag | Lot | Location |
|---------|------|------|-------|------|-----|----------|
| 1323 (i) | 1933 | TO | Lancing | 2005 | 706 | Mid-Hants |
| 082232 | 1964 | | | | | |
| DS70266 | 1968 | | | | | |

Remarks: P'82, but for sale '84

| Numbers | Year | Type | Built | Diag | Lot | Location |
|---------|------|------|-------|------|-----|----------|
| 1323 (ii) | 1939 | PMVY | Ashford | 3103 | 1031 | Tanfield ? |
| 041468 | | | | | | |
| DB975960 | 1980 | | | | | |

Remarks: P'90 by Stephenson & Hawthorn Loco Trust

| 1333 | 1939 | PMVY | Ashford | 3103 | 1031 | Market Bosworth |

Remarks: P'81?

| 1336 (i) | 1939 | PMVY | Ashford | 3103 | 1031 | Great Central |

Remarks: Body P'?

| 1336 (ii) | 1933 | TO | Eastleigh | 2005 | 706 | Bluebell |
| 081901 | 1962 | | | | | |
| DS70313 | 1970 | | | | | |

Remarks: P'88

| 1346 | 1933 | TO | Eastleigh | 2005 | 706 | K&ESR |
| DS70201 | 1961 | | | | | |
| 083181 | 1975 | | | | | |
| K&ESR 78 | 1982 | | | | | |

Remarks: P'82

| 1360 | 1939 | PMVY | Ashford | 3103 | 1031 | W Somerset |

Remarks: P'85

1365 – see 7866

| 1367 | 1939 | PMVY | Ashford | 3103 | 1031 | Tyseley |

Remarks: P'83

| 1375 | 1939 | PMVY | Ashford | 3103 | 1031 | Great Central |

Remarks: Body P'? by Thompson B1 Soc

| 1381 | 1930 | TO | Eastleigh | 2005 | 461 | Swanage |
| DS70175 | 1962 | | | | | |

Remarks: P'79

| 1391 | 1939 | PMVY | Ashford | 3103 | 1031 | Steamtown |

Remarks: P'83

| 1396 | 1939 | PMVY | Ashford | 3103 | 1031 | E Somerset |

Remarks: P'73

| 1418 | 1951 | CCTY | Ashford | 3101 | 3702 | Brecon Mountain |

Remarks: P'87

| Numbers | Year | Type | Built | Diag | Lot | Location |
|---------|------|------|-------|------|-----|----------|
| 1432 | 1951 | CCTY | Ashford | 3101 | 3702 | Southport |

Remarks: P'?

| 1439 | 1951 | CCTY | Ashford | 3101 | 3702 | Chappel |

Remarks: P'87

| 1449 | 1951 | CCTY | Ashford | 3101 | 3702 | Swindon |

Remarks: P'83 by Port Line Loco group, at Blunsdon till '88

| 1456 DS70285 | 1947 1967 | TO | Eastleigh | 2017 | 3240 | * Bluebell |

Remarks: P'80

| 1457 DS70262 | 1948 1967 | TO | Eastleigh | 2017 | 3240 | Swanage |

Remarks: P'88, to Swindon for restoration

| 1458 | 1951 | PMVY | Wolverton | 3103 | | W Somerset |

Remarks: P'84 by GW Rolling Stock Fund

| 1461 | 1951 | PMVY | Wolverton | 3103 | | Hayling Island |

Remarks: P'87 by HI Rly Soc

| 1464 (i) | 1951 | PMVY | Wolverton | 3103 | | W Somerset |

Remarks: P'85

| 1464 (ii) | 1950 | TO | Eastleigh | 2017 | 3581 | Bluebell |

Remarks: P'68 by SCPG to complement 'Clan Line', & at Ashford till the evacuation in '78

| 1469 K&WVR 5 | 1950 | TO | Eastleigh | 2017 | 3581 | Worth Valley |

Remarks: P'69 by Vintage Carriages Trust

| 1470 K&WVR 114 | 1951 1982 | PMVY | Wolverton | 3103 | | Steamtown |

Remarks: P'81 after filming The Wall & on Worth Valley as a Store van till late '80s

| 1481 | 1950 | TO | Eastleigh | 2017 | 3581 | Bluebell |

Remarks: P'70

| 1482 DS70314 | 1950 | TO | Eastleigh | 2017 | 3581 | Bluebell |

Remarks: P'73 after its discovery at Bellahouston by the Scottish RPS; its journey south led to the sale of the Bluebell's Caledonian coach

| Numbers | Year | Type | Built | Diag | Lot | Location |
|---------|------|------|-------|------|-----|----------|
| 1497 | 1951 | PMVY | Wolverton | 3103 | | IoWSR |

*Remarks:* P'82 (u/f for vintage coach body?)

| 1517 | 1947 | PMVY | Ashford | 3103 | 3229 | |

*Remarks:* P'81? on Worth Valley for film *The Wall*; underframe since converted to crane runner.

| 1533 | 1947 | PMVY | Ashford | 3103 | 3229 | IoWSR |

*Remarks:* P'82 (u/f for vintage coach body?)

| 1550 | 1947 | PMVY | Ashford | 3103 | 3229 | |

*Remarks:* P'81 on Worth Valley for film *The Wall*, & though moved to Steamtown by '84 was not found there '90

| 1563 | 1950 | PMVY | Ashford | 3103 | 3590 | Market Bosworth |

*Remarks:* P'82?

| 1566 | 1950 | PMVY | Ashford | 3103 | 3590 | IoWSR |

*Remarks:* P'81 (u/f for vintage coach body?)

| 1603 | 1950 | PMVY | Ashford | 3103 | 3590 | IoWSR |

*Remarks:* P'82 (u/f for vintage coach body?)

| 1617 | 1950 | PMVY | Ashford | 3103 | 3590 | IoWSR |

*Remarks:* P'82 (u/f for vintage coach body?)

| 1633 | 1950 | PMVY | Lancing | 3103 | 3590 | W Somerset |

*Remarks:* P'84

| 1650 | 1950 | PMVY | Lancing | 3103 | 3590 | E Somerset |

*Remarks:* P'86 for stores use

| 1669 | 1950 | PMVY | Lancing | 3103 | 3590 | IoWSR |

*Remarks:* P'82 (u/f for vintage coach body?)

| 1692 | 1943 | PMVY | Lancing | 3103 | 1659 | IoWSR |
| 1052 | 1950 | | | | | |
| 082975 | 1966 | | | | | |

*Remarks:* To IoW in 1950, P'76.

| 1698 | 1943 | PMVY | Lancing | 3103 | 1659 | Bitton |

*Remarks:* P' ?, grounded as store

| 1703 | 1943 | PMVY | Lancing | 3103 | 1659 | Foxfield |

*Remarks:* P'82? (u/f intended for MR 2741 but being used as store)

| Numbers | Year | Type | Built | Diag | Lot | Location |
|---------|------|------|-------|------|-----|----------|
| 1706 | 1943 | PMVY | Lancing | 3103 | 1659 | Great Central |

Remarks: P'84 by GCR member.

| 1711 | 1943 | PMVY | Lancing | 3103 | 1659 | Embsay |

Remarks: P'82?

| 1712 | 1943 | PMVY | Lancing | 3103 | 1659 | Bitton |

Remarks: P' ?

| 1720 | 1943 | PMVY | Lancing | 3103 | 1659 | IoWSR |
| 1048 | 1950 | | | | | |
| DS70257 | | | | | | |
| 082056 | 1967 | | | | | |

Remarks: To IoW 1950, P'85 (Underframe of this or 1134 used to carry the body of LCDR BT 653, the spare body grounded as C&W Dept store)

| 1745 | 1938 | CCTY | Eastleigh | 3101 | 972 | K&ESR |
| KESR 76 | 1982 | | | | | |

Remarks: P'82

| 1750 | 1938 | CCTY | Eastleigh | 3101 | 972 | IoWSR |

Remarks: P'81, body grounded as Loco Dept store & underframe used under the North London body (IoWR 46)

| 1765 | 1938 | CCTY | Eastleigh | 3101 | 972 | St Leonards |

Remarks: P'?? by SEG, on Nene Valley till '86 then Brighton till '91

| 1768 | 1938 | CCTY | Eastleigh | 3101 | 972 | Mid-Hants |

Remarks: P'77

| 1783 | 1942 | PMVY | Lancing | 3103 | 1191 | IoWSR |

Remarks: P'81 (u/f for vintage coach body?)

| 1788 | 1942 | PMVY | Lancing | 3103 | 1191 | Bluebell |

Remarks: P'82, currently serving as a store at W Hoathly

| 1803 | 1942 | PMVY | Lancing | 3103 | 1191 | IoWSR |

Remarks: P'82 (u/f for vintage coach body?)

| 1808 | 1942 | PMVY | Lancing | 3103 | 1191 | K&ESR |
| KESR 74 | | | | | | |

Remarks: P'81, given gangway at one end in '84 for use in 'Wealden Pullman' set.

| 1811 | 1942 | PMVY | Lancing | 3103 | 1191 | Bodmin |

Remarks: P'86

| Numbers | Year | Type | Built | Diag | Lot | Location |
|---------|------|------|-------|------|-----|----------|
| 1851 | 1940 | PMVY | Eastleigh | 3103 | 1092 | Mid-Hants |

Remarks: P'76, now used as a store.

| 1856 | 1940 | PMVY | Eastleigh | 3103 | 1092 | Bo'ness |

Remarks: P'82? by SRPS, at Falkirk till '88

| 1863 | 1940 | PMVY | Eastleigh | 3103 | 1092 | Gloucs-Warks |

Remarks: P'82 by 35006 Association

| 1865 | 1940 | PMVY | Eastleigh | 3103 | 1092 | Midland |

Remarks: P'87, its u'frame to be shortened for use as chassis for MR 211 (qv)

| 1867 | 1940 | PMVY | Eastleigh | 3103 | 1092 | Middleton |
|      | 198? | TY   |           |      |      |           |

Remarks: P'82? & rebuilt as passenger coach

| 1874 | 1940 | PMVY | Eastleigh | 3103 | 1092 | Derby ? |

Remarks: P'88 by Hartland Pres Grp, at Shaws Metals (may have accompanied 'Hartland' to Great Central '91)

| 1925 | 1938 | PMVY | Ashford | 3103 | 973 | Rutland |
| 1930 | 1938 | PMVY | Ashford | 3103 | 973 | IoWSR |

Remarks: P'82 (u/f for vintage coach body?)

| 1937 | 1938 | PMVY | Ashford | 3103 | 973 | Manchester Liverpool Rd |
| 1964 | 1938 | PMVY | Ashford | 3103 | 973 | W Somerset |

Remarks: P'85

| 1990 | 1951 | CCTY | Ashford | 3101 | 3702 | Nene Valley |

Remarks: P'81?

| 2084 | 1943 | PMVY | Lancing | 3103 | 1659 | Middleton |
|      | 198? | TY   |         |      |      |           |

Remarks: P'?? & rebuilt as passenger coach

| 2105 | 1942 | PMVY | Lancing | 3103 | 1191 | N Woolwich |
| 2142 | 1942 | PMVY | Lancing | 3103 | 1191 | Preston Pk |
| 2151 | 1942 | PMVY | Lancing | 3103 | 1191 | Buxton |

Remarks: P'81 & on Worth Valley till '??

| 2157 | 1942 | PMVY | Lancing | 3103 | 1191 | E Somerset |

Remarks: P'86 for stores use

| Numbers | Year | Type | Built | Diag | Lot | Location |
|---------|------|------|-------|------|-----|----------|
| 2158 | 1942 | PMVY | Lancing | 3103 | 1191 | Market Bosworth |

Remarks: P'??

| 2186 DS150 | 1934 1956 | PMVY | Ashford | 3103 | | Bluebell |

Remarks: P'79 by Maunsell Loco Soc

| 2188 DS11 | 1934 | PMVY | Ashford | 3103 | | Mid-Hants |

Remarks: P'78

| 2196 DS93 | 1934 | PMVY | Ashford | 3103 | | Mid-Hants |

Remarks: P'76

| 2213 DS70154 | 1935 1961 | PMVY | Ashford | 3103 | | Bitton ? |

Remarks: P'90 by Chichester & Midhurst RPS, resold to Avon Valley '91

| 2225 DS70156 | 1935 1962 | PMVY | Ashford | 3103 | | Tanfield ? |

Remarks: P'90 by Stephenson & Hawthorn Loco Trust

| 2239 | 1951 | CCTY | Ashford | 3101 | 3702 | Dartford |

Remarks: P'87 by N Downs Stm Rly, stored at Rochester till '88

| 2276 DS70202 | 1929 1963 | CCTY | Ashford | 3101 | 277 | Bluebell |

Remarks: P'74

| 2298 | 1930 | PMVG | Ashford | 3100 | 443 | Bluebell |

Remarks: Gangwayed Bogie Luggage van built on a former LSWR 51ft underframe (ex-BT or C). P' ?

| 2339 DS70076 K&ESR 77 | 1930 1960 1982 | PMVG | Ashford | 3098 | | K&ESR |

Remarks: Built on a former LSWR 49ft underframe (ex-Compo) lengthened by 2ft. P'82

| 2356 081315 | 1931 c1962 | TK | Eastleigh | 2003 | 494 | Bluebell |

Remarks: P'73

| 2400 082949 | 1931 1971 | CCTY | Selhurst | 3101 | | Eastleigh |

Remarks: P'84? by Eastleigh RPS

| Numbers | Year | Type | Built | Diag | Lot | Location |
|---|---|---|---|---|---|---|
| 2439<br>DS70324 | 1931<br>1971 | CCTY | Selhurst | 3101 | | Pitsford |

*Remarks:* P'90

| 2462<br>DS70141 | 1931<br>1961<br>1982 | PMVG<br><br>RK | Ashford<br><br>Bluebell | 3099 | 573 | Bluebell |

*Remarks:* Built on a former LSWR 51ft underframe (ex-BT or C) lengthened by 2ft. Used in CasEvac Train 34/334 during WW2. P'81, used as Kitchen & Store from '83

| 2464 | 1931 | PMVG | Ashford | 3099 | 573 | California, USA |

*Remarks:* Second-hand u'frame as per 2462 above. Given Pullman livery in 1962 & used to carry Churchill's coffin after the State Funeral in 1965, then exported to 'City of Industry' Los Angeles

| 2504 | 1955 | CCTY | Lancing | 3101 | 3764 | Brecon Mountain |

*Remarks:* P'87

| 2515 | 1951 | BTK | Eastleigh | 2123 | | Bluebell |

*Remarks:* Semi-open. P'73

| 2524 | 1955 | CCTY | Lancing | 3101 | 3764 | Brecon Mountain |

*Remarks:* P'87

| 2530 | 1955 | CCTY | Lancing | 3101 | 3764 | N Yorks Moors |

*Remarks:* P'82

| 2531 | 1955 | CCTY | Lancing | 3101 | 3764 | Bluebell |

*Remarks:* P'81 by Camelot Soc

| 2768<br>DS70172 | 1932<br>1962 | BTK | Eastleigh<br>Longhedge | 2102 | 633 | Swanage |

*Remarks:* P'81 by SST

| 2850<br>CWT 13<br>99013 plated | 1945<br>1964 | BTK | Eastleigh | 2121 | 3043 | - |

*Remarks:* Latterly Chipman's Staff coach. P'78 on Mid-Hants, but body dismantled '88; underframe transferred to Swanage '90 as crane runner.

3187/90 – see LSWR 1282 & 1353

| 3193<br><br>DS70133 | 1923<br><br>1964 | BTK | Eastleigh | LSW24c<br>213 | | K&ESR |

*Remarks:* 'Ironclad' P'89 ex Marple & Gillott, at Stewarts Lane till swopped for BR 35326 (qv) in '91

| Numbers | Year | Type | Built | Diag | Lot | Location |
|---------|------|------|-------|------|-----|----------|
| 3204 | 1925 | BTK | Eastleigh | LSW24c 213 | | W Somerset |
| DS70085 | 1959 | | | | | |

Remarks: 'Ironclad' P'73 by S&DR Trust, at Radstock till '75, later sold to WSR Assoc

| 3554 | 1924 | BTK | Metro C&W | SEC | | Worth Valley |
| K&WVR 1 | | | | | | |

Remarks: P'62 for Westerham branch scheme, but stored till sold to Vintage Carriage Trust in '65

| 3687 | 1929 | BTK | Eastleigh | 2105 | 498 | Bluebell |
| DS70160 | 1962 | | | | | |
| 083409 | 1981 | | | | | |

Remarks: P'91

| 3690 | 1931 | BTK | Eastleigh | 2105 | 498 | Tunbridge Wells |
| DS70163 | 1962 | | | | | |

Remarks: In SR Control Train till '80. P'88, at Great Central till sale to TWERPS

| 3719 | 1930 | BTK | Eastleigh | 2101 | 489 | Mid-Hants |
| DS70168 | 1962 | | | | | |

Remarks: P'76

| 3724 | 1930 | BTK | Eastleigh | 2101 | 487 | Bluebell |
| CWT 7 | | | | | | |
| 99007 plated | | | | | | |

Remarks: Latterly Chipman's Spray coach. P'87, utilised as Exhibition coach at Horsted Keynes

| 3733 | 1951 | SCVY | | | | * NRM |

| 4035 | 1949 | BTK | Eastleigh | 2123 | 3249 | N Yorks Moors |
| CWT 10 | 1964 | | | | | |
| 99010 plated | | | | | | |

Remarks: Latterly Chipman's Staff coach. P'88

| 4036 | 1949 | BTK | Eastleigh | 2123 | 3249 | Bluebell |
| CWT 12 | 1964 | | | | | |
| 99012 plated | | | | | | |

Remarks: Latterly in Chipman's weed-killing train. Pc'82, intended merely for spares

| 4211 | 1947 | BTK | B R C W | 2124 | | Mid-Hants |
| DS70319 | 1966 | | | | | |
| | 1976 | BTKB | Mid-Hants | | | |
| | 1989 | BTKD | Mid-Hants | | | |

Remarks: P'76 & modified to include a buffet

| 4227 | 1948 | BTK | B R C W | 2124 | | Bluebell |
| DW150385 | 1966 | | | | | |

Remarks: P'80, at Bristol Mus till '87

| Numbers | Year | Type | Built | Diag | Lot | Location |
|---------|------|------|-------|------|-----|----------|
| 4279 DS70248 | 1948 | BTK | B R C W | 2125 | | Bluebell |

*Remarks:* Semi-open. P'70

| 4365 RCT 1 Army 5200 | 1948 1967 | BTK | Eastleigh | 2123 | 3240 | Swanage |

*Remarks:* W'66 & sold to the Army, P'78 from MoD Bicester by SST members

| 4366 Army 5201 | 1948 | BTK | Eastleigh | 2123 | 3240 | Swanage |

*Remarks:* W'66 & sold to the Army, P'85 from MoD Kineton by SST

| 4367 Army 5202 | 1948 1966 | BTK | Eastleigh | 2123 | 3240 | Mid-Hants |

*Remarks:* P'89 ex MODAD Long Marston

| 4409 | 1931 1938 | MTY MTZ | Lancing Ashford | 3152 3159 | | Didcot |

*Remarks:* P'? by GWS

| 4430 | 1933 | MTZ | Lancing | 3157 | | Bluebell |

*Remarks:* P'81

| 4432 K&ESR 53 | 1933 1972 | BUO | Eastleigh | 2654A | 708 | K&ESR |

*Remarks:* P'65

| 4438 7920 DB975279 K&ESR 72 | 1933 1959 1973 1980 | BUO Ward | Eastleigh Lancing | 2654 | 708 4559 | K&ESR |

*Remarks:* Converted 1959 to 'Ward Car' for Lourdes pilgrims. P'80

| 4441 082444 | 1933 1966? | BUO | Eastleigh | 2654A | 708 | Bluebell |

*Remarks:* P'73

| 4443 K&ESR 27 K&ESR 54 | 1933 1967 1972 | BUO | Eastleigh | 2654 | 708 | K&ESR |

*Remarks:* P'65

| 4444 7921 AD 777 | 1933 1959 | BUO Ward | Eastleigh Lancing | 2654 | 708 4559 | Bluebell |

*Remarks:* P'80 from MOD Bramley with 'rotten' roof & became second Sheffield Park Buffet 1981-6

| Numbers | Year | Type | Built | Diag | Lot | Location |
|---------|------|------|-------|------|-----|----------|
| 4449 | 1933 | BUO | Eastleigh | 2654 | 708 | |
| 7923 | 1959 | Ward | Lancing | | 4559 | |
| DB975406 | 1974 | | | | | |

*Remarks:* P'78 on Mid-Hants & restored for carriage of handicapped. Damaged in shunting accident 12/83 & broken up for spares by Swanage RPS members in '84.

| | | | | | | |
|---------|------|------|-------|------|-----|----------|
| 4594 | 1938 | CCT | Eastleigh | 3182 | 975 | Swanage |

*Remarks:* P'77 by SST members

| | | | | | | |
|---------|------|------|-------|------|-----|----------|
| 4595 | 1938 | CCT | Eastleigh | 2182 | 975 | E Kent |

*Remarks:* Body & underframe grounded at Ramsgate '80. P'91, getting Bulleid EPB bogies, buffers & drawgear when lifted

| | | | | | | |
|---------|------|------|-------|------|-----|----------|
| 4601 | 1949 | CCT | Lancing | 3182 | 3228 | Bluebell |

*Remarks:* Specially strengthened for the carriage of elephants. P'81

| | | | | | | |
|---------|------|------|-------|------|-----|----------|
| 4605 | 1949 | CCT | Lancing | 3182 | 3228 | IoWSR |
| DB975967 | 1980 | | | | | |

*Remarks:* P'90, u'frame intended to carry restored body of LCDR T 348 (qv)

| | | | | | | |
|---------|------|------|-------|------|-----|----------|
| 4920 | 1939 | POS | Eastleigh | 3192 | 1043 | * Nene Valley |

*Remarks:* P'77? here?

| | | | | | | |
|---------|------|------|-------|------|-----|----------|
| 4922 | 1939 | POS | Eastleigh | 3192 | 1043 | Bluebell |

*Remarks:* P'78

| | | | | | | |
|---------|------|------|-------|------|-----|----------|
| 4958 | 1939 | POT | Eastleigh | 3196 | 999 | Mid-Hants |

*Remarks:* P'77

| | | | | | | |
|---------|------|------|-------|------|-----|----------|
| 5153 | 1928 | CK | Eastleigh | 2302 | 160 | K&ESR |
| KESR 55 | 1972 | | | | | |

*Remarks:* P'65

| | | | | | | |
|---------|------|------|-------|------|-----|----------|
| 5546 | 1927 | C | Lancing | 50 | | Bluebell |
| 1050 | 1943 | T | | | | |

*Remarks:* Built using the body of SER Second 792, part-body of SER Third 568 & a section of an unidentified third body on a new underframe. P'63

| | | | | | | |
|---------|------|------|-------|------|-----|----------|
| 5600 | 1930 | CK | Eastleigh | 2304 | 498 | K&ESR |
| DS70155 | 1962 | | | | | |
| KESR 91 | 1990 | | | | | |

*Remarks:* P'90 by Tenterden Rolling Stock Group

| | | | | | | |
|---------|------|------|-------|------|-----|----------|
| 5618 | 1931 | CK | Eastleigh | 2302 | 495 | K&ESR |
| KESR 26 | 1967 | | | | | |
| KESR 56 | 1972 | | | | | |

*Remarks:* P'65

| Numbers | Year | Type | Built | Diag | Lot | Location |
|---------|------|------|-------|------|-----|----------|
| 5644<br>CWT 8<br>99008 plated | 1931 | CK | Eastleigh | 2304 | | Bluebell |

*Remarks:* Latterly in Chipman's weed-killing train. P'89

| Numbers | Year | Type | Built | Diag | Lot | Location |
|---------|------|------|-------|------|-----|----------|
| 5761 | 1947 | CK | Eastleigh | 2318 | 3235 | Swanage |

*Remarks:* P'70, at Longmoor till '71, then Ashford till '78 & Mid-Hants till '84

| Numbers | Year | Type | Built | Diag | Lot | Location |
|---------|------|------|-------|------|-----|----------|
| 5768 | 1947 | CK | Eastleigh | 2318 | | Bluebell |

*Remarks:* P'68 by the Bulleid Society, at Longmoor till 1971

| Numbers | Year | Type | Built | Diag | Lot | Location |
|---------|------|------|-------|------|-----|----------|
| 6164<br>6349 | 1924<br>1937 | C | Lancing | 337<br>373 | | IoWSR |

*Remarks:* LBSCR design, & though allocated No.7 it was probably never borne. P'67, at Newport till '71

| Numbers | Year | Type | Built | Diag | Lot | Location |
|---------|------|------|-------|------|-----|----------|
| 6575 | 1929 | BCK | Eastleigh | 2401 | 363 | Bluebell |

*Remarks:* P'60

| Numbers | Year | Type | Built | Diag | Lot | Location |
|---------|------|------|-------|------|-----|----------|
| 6601<br>DW150386 | 1930<br>1965 | BCK | Eastleigh | 2401 | 462 | Mid-Hants |

*Remarks:* Latterly a mess van, becoming an office in '76. P'78

| Numbers | Year | Type | Built | Diag | Lot | Location |
|---------|------|------|-------|------|-----|----------|
| 6686 | 1935 | BCK | Eastleigh | 2403 | 799 | Bluebell |

*Remarks:* P'67 by Southern Loco Pres Co at Droxford, briefly in Fareham goods shed '70 then at Longmoor till '71

| Numbers | Year | Type | Built | Diag | Lot | Location |
|---------|------|------|-------|------|-----|----------|
| 6697<br>CWT 11<br>99011 plated | 1935 | BCK | Eastleigh | 2403 | 799 | Mid-Hants |

*Remarks:* Latterly in Chipman's stock. P'84

| Numbers | Year | Type | Built | Diag | Lot | Location |
|---------|------|------|-------|------|-----|----------|
| 6699<br>CWT 9<br>99009 plated | 1935<br>1960 | BCK<br>DTC | Eastleigh | 2403<br>4634 | 799 | Horsham |

*Remarks:* Latterly Chipman's Spray coach. P'89 by SST, for Swanage but currently stored

| Numbers | Year | Type | Built | Diag | Lot | Location |
|---------|------|------|-------|------|-----|----------|
| 7200<br>DS227 | 1924<br>1958 | FK | Eastleigh | 476 | | K&ESR |

*Remarks:* 'Ironclad' P'89 ex Marple & Gillott, at Stewarts Lane till swopped for BR 35326 (qv) in '91

| Numbers | Year | Type | Built | Diag | Lot | Location |
|---------|------|------|-------|------|-----|----------|
| 7400<br>O81621<br>K&ESR 57 | 1929<br>1961<br>1972 | FK | | 2503 | 376 | K&ESR |

*Remarks:* P'71

| Numbers | Year | Type | Built | Diag | Lot | Location |
|---------|------|------|-------|------|-----|----------|
| 7679 | 1947 | sRFO | Eastleigh | 2507 | 3234 | - |

*Remarks:* P'65 at Droxford by Sadler Rail Coach Ltd, its remains set on fire by vandals & destroyed '68.

| Numbers | Year | Type | Built | Diag | Lot | Location |
|---------|------|------|-------|------|-----|----------|
| 7798 | 1931 | SO | Eastleigh | 2653 | 463 | K&ESR |
| DS70109 | 1961 | | | | | |
| K&ESR 58 | 1972 | | | | | |

*Remarks:* Latterly mess van; P'71

7851 – see LSWR 4151

| Numbers | Year | Type | Built | Diag | Lot | Location |
|---------|------|------|-------|------|-----|----------|
| 7864 | 1932 | RF | Eastleigh | 2656 | 635 | Bluebell |
| | 1947 | RB | | 2659 | | |

*Remarks:* P'62, Sheffield Park's buffet till '81

| Numbers | Year | Type | Built | Diag | Lot | Location |
|---------|------|------|-------|------|-----|----------|
| 7866 | 1927 | RTO | Eastleigh | 2652 | 99 | Bluebell |
| 1365 | 1930 | TO | | | | |
| 6802 | 1944 | | | | | |
| 7841 | 1947 | RCO | | 2658 | | |

*Remarks:* In Ambulance Train 68 1944-6. P'63

| Numbers | Year | Type | Built | Diag | Lot | Location |
|---------|------|------|-------|------|-----|----------|
| 8143 | 1925 | DMBT | Metro C&W | | | * NRM |
| Set 1293 | | | | | | |
| Set 4308 | | | | | | |

*Remarks:* '3-SUB'. P'63, stored Brighton till '77 & restored by BREL York '79. At NRM York except for 'NRM On Tour' display at Swindon 1990-1 & some Open Days

| Numbers | Year | Type | Built | Diag | Lot | Location |
|---------|------|------|-------|------|-----|----------|
| 8144 | 1925 | DMBT | Metro C&W | | | * |
| Set 1293 | | | | | | |
| Set 4308 | | | | | | |

*Remarks:* '3-SUB'. P'63 with its twin above, but broken-up at York '79 to provide parts.

| Numbers | Year | Type | Built | Diag | Lot | Location |
|---------|------|------|-------|------|-----|----------|
| 10096 | 1938 | TTK | Eastleigh | | | St Leonards |

*Remarks:* '4-COR'. P'72 by SEG member, at Ashford till '76, Nene Valley till '86, Brighton till '91

| Numbers | Year | Type | Built | Diag | Lot | Location |
|---------|------|------|-------|------|-----|----------|
| 10239 | 1946 | TT | Eastleigh | | | Selhurst |

*Remarks:* Augmentation coach, in '4-SUB' Set 4732 from 1951. P'84 by BR, initially at Brighton

| Numbers | Year | Type | Built | Diag | Lot | Location |
|---------|------|------|-------|------|-----|----------|
| 10656 | 1937 | DTCL | Eastleigh | | | * Brighton Works |
| Set 2090 | | | | | | |
| 99951 plated | | | | | | |

*Remarks:* '2-BIL'. P'7?, at Brighton till '89

| Numbers | Year | Type | Built | Diag | Lot | Location |
|---------|------|------|-------|------|-----|----------|
| 11161 | 1937 | DMBTO | Eastleigh | | | St Leonards |
| Set 3065 | | | | | | |
| Set 3142 | 1945 | | | | | |

*Remarks:* '4-RES'. P'72 by SEG, at Ashford till '76, Nene Valley till '86, Brighton till '91

| Numbers | Year | Type | Built | Diag | Lot | Location |
|---------|------|------|-------|------|-----|----------|
| 11179<br>Set 3131 | 1937 | DMBTO | Eastleigh | | | * NRM |

*Remarks:* '4-COR'. P'72, stored Brighton till '77, restored by NRM '79 & at York apart from 'NRM On Tour' trip to Swindon 1990-1

| Numbers | Year | Type | Built | Diag | Lot | Location |
|---------|------|------|-------|------|-----|----------|
| 11187<br>Set 3135 | 1937 | DMBTO | Eastleigh | | | Nene Valley |

*Remarks:* '4-COR'. P'72 & placed in owner's front garden at Cheshunt till moved to Nene Valley in '81

| Numbers | Year | Type | Built | Diag | Lot | Location |
|---------|------|------|-------|------|-----|----------|
| 11201<br>Set 3142 | 1938 | DMBTO | Eastleigh | | | St Leonards |

*Remarks:* '4-COR'. P'72 by SEG, at Ashford till '76, Nene Valley till '86, Brighton till '91

| Numbers | Year | Type | Built | Diag | Lot | Location |
|---------|------|------|-------|------|-----|----------|
| 11773 | 1932 | TCK | Eastleigh | | | Swanage |

*Remarks:* '6-PUL'. P'72 by SEG member, at Ashford till '76, Nene Valley till '84 then Blunsdon. Moved into Swindon Wks '89 but gone by 10/90

| Numbers | Year | Type | Built | Diag | Lot | Location |
|---------|------|------|-------|------|-----|----------|
| 11825 | 1937 | TCK | Eastleigh | | | St Leonards |

*Remarks:* '4-COR'. P'72 by SEG member, at Ashford till '76, Nene Valley till '86, Brighton till '91

| Numbers | Year | Type | Built | Diag | Lot | Location |
|---------|------|------|-------|------|-----|----------|
| 12123<br>Set 2090<br>99952 plated | 1937 | DMBTL | Eastleigh | | | * Brighton |

*Remarks:* '2-BIL'. P'7?

| Numbers | Year | Type | Built | Diag | Lot | Location |
|---------|------|------|-------|------|-----|----------|
| 12354 | 1948 | TTO | Eastleigh | | | Selhurst |

*Remarks:* '4-SUB'. P'84 by BR, firstly at Brighton

| Numbers | Year | Type | Built | Diag | Lot | Location |
|---------|------|------|-------|------|-----|----------|
| 12529 | 1938 | TRB | Eastleigh | | | * |

*Remarks:* '4-BUF'. P'72 by the NRM, stored at Brighton till '77 & loaned to Nene Valley in '78. Set on fire by vandals on 20/10/78 and burned out!

| Numbers | Year | Type | Built | Diag | Lot | Location |
|---------|------|------|-------|------|-----|----------|
| 12613 | 1937<br>1954 | TRT<br>TRB | B R C W | | | Shepherds Bush |

*Remarks:* '4-RES'. Fire damaged in '54; rebuilt as prototype BR RB. P'72 at H&G Car Parks, Sterne St/Wood Lane

| Numbers | Year | Type | Built | Diag | Lot | Location |
|---------|------|------|-------|------|-----|----------|
| 12795<br>Set 4732 | 1951 | DMBTO | Eastleigh | | | Selhurst |

*Remarks:* '4-SUB'. Built on ex-SECR '3-SUB' underframe from Set 8309. P'84 by BR, initially at Brighton

| Numbers | Year | Type | Built | Diag | Lot | Location |
|---------|------|------|-------|------|-----|----------|
| 12796<br>Set 4732 | 1951 | DMBTO | Eastleigh | | | Selhurst |

*Remarks:* '4-SUB'. Built on ex-SECR '3-SUB' underframe from Set 8310. P'84 by BR, initially at Brighton

| Numbers | Year | Type | Built | Diag | Lot | Location |
|---------|------|------|-------|------|-----|----------|
| 13003 | 1949 | DMBT | Lancing | | | nr Ashford |
| Set 4002 | | | | | | |
| Set 4902 | 1970 | | | | | |

*Remarks:* '4-DD'. P'72 & at Ashford till '84. Seen on farm between Molash & Shottenden (off A252) during Sept'87

| Numbers | Year | Type | Built | Diag | Lot | Location |
|---------|------|------|-------|------|-----|----------|
| 13004 | 1949 | DMBT | Lancing | | | Pitsford |
| Set 4002 | | | | | | |
| Set 4902 | 1970 | | | | | |

*Remarks:* '4-DD'. P'72 & at Ashford till '84, then stored at Silvertown till '86?

| Numbers | Year | Type | Built | Diag | Lot | Location |
|---------|------|------|-------|------|-----|----------|
| 13503 | 1949 | TT | Lancing | | | - |

*Remarks:* '4-DD'. P'72 & at Ashford till cut up by BR contractors in '84.

*Others:*
Body of an unidentified PMVY grounded at Blaenavon
Unidentified BY on Swindon Ry Engineering's premises '90

One of the most extraordinary passenger trains to run in Britain was the 'double-decker' unit, two of which were used on Dartford line trains from 1949. They were not successful, mainly on account of the cramped conditions and the amount of time taken for passengers to alight and enter. Two vehicles survive, one of which is to be found at Pitsford on the Northampton & Lamport Railway. It is DMBT No 13004. *Murray Brown*

# THE LONDON, MIDLAND & SCOTTISH RAILWAY GROUP

| Numbers | Year | Type | Built | Diag | Lot | Location |
|---------|------|------|-------|------|-----|----------|

## CALEDONIAN RAILWAY

41 – see WCJS 484

| 426 | 1914 | T | St Rollox? | 118 | | Bo'ness |
| 16498 | 1923 | | | | | |
| 15498 | 1933 | | | | | |

*Remarks:* Sold to RN '54?. P'70 by SRPS from RNAD Bandeath, at Falkirk till Dec'87; body dismantled '89

| 464 | 1921 | BCK | St Rollox | 111A? | | Bo'ness |
| 16050 | 1923 | | | | | |
| 7369 | 1933 | | | | | |
| 99802 plated | | | | | | |

*Remarks:* Restored by BR in '58. P'68 by SRPS, at Falkirk till '88

| 1375 | 1921 | TK | St Rollox | 124? | | Bo'ness |
| 17430 | 1923 | | | | | |
| 3339 | 1933 | | | | | |
| 99803 plated | | | | | | |

*Remarks:* Restored by BR in '58. P'68, moved to Bluebell in '69. Sold to SRPS after dealings over Bulleid TO 1482, moved to Falkirk in '74 & there till '88

## GLASGOW & SOUTH WESTERN RAILWAY

| 122 | 1901 | BZ | Kilmarnock | 55 | | Bo'ness |
| DM284290 | | | | | | |

*Remarks:* P'67 by SRPS, at Falkirk till '88

| 731 | 1914 | TK | B R C W | 42? | | Bo'ness |
| 8205 | 1923 | | | | | |

*Remarks:* Sold to RN in ' ? P'70 by SRPS from RNAD Bandeath, at Falkirk till Dec'87

| Numbers | Year | Type | Built | Diag | Lot | Location |
|---------|------|------|-------|------|-----|----------|

## HIGHLAND RAILWAY

| Numbers | Year | Type | Built | Diag | Lot | Location |
|---------|------|------|-------|------|-----|----------|
| 5 | c1870 | BY | Metro C&W | 32 | | Strathspey |
| | 1919 | BY | Lochgorm | | | |
| 7371 | 1923 | | | | | |
| SR 151 | | | | | | |

*Remarks:* Rebuilt 1919; P after '65 from Inchlea by SRPS, but restored at ? till '82 ?

| Numbers | Year | Type | Built | Diag | Lot | Location |
|---------|------|------|-------|------|-----|----------|
| 57A | 1899 | Priv | Wolverton | - | | * NRM |

*Remarks:* Duke of Sutherland's 8-wheel Clerestory Saloon, in use till 1949 then stored at Wolverton. Sold to National Collection '57, at Clapham '63-75. To Swindon '90 for 'NRM On Tour' exhibition, returned to York 5/91

| Numbers | Year | Type | Built | Diag | Lot | Location |
|---------|------|------|-------|------|-----|----------|
| 58A | 1909 | Priv | Lochgorm | - | | BC, Canada |

*Remarks:* Duke of Sutherland's 4-wheel Clerestory Saloon, used till '49. P'50 at New Romney with its 0-4-4T 'Dunrobin' till '65, then to Fort Steele Historical Mus.

| Numbers | Year | Type | Built | Diag | Lot | Location |
|---------|------|------|-------|------|-----|----------|
| 89 | 1908 | CZ | Lochgorm | 59 | | Bo'ness |
| 18693 | 1923 | | | | | |
| 27236 | 1933 | | | | | |
| Dep'tl No | ? | | | | | |
| 17 | 1968 | | | | | |

*Remarks:* P'65 by SRPS, restored at Lochgorm Works, Inverness in '68 (with the erroneous number 17) & at Falkirk till Dec'87

*Others:*
2 bodies at Strathspey (both once grounded at Tomintoul, but the coupé built 1888 since scrapped)

## LANCASHIRE & YORKSHIRE RAILWAY

1 – see also 135

| Numbers | Year | Type | Built | Diag | Lot | Location |
|---------|------|------|-------|------|-----|----------|
| 1 | 1906 | Spec | Newton Heath | 80 | B23 | N Norfolk |
| 10701 | 1923 | | | | | |
| 168822 | 1925 | | | | | |
| 45037 | 1933 | | | | | |

*Remarks:* Directors' Saloon. P'69 by M&GNJRS

| Numbers | Year | Type | Built | Diag | Lot | Location |
|---------|------|------|-------|------|-----|----------|
| 50 | 1911 | FO | Newton Heath | 125 | S26 | Midland |
| 10722 | 1923 | | | | | |
| 995 | 1933 | | | | | |
| DM395001 | 1952 | | | | | |

*Remarks:* Reported to be for Lord Derby while being built, but completed as Family Saloon. P'70 by Derby Corp, stored at Derby till '75

| Numbers | Year | Type | Built | Diag | Lot | Location |
|---------|------|------|-------|------|-----|----------|
| 135 | 1908 | Spec | Newton Heath | 22 | V3 | Worth Valley |
| 10772 | 1923 | | | | | |
| 45038 | 1933 | | | | | |

*Remarks:* Originally 6-wheel Clerestory Directors' Saloon No.1, built Miles Platting 1878. Rebuilt as shown & mounted on bogies; remained in use till 1962 at least. P'?? (K&WVR stockbook also quotes No.2)

| 247 | 1923 | Spec | Newton Heath | 150 | E32 | Worth Valley ? |
|-----|------|------|--------------|-----|-----|----------------|
| 10825 | 1923 | | | | | |
| 45017 | 1933 | | | | | |

*Remarks:* Built Newton Heath 1917 as TK to Lot W30, converted as Staff Car for US Ambulance Train No.59 (Coach B No.5902), then rebuilt as Medical Officer's Saloon. P'72 by HRSG, intended for Severn Valley but sent to Dinting '74 instead & there till '90

| 293 | 1913 | Spec | Newton Heath | | K27 | Midland |
|-----|------|------|--------------|--|-----|---------|
| 10874 | 1923 | | | | | |
| 45050 | 1933 | | | | | |
| Dynamometer Car No.1 | | | | | | |

*Remarks:* Dynamometer Car. Accuracy of equipment suspect, confirmed after grouping; rebuilt 1929 with gangway at one end. In use till P'71 with instrumentation intact

| 631 | | TZ ? | | 8 ? | | W Somerset |
|-----|--|------|--|-----|--|------------|

*Remarks:* Body grounded at Minehead in two halves

| 1474 | 1910 | BT | Newton Heath | 94 | D26 | Worth Valley |
|------|------|----|--------------|----|-----|--------------|
| 12885 | 1923 | | | | | |
| 23964 | 1933 | | | | | |
| ? | 195x | | | | | |
| K&WVR 102 | | | | | | |

*Remarks:* Staff van from 50's. P'65 by L&Y Saddletanks Fund (now L&YRPS) & restoration begun '74

| 1856 | 1909 | BTK | | 91 | W29 | E Lancs |
|------|------|-----|--|----|-----|---------|
| 24C | 1915 | | | | | |
| 13245 | 1923 | | | | | |
| 6513 | 1933 | | | | | |
| DB975154 | | | | | | |

*Remarks:* Part of WW1 Ambulance Train No 24. Latterly Exhibition van. P'76

## LONDON & BIRMINGHAM RAILWAY

| 2 | 1842 | ROY | Hooper | - | - | * NRM |
|---|------|-----|--------|---|---|-------|

*Remarks:* Queen Adelaide's 4-wheel coach. Stored at Wolverton from c1850-1963, then at Clapham till '75. Moved to Swindon for 'NRM On Tour' exhibition '90-1

| Numbers | Year | Type | Built | | Diag | Lot | Location |
|---------|------|------|-------|---|------|-----|----------|

# LONDON & NORTH WESTERN RAILWAY

[Diagrams per c1915 Book; those in brackets are page number in 1903 Diag Book]

| Numbers | Year | Type | Built | | Diag | Lot | Location |
|---------|------|------|-------|---|------|-----|----------|
| | 1869 | ROY | Wolverton | | - | - | * NRM |
| 802 | 1933 | | | | | | |

*Remarks:* Originally two separate 6-wheel vehicles built for Queen Victoria's use, the bodies united on a new underframe with two 6-wheel bogies in 1895. Used by the monarch till replaced by the vehicles above, but remained in store at Wolverton till 1963, then at Clapham till '75

| Numbers | Year | Type | Built | | Diag | Lot | Location |
|---------|------|------|-------|---|------|-----|----------|
| | 1902 | ROY | Wolverton | | - | | * NRM |
| 800 | 1933 | | | | | | |

*Remarks:* King Edward's 12-wheel Clerestory Saloon. Replaced 1941, P'47 but remained in store at Wolverton till '63, then at Clapham till '75. Refurbished at Wolverton 1979/80

Although the National Railway Museum has a wonderful selection of coaches, it is probably best known in rolling stock terms for its collection of Royal vehicles. They don't come much earlier than this — London & Birmingham 1842-built No 2 which is known as Queen Adelaide's coach. It spent over 100 years stored at Wolverton Works! This view shows the venerable vehicle on display at the NRM on 11 August 1982. *John Lloyd*

| Numbers | Year | Type | Built | Diag | Lot | Location |
|---------|------|------|-------|------|-----|----------|
| | 1902 | ROY | Wolverton | - | | * NRM |
| 801 | 1933 | | | | | |

*Remarks:* Queen Alexandra's 12-wheel Clerestory Saloon. Replaced 1941, P'47 but remained in store at Wolverton till '63, then at Clapham till '75. Refurbished at Wolverton 1979/80

| | 1889 | Insp | Wolverton | | | K&ESR |
| ED33 | 1923 | | | | | |
| 45021 | 1933 | | | | | |
| Army 3005 | | | | | | |
| K&ESR 82 | 1985 | | | | | |

*Remarks:* 6-wheel Inspection Saloon, OOU by Mar'40. Sold to Army, moved to Melbourne Mil Rly May'40; to Longmoor during '45 for use in the Officers' Train. P'70 (donated to Transport Trust), removed to Severn Valley in '71 & remained there till sold '85

| 20 | 1909 | POS | Wolverton | 406 | | Tyseley |
| 9520 | 1912 | | | | | |
| 3227 | 1926 | | | | | |
| 30244 | 1933 | | | | | |
| | 1945 | POT | | | | |

*Remarks:* Arms & net removed in '45, used as tender till withdrawn. P'61 by RPS, at Hednesford till ' ? then at Chasewater till sold '83

| 31E | 1915 | DMBTO | Metro C&W | | | * NRM |
| 5751 | 1926 | | | | | |
| 28249 | 1933 | | | | | |

*Remarks:* 'Oerlikon' equipped EMU coach. P' ? but stored at Brighton till '77. To Swindon for 'NRM On Tour' exhibition '90, returned to York 4/91

| 68 | 1877 | Obs | Wolverton | | | Quainton |

*Remarks:* 4-wheel Observation Saloon. W'02, body sold & grounded. P'75

| 74 | 1903 | Spec | Wolverton | 1 | | Tyseley |
| 5074 | 1910 | | | | | |
| 10506 | 1924 | | | | | |
| 806 | 1933 | | | | | |

*Remarks:* Clerestory Semi-Royal Saloon. W'71

| 112 (i) | 1883 | SLF | Wolverton | (6) | | Homefield |
| 2112 | 1907? | | | 21 | | |
| 2112A | 1910? | | | | | |

*Remarks:* Orig no. guessed from known final number; probably to duplicate list when next 112 was built in 1907. W'20, body grounded. P'78? by Resco

| Numbers | Year | Type | Built | Diag | Lot | Location |
|---------|------|------|-------|------|-----|----------|
| 112 (ii) | 1907 | SLF | Wolverton | 16 | | Quainton |
| 5112 | 1912 | | | | | |
| 10337 | 1927 | | | | | |
| 481 | 1933 | | | | | |
| DM198512 | 1937 | | | | | |
| DM395017 | 1952 | | | | | |

*Remarks:* 12-wheel. Rebuilt 1937 after withdrawal, later (probably 1952) converted to Cinema coach. P'73

| Numbers | Year | Type | Built | Diag | Lot | Location |
|---------|------|------|-------|------|-----|----------|
| 159 | 1891 | RF | Wolverton | (19) | | St Leonards |
| 5159 | 1912 | | | | | |
| 99880 plated | | | | | | |

*Remarks:* Used in WW1 Ambulance Train, probably No 18. Body P'78 by Resco from Bognor, rebuilt on LMS 42ft u'frame & mounted on Gresley bogies by '84. Leased to GS&WR for the 'Royal Scotsman' set till '89, then in abortive 'Queen of Scots', both based at Steamtown; into storage '91

| Numbers | Year | Type | Built | Diag | Lot | Location |
|---------|------|------|-------|------|-----|----------|
| 249 | 1901 | RF | Wolverton | (15) | | Quainton |
| 5249 | 1912 | | | 29 | | |
| 10411 | 1924 | | | | | |
| 77 | 1933 | | | | | |

*Remarks:* Clerestory. Reserved for Staff on the Royal Train from 1905 till P'67. In store till '70

| Numbers | Year | Type | Built | Diag | Lot | Location |
|---------|------|------|-------|------|-----|----------|
| 275 ? | 1908 | OCTY | | | | * NRM |
| 11275 | 1914 | | | | | |
| 4984 | 1924 | | | | | |
| 41621 | 1933 | | | | | |

*Remarks:* Restored at Wolverton

| Numbers | Year | Type | Built | Diag | Lot | Location |
|---------|------|------|-------|------|-----|----------|
| 303 | 1905 | BFK | Wolverton | 127 | | * NRM |
| 5624 | 1913 | | | | | |
| 10070 | 1925 | | Wolverton | 127A | | |
| 5154 | 1933 | | | | | |

*Remarks:* Originally built with Cove roof, to Royal Train 1924, rebuilt with Clerestory roof 1925 as 'Power Car' (fitted with two diesel generators in the Brake section). Body mounted on new LMS chassis c1937. P'77

| Numbers | Year | Type | Built | Diag | Lot | Location |
|---------|------|------|-------|------|-----|----------|
| 310 | 1905 | BFK | Wolverton | 127 | | * NRM |
| 5625 | 1912 | | | | | |
| 10071 | 1925 | | Wolverton | 127B | | |
| 5155 | 1933 | | | | | |
| 95401 plated | | | | | | |

*Remarks:* As above, but rebuilt 1925 as the 'Escort Car'. P'77, restored by BREL Wolverton '79 & used as Steam Loco Support coach till '85. To Swindon for 'NRM On Tour' exhibition '90, returned to York 5/91

| Numbers | Year | Type | Built | Diag | Lot | Location |
|---------|------|------|-------|------|-----|----------|
| 1503 | 1913 | Obs | Wolverton | M50 | | Bluebell |
| 5316 | 1923 | | | | | |
| 15843 | 1933 | | | | | |

*Remarks:* Observation Saloon; P'63

| Numbers | Year | Type | Built | Diag | Lot | Location |
|---|---|---|---|---|---|---|
| 2997 | 1920 | CK | Wolverton | 131 | | Steamtown |
| 8107 | 1924 | | | | | |
| 4772 | 1933 | | | | | |
| DM395136 | 1955 | | | | | |

*Remarks:* P'78 by GCR Coach Group & at Quainton till sold to R Edmondson '87

| ??? | 187x | TY | Wolverton | (102) | | Quainton |
| 4569 | | | | | | |

*Remarks:* Body grounded at Dunsmore. P'82 by 6024 Soc (an identical but unidentified body from same site is beside this one)

| 5000 | 1920 | Spec | Wolverton | 12 | | * NRM |
| 45000 | 1933 | | | | | |
| 2911 | 1983 | | | | | |

*Remarks:* Chairman's Saloon, later LMS President's Saloon then incorporated into Royal Train. W'90 & claimed for National Collection

| 5318 | 1913 | Spec | Wolverton | 2 | | N Norfolk |
| 10500 | 1924 | | | | | |
| 45002 | 1933 | | | | | |

*Remarks:* 12-wheel Directors' Saloon. P'69 by M&GNJRS

| 7080 | 1917 | BT | Wolverton | 333 | | Chasewater |
| 7048 | 1926 | | | | | |
| 22687 | 1933 | | | | | |

*Remarks:* Sold to Cannock & Rugeley Collieries '58. P'64 & at Hednesford till c1965-70

| 7340 | 1921 | BT | Wolverton | 333 | | Chinnor |
| 7107 | 1924 | | | | | |
| 22736 | 1933 | | | | | |
| DM395209 | 1958 | | | | | |

*Remarks:* W'57 for use as a Riding van. P'77 by GCR Coach Group & at Quainton till sold '90

| 8898 | 1920 | BG | Wolverton | 378 | | Steamtown |
| 2362 | 1926 | | | | | |
| 32745 | 1933 | | | | | |
| DM395455 | 1958 | | | | | |

*Remarks:* Originally a Ward Car, built 1916 for Home Ambulance Train No.7, but rebuilt as BG on repurchase after WW1. Ended its career based at Watford. P'88 by R Edmondson

| ? | 1905 | BG | Wolverton | | | Chasewater |
| ? | 1910 | | | | | |
| DM01836 | | | | | | |

*Remarks:* P' ? by L&NW Society

| Numbers | Year | Type | Built | Diag | Lot | Location |
|---------|------|------|-------|------|-----|----------|
| ? | 1891 | BZ | Wolverton | 385 | | Quainton |
| ? | 1910 | | | | | |
| ? | 1923 | | | | | |
| ? | 1933 | | | | | |
| DM279982 | | | | | | |

*Remarks:* P'76 by GCR Coach Group but promptly resold to QRS.

| Numbers | Year | Type | Built | Diag | Lot | Location |
|---------|------|------|-------|------|-----|----------|
| 11010 | 1913 | CCTZ | Wolverton | 444 | | Lakeside |
| 4041 | 1923 | | | | | |
| 36903 | 1933 | | | | | |
| DM395081 | 1954 | | | | | |

*Remarks:* P'81 for grounding, its u'frame wanted for the NLR teak body, but later prepared as mobile museum plus membership office

| Numbers | Year | Type | Built | Diag | Lot | Location |
|---------|------|------|-------|------|-----|----------|
| 11388 | 1911 | CCTZ | Wolverton | 444 | | Quainton |
| 4118 | 1926 | | | | | |
| 36895 | 1933 | | | | | |
| CND395080 | | | | | | |

*Remarks:* Latterly used as a Cell Truck. P' ? by GCR Coach Group

For many years, just to the north of Watford on the east side of the line, could be seen this somewhat battered gem — LNWR BG No TDM395455. Its final use was as an operating department instruction coach. Salvation came in 1988, courtesy of coach restorer, owner, and train operator Rick Edmondson, who moved it for safe keeping to Steamtown, Carnforth. *Mike Robinson*

| Numbers | Year | Type | Built | Diag | Lot | Location |
|---------|------|------|-------|------|-----|----------|
| 11433 ? | 1915 | CCTZ | Wolverton | 444a | | Llangollen |
| 4167 ? | 1923 | | | | | |
| 36954 | 1933 | | | | | |
| DM395149 | 1956 | | | | | |

*Remarks:* Latterly one of Messrs. Pooley's vans. P'80, at Steamport till'86 (though No.11429 is possible, 11433 is more likely)

| | | | | | | |
|---------|------|------|-------|------|-----|----------|
| 12196 | 1916 | CCTZ | Wolverton | 444a | | Swanage |
| 4183 | 1926 | | | | | |
| 36966 | 1933 | | | | | |
| DM395358 | 1958 | | | | | |

*Remarks:* Latterly one of Messrs. Pooley's vans. P'80 by LMSSPG

| | | | | | | |
|---------|------|------|-------|------|-----|----------|
| 12220 | 1922 | CCTZ | Wolverton | 444a | | W Somerset |
| 4207 | 1928 | | | | | |
| 36992 | 1933 | | | | | |
| DM395273 | 1957 | | | | | |

*Remarks:* Latterly one of Messrs. Pooley's vans. P'73 by HRSG, later sold to 2857 Soc; restored as a mobile workshop & on Severn Valley till '82, then at Buxton till sold '91 (underframe intended for coach body)

| | | | | | | |
|---------|------|------|-------|------|-----|----------|
| ? | | CCTZ | Wolverton | 444a | | Nene Valley |

*Remarks:* P pre'76

*Others:*
Unidentified body also at Quainton (identical to 4569 qv)
An Ambulance coach underframe on Bluebell Ry for LBSCR 142 (qv) (Army No. 80.081, formerly at Steamtown)
A former Camping Coach at Aberystwyth, once used by Vale of Rheidol Supporters Assoc, was scrapped in 1991

# LONDON, TILBURY & SOUTHEND RAILWAY

| | | | | | | |
|---|------|------|---|---|---|---|
| ? | 1876 | CY | | | | ? |

*Remarks:* P'70 by the Lea Valley Rly Grp (ancestor of RVP), the body from Corringham, the underframe from Thames Haven. Reported given to two members in '72

see also MR 228

# MANCHESTER SOUTH JUNCTION & ALTRINCHAM RAILWAY

| | | | | | | |
|-------|------|---|---------------|------|-----|---------|
| 114 | 1931 | C | Metro-Cammell | 1726 | 505 | Midland |
| 29663 | 1948 | | | | | |

*Remarks:* P'71 by Derby Museum, stored on siding at Derby till '75

| | | | | | | |
|-------|------|---|---------------|------|-----|---------|
| 117 | 1931 | C | Metro-Cammell | 1726 | 505 | Midland |
| 29666 | 1948 | | | | | |

*Remarks:* P'71 by AERPS, on Yorkshire Dales '72-83

| Numbers | Year | Type | Built | Diag | Lot | Location |
|---------|------|------|-------|------|-----|----------|
| 121 | 1931 | C | Metro-Cammell | 1726 | 505 | Midland |
| 29670 | 1948 | | | | | |

*Remarks:* P'71 by AERPS, on Yorkshire Dales '72-83

see also MS&LR 1076

## MARYPORT & CARLISLE RAILWAY

| | | | | | | |
|---------|------|------|-------|------|-----|----------|
| 11 | 1875 | TZ | B R C W | | | Chasewater |

*Remarks:* Sold for miners' use in 1930's. P'60 by RPS

## MIDLAND RAILWAY

| | | | | | | |
|---------|------|------|-------|------|-----|----------|
| 78 | c1865 | TY | Gloucester | - | - | Midland |
| c462-661 | ? | | Wagon Co | | | |

*Remarks:* Body grounded at E Bridgford c1900. P'83, to be mounted on LSWR u/f bought from Cranmore '90 once it has been lengthened

| | | | | | | |
|---------|------|------|-------|------|-----|----------|
| 184 | 1913 | BZ | Derby | 530A | 788 | Dalmellington |
| 34147 | 1933 | | | | | |
| DM395092 | 1954 | | | | | |

*Remarks:* P'91 by Ayrshire RPS

| | | | | | | |
|---------|------|------|-------|------|-----|----------|
| 211 | 1875 | FY | Metro C&W | | | Midland |
| | c1880 | FZ | | | | |
| c2561-2660 | 1902 | | | | | |

*Remarks:* Body grounded as a shed/summerhouse at Shepshed, probably pre-1914. P'89 (to be mounted on a shortened u'frame ex SR PMV 1865?)

| | | | | | | |
|---------|------|------|-------|------|-----|----------|
| 228 | 1922 | PMV | Derby | 1198 | 969 | Foxfield |
| LTSR 1 | | | | | | |
| 37797 | 1933 | | | | | |
| (37867) | 1934 | | | | | |
| 38268 | 1935 | | | | | |

*Remarks:* W'55, sold to Boots, Nottingham. P'68

| | | | | | | |
|---------|------|------|-------|------|-----|----------|
| 253 | 1884 | BTZ | Derby | 504 | 118 | Midland |
| 7243 | 1910 | | | | | |
| DM7243 | 1924? | | | | | |

*Remarks:* Sold to Shotton steelworks in ' ? Donated to MRT by British Steel in '72 but stored in Derby till '75

| | | | | | | |
|---------|------|------|-------|------|-----|----------|
| 375 | 1913 | TL | Derby | 1056 | 799 | - |
| 18828 | 1933 | | | | | |
| DM395031 | 1952 | | | | | |
| L&HR 72 | | | | | | |

*Remarks:* Clerestory. P'68, stored at Carnforth till '70, then at Haverthwaite. Body destroyed by fire on 5/10/81 (see *Steam World* No.9), underframe since used as a flat wagon.

| Numbers | Year | Type | Built | Diag | Lot | Location |
|---|---|---|---|---|---|---|
| c395-487 | 1885 | CL | Derby | 512 | 105 | Midland |
| 3537 | 1902 | | | | | |
| 03537 | c1910 | | | | | |

*Remarks:* Body P'74? from Long Eaton in two halves; one half at Butterley E yard, other became Station Booking Office till moved to Hammersmith '86, Swanwick '87

| 435 | 1905 | BTK | Derby | 476 | 593 | - |
| 6437 | 1933 | | | | | |
| DM198715 | 1945 | | | | | |

*Remarks:* Clerestory. P'71 from Bath as a Tool Van complete with all tools & stored in Derby till '75. All but its framework dismantled before moving to Butterley, & the remainder dismantled in '85; u'frame overhauled to carry the body of MR CK 2885 (qv)

| ? | 1885 | C | Derby | 513? | 108? | Midland |
| 3575 | 1902 | | | | | |
| 03575 | c1910 | | | | | |

*Remarks:* W'27, body grounded at Warsop. Part-body P'80 & grounded to west of Butterley north platform

| 634 | 1905 | TK | Derby | 473 | 618 | - |
| 3186 | 1933 | | | | | |
| DM195955 | 1951 | | | | | |
| K&WVR 101 | | | | | | |

*Remarks:* Clerestory. Used by Civil Engineers from 1951. P'65, on Worth Valley till '71, then stored in Derby in Derby till '75. All but its framework dismantled before moving to Butterley, & the remainder dismantled in '85

| 851 | 1914 | T | Derby | 487 | 802 | Midland |
| 14140 | 1933 | | | | | |

*Remarks:* W'47. Body P' ? (stored till '77?)

| ? | 1885 | CZ | Derby | 516 | 111 | * NRM |
| 34xx | 1902 | | | | 141 | |
| ? | | | | | | |
| 901 | 1975 | | | | | |

*Remarks:* Sold 1922 to CWS, used in their soap works at Irlam (Lancs) till P'60. Restored at Wolverton in '75, adopting the identity of a known twin-sister!

| ? | 1886 | CZ | Derby | 516? | 141? | Worth Valley |
| 34xx | 1902 | | | | | |
| ? | | | | | | |
| DM284677 | | | | | | |

*Remarks:* P'68 by Vintage Carriage Trust

| 1119 | 1886 | TZ | Derby | 493 | 142? | Midland |
| 01119 | 1913 | | | | | |

*Remarks:* Body P'80 from Warsop & mounted on the chassis of the late BZ 483 on 2/8/80

| Numbers | Year | Type | Built | Diag | Lot | Location |
|---------|------|------|-------|------|-----|----------|
| 1250 | 1921 | BT | Derby | 1246 | 884 | Midland |
| 23293 | 1933 | | | | | |
| DM395525 | | | | | | |

Remarks: W'58, became mobile Test Laboratory.

| | | | | | | |
|---------|------|------|-------|------|-----|----------|
| c1621-3 ? | 1884 | TOZ | Derby | 465 | 104 | Foxfield |
| 2741 | 1902 | | | | | |

Remarks: Picnic Saloon. W'30's, body grounded. P'76, intended to be mounted on u/f from SR PMV 1703 at some time. (May be a FOZ to same Diag but Lot 103)

| | | | | | | |
|---------|------|------|-------|------|-----|----------|
| 1805 | 1923 | TO | Derby | | | Nene Valley |
| 7629 | 1933 | | | | | |
| DM395562 | | | | | | |

Remarks: P'78 by R Edmondson (built by the LMS but listed on p175 of the MR Diagram Book, which is why it appears here!)

| | | | | | | |
|---------|------|------|-------|------|-----|----------|
| 1910 | 1912 | ROY | Derby | 597 | 745 | Midland |
| 2795 | c1923 | Spec | | | | |
| 809 | 1933 | | | | | |
| | 1951 | FO | | | | |

Remarks: Clerestory. Royal Saloon, then VIP Saloon till '33, Semi-Royal Saloon or in storage till '51, finally used in N Wales tourist trains. P'63 by RPS at Cannock Wood colliery, stored at Derby Works '71-9, then to Butterley. Sold to MRT in '81

| | | | | | | |
|---------|------|------|-------|------|-----|----------|
| 2234 | 1904 | Spec | Derby | 479 | | * NRM |
| | 1917 | Insp | Derby | 478 | 578 | |
| 45010 | 1933 | | | | | |

Remarks: Steam Railmotor, converted to Officers' Saloon in 1907, but retaining engine unit till 1917. P'68 by George Dow & moved to a siding at Machynlleth (C Wales) for use as a holiday home till sold to NRM in March '77

| | | | | | | |
|---------|------|------|-------|------|-----|----------|
| 2885 | 1905 | CK | Derby | 469 | 616 | Midland |
| 4876 | 1933 | | | | | |

Remarks: Clerestory. W'48, body grounded for use as summer house at Hazelwood (nr Duffield). P'88 & mounted on u/f from 435 (qv)

| | | | | | | |
|---------|------|------|-------|------|-----|----------|
| 2944 | 1904 | BCK | Derby | 470 | 569 | Midland |
| 7263 | 1933 | | | | | |
| DM198829 | 1947 | | | | | |

Remarks: Clerestory. Became Tool Van, then Bridge Testing unit. P'71 at Quainton, sold to Derby Corp '72 but stored in Derby '74-5

| | | | | | | |
|---------|------|------|-------|------|-----|----------|
| ? | 1922 | TK | Derby | 1282 | 973 | Whitehead, NI |
| ? | 1933 | | | | | |
| 238 | 1942 | | | J12 | | |
| 340 | 1959 | | | | | |

Remarks: Re-bogied for 5'3" gauge when sent to NCC in 1942 to replace war-damaged stock. P'75 by RPSI

| Numbers | Year | Type | Built | Diag | Lot | Location |
|---------|------|------|-------|------|-----|----------|
| ? | 1922 | TK | Derby | 1282 | 973 | Whitehead, NI |
| ? | 1933 | | | | | |
| 241 | 1942 | | | J12 | | |
| 342 | 1959 | | | | | |

Remarks: Re-bogied for 5'3" gauge when sent to NCC in 1942 to replace war-damaged stock. P'75 by RPSI

(The two coaches above are the only survivors from the following group exported to Ireland: original/1933 numbers were - 632/3225, 886/3228, 2986/3234, 2993/3235, 3300/3236 & 3339/3238)

| Numbers | Year | Type | Built | Diag | Lot | Location |
|---------|------|------|-------|------|-----|----------|
| c3001-3056 | 1897 | BZ | Derby | 530 | 400 | ⸗ |
| 483 (or 485?) | 1903 | | | | | |
| c33930-70 | 1933 | | | | | |
| DM297290 | | | | | | |

Remarks: Clerestory. P' ? by MRT from Inverness, but stored in Derby till '75. Body destroyed by fire on 6/2/80, its u'frame used to carry the body of 1119 (qv).

| Numbers | Year | Type | Built | Diag | Lot | Location |
|---------|------|------|-------|------|-----|----------|
| c3137-3218 | 1902 | BZ | Derby | 530 | 519 | Midland |
| c85-574 | 1903 | | | | | |
| c34069-144 | 1933 | | | | | |
| DM198587 | | | | | | |

Remarks: Clerestory. P' ? from Wakefield, stored in Derby till '75

(Of the two 6-wheel Passenger Brakes above, one was preserved '71 & the other '74)

| Numbers | Year | Type | Built | Diag | Lot | Location |
|---------|------|------|-------|------|-----|----------|
| 3335 | 1909 | BCK | Derby | 472 | 686 | ⸗ |
| 7300 | 1933 | | | | | |

Remarks: Clerestory. W'47, body sold. P' ? from Littleover by MRT, but dismantled for spares in '84. (data may be in error: Wyvern No 58 refers to this as BT)

| Numbers | Year | Type | Built | Diag | Lot | Location |
|---------|------|------|-------|------|-----|----------|
| 3421 | 1922 | CK | Derby | 1281 | 971 | Whitehead, NI |
| 4914 | 1933 | | | | | |
| 68 | 1942 | | | F3 | | |
| 274 | 1959 | | | | | |

Remarks: Re-bogied for 5'3" gauge when sent to NCC in 1942 to replace war-damaged stock. P'75 by RPSI

| Numbers | Year | Type | Built | Diag | Lot | Location |
|---------|------|------|-------|------|-----|----------|
| 3463 | 1914 | RU | Derby | 575 | 843 | * NRM |
| 166 | 1933 | | | | | |

Remarks: 12-wheel Clerestory. OOU at Burton in '54 when BR persuaded by enthusiast to preserve it. Restored in '57, at Clapham '63-75

| Numbers | Year | Type | Built | Diag | Lot | Location |
|---------|------|------|-------|------|-----|----------|
| 8272 | 1916 | CCTY | Derby | | 893 | Midland |
| DM395106 | | | | | | |

Remarks: Motor Car Van

| Numbers | Year | Type | Built | Diag | Lot | Location |
|---------|------|------|-------|------|-----|----------|
| ? | c1885 | BY | Derby | 529 | 11 or later | Chasewater |

Remarks: P' ? by RPS

| Numbers | Year | Type | Built | Diag | Lot | Location |
|---------|------|------|-------|------|-----|----------|

*Others:*
Body of unidentified 7-compartment bogie Third P'89 at Foxfield

# NORTH LONDON RAILWAY

| Numbers | Year | Type | Built | Diag | Lot | Location |
|---------|------|------|-------|------|-----|----------|
| 31 ? | 1910 | BTY | Wolverton | | | K&ESR |
| K&ESR 101 | 1964 | | | | | |
| K&ESR 67 | 1978 | | | | | |

*Remarks:* Sold to Woolwich Arsenal c1933. P'64

| Numbers | Year | Type | Built | Diag | Lot | Location |
|---------|------|------|-------|------|-----|----------|
| 32 | 1872 | Spec | Bow | | | * Swindon |
| 1032 | | | | | | |
| 45003 | 1933 | | | | | |

*Remarks:* 4-wheel Directors' Saloon. P' ?, stored at Lostock Hall till ' ? then at Clapham till ' ?. To 'NRM On Tour' exhibition '90

| Numbers | Year | Type | Built | Diag | Lot | Location |
|---------|------|------|-------|------|-----|----------|
| ? | 186x | FY | Bow | | | IoWSR |
| 46 | 1898 | CY | | | | |
| (6336) | SR | | | | | |

*Remarks:* Sold to IoWR in 1898, W'26 before SR No. was painted on. Body P' ?, mounted on underframe from SR PMV No.1750 since '83 (built 1864 or 1869)

| Numbers | Year | Type | Built | Diag | Lot | Location |
|---------|------|------|-------|------|-----|----------|
| ? | | FY | Bow | | | Lakeside |

*Remarks:* Body grounded at Ulverston Station ' ? P'71 & still in use as a store.

| Numbers | Year | Type | Built | Diag | Lot | Location |
|---------|------|------|-------|------|-----|----------|
| ? | | FY | | | | Great Central |

*Remarks:* Body P'76 from Rugby

| Numbers | Year | Type | Built | Diag | Lot | Location |
|---------|------|------|-------|------|-----|----------|
| ? | | FY | | | | Dean Forest |

*Remarks:* Body

| Numbers | Year | Type | Built | Diag | Lot | Location |
|---------|------|------|-------|------|-----|----------|
| ? | 1880 | BY | Bow | | | Tyseley |

*Remarks:* Body P'89

*Others:*
Unidentified body on platform at Castle Hedingham

# NORTH STAFFORDSHIRE RAILWAY

| Numbers | Year | Type | Built | Diag | Lot | Location |
|---------|------|------|-------|------|-----|----------|
| 61 | 1870's | | | | | Foxfield |
| 061 | 1890's | | | | | |

*Remarks:* Body P'76

| Numbers | Year | Type | Built | Diag | Lot | Location |
|---------|------|------|-------|------|-----|----------|
| 127 | 1880's | | | | | Foxfield |

*Remarks:* Body P'80

(The above pair withdrawn before new 61 & 127 built to Diag.12 in period 1891-1907)

| Numbers | Year | Type | Built | Diag | Lot | Location |
|---------|------|------|-------|------|-----|----------|
| ? | 187x | FY | | 16 | | Cheddleton |

*Remarks:* Body grounded c1909 as holiday home in a wood at Loggerheads. Disused from c1960, P'85

*Others:*
Unidentified body P'89 at Foxfield (tentative ident only)

## SOMERSET & DORSET JOINT RAILWAY

see Southern Railway Group

## WEST COAST JOINT STOCK

[Diagrams per HMRS Register]

| Numbers | Year | Type | Built | Diag | Lot | Location |
|---------|------|------|-------|------|-----|----------|
| 102 | 1874 | SLFZ | Wolverton | | | Quainton |
| 119 | 1883 | COZ | | 23 | | |
| 2119 | 1899 | | | | | |
| | 1903 | Insp | | | | |
| 2119A | 1910 | | | | | |
| 010393 | 1923 | | | | | |
| 45024 | 1933 | | | | | |

*Remarks:* To LNWR 1883 & converted to Family Saloon, rebuilt as Inspection Saloon 1903. Body grounded 1945 as a dwelling & so used till c1970. Donated to Quainton Sept'82; mounted on GNoSR 4-wh (ex 6-wh) chassis (MOD 48103) in '??

Only grounded bodies survive from the North Staffordshire Railway and these total four. One of them is NSR Third No 061, dating from the 1870s, and it can be found at the Foxfield Railway. *Hugh Madgin*

| Numbers | Year | Type | Built | Diag | Lot | Location |
|---------|------|------|-------|------|-----|----------|
| 186 | 1883 | POS | Wolverton | 87 | | * NRM |
| 3234 | 1923 | | | | | |
| 30384 | 1933 | | | | | |

*Remarks:* 8-wheel radial chassis. Entered service 1/7/1885, given new underframe with bogies 1896, its body rebuilt 1908 & withdrawn March'34. Underframe replaced by one of the original type for exhibition in 1938. Stored at Wolverton & Lostock Hall till ' ? then at Clapham till ' ?

| Numbers | Year | Type | Built | Diag | Lot | Location |
|---------|------|------|-------|------|-----|----------|
| 200 | 1900 | RF | Wolverton | LNW29 | | * NRM |
| 5200 | 1914 | | | | | |
| 10400 | 1923 | | | | | |
| 76 | 1933 | | | | | |

*Remarks:* Allocated to Royal Train from 1904, transferred to LNWR stock 1914, LMS underframe fitted 1938 & in use till W'56. P'58?, stored at Wolverton till '63, then at Clapham till '75. Restored at Wolverton '77-9. To 'NRM On Tour' exhibition '90-1

| Numbers | Year | Type | Built | Diag | Lot | Location |
|---------|------|------|-------|------|-----|----------|
| 2xx | 1902 | TK | Wolverton | 51 | | Strathspey |
| 47xx | 1923 | | | | | |
| 2xxx | 1933 | | | | | |
| DM198614 | | | | | | |

*Remarks:* P'82

| Numbers | Year | Type | Built | Diag | Lot | Location |
|---------|------|------|-------|------|-----|----------|
| 484 | 1897 | RF | Wolverton | LNW41 | | St Leonards |
| 41 | 1905 | | | | | |
| | 1918 | | St Rollox | CR63A | | |
| 15555 | 1923 | | | | | |
| 45018 | 1933 | Insp | | | | |
| 99052 plated | | | | | | |

*Remarks:* 12-wheel. To Caledonian 1905, rebuilt '18 with new 4-wheel bogies & fitted with new BRCW u'frame '27. Classed as Inspection Saloon from '33, & given new Gresley bogies '55. One end collision damaged '60 & rebuilt akin to DMU. W'72 & sold to W McAlpine, resold to Resco '82, leased to GS&WR for 'Royal Scotsman' till '89, in abortive 'Queen of Scots' '90; based Steamtown till moved to storage '91

| Numbers | Year | Type | Built | Diag | Lot | Location |
|---------|------|------|-------|------|-----|----------|
| 487 | 1892 | RFO | Wolverton | 1 | | Woolwich |
| 303 | 1905 | | | | | |
| 5303 | 1910 | | | 31? | | |
| | 1916 | RF | | 31A | | |

*Remarks:* 12-wheel Clerestory. Transferred to LNWR, modified for use in Ambulance Train 1916, returned by '20 & withdrawn c'22. Body grounded as dwelling on South Coast till P'88 by R Edmondson

# LONDON, MIDLAND & SCOTTISH RAILWAY

| Numbers | Year | Type | Built | Diag | Lot | Location |
|---------|------|------|-------|------|-----|----------|
| 46 | 1925 | CCT | Derby | 1875 | 160 | Foxfield |
| 37508 | 1933 | | | | | |

*Remarks:* Scenery van. P'68

149 – see 9355

| Numbers | Year | Type | Built | Diag | Lot | Location |
|---------|------|------|-------|------|-----|----------|
| 378 DB975181 | 1951 1972 | SLF | Wolverton | 2166 | 1570 | N Yorks Moors |

*Remarks:* 12-wheel. P'79

| 379 DB975182 | 1951 1972 | SLF | Wolverton | 2166 | 1570 | Chappel |

*Remarks:* 12-wheel. P'79

| 380 DB975183 | 1951 1972 | SLF | Wolverton | 2166 | 1570 | Great Central |

*Remarks:* 12-wheel. P'82 by RVP

| 381 DB975184 | 1951 1972 | SLF | Wolverton | 2166 | 1570 | Mid-Hants |

*Remarks:* 12-wheel. P'83

| 394 SR 179 | 1951 | SLF | Wolverton | 2166 | 1584 | Strathspey |

*Remarks:* 12-wheel.

| 395 99055 plated | 1951 | SLF | Wolverton | 2166 | 1584 | Steamtown |

*Remarks:* 12-wheel. P'?? by W H McAlpine

| 398 DB975188 | 1951 | SLF | Wolverton | 2166 | 1584 | Bluebell |

*Remarks:* 12-wheel. P'74

| 592 DM395922 | 1933 | SLT | Derby | 1863 | 699 | Quainton |

*Remarks:* P'77 by GCR Coach Group member

| 603 | 1951 | SLT | Derby | 2169 | 1574 | Bluebell |

*Remarks:* P'??, at Steamtown till '82

| 612 | 1952 | SLT | Derby | 2169 | 1628 | Midland |

| 615 | 1952 | SLT | Derby | 2169 | 1628 | W Somerset |

*Remarks:* P'77 by S&DR Trust

| 617 | 1952 | SLT | Derby | 2169 | 1628 | Dean Forest |

*Remarks:* P'80 by Purbeck School, Dorset as a base for field studies: 4 compartments and the pantry removed to make space for kitchen/dining area

| 621 SR 180 | 1952 | SLT | Derby | 2169 | 1628 | Strathspey |

| Numbers | Year | Type | Built | Diag | Lot | Location |
|---------|------|------|-------|------|-----|----------|
| 622 | 1952 | SLT | Derby | 2169 | 1628 | Bo'ness |

Remarks: P'?? by SRPS, at Falkirk till Dec'87

| Numbers | Year | Type | Built | Diag | Lot | Location |
|---------|------|------|-------|------|-----|----------|
| 623 | 1952 | SLT | Derby | 2169 | 1628 | Bluebell |

Remarks: P'77

| Numbers | Year | Type | Built | Diag | Lot | Location |
|---------|------|------|-------|------|-----|----------|
| 624 | 1952 | SLT | Derby | 2169 | 1628 | N Norfolk |

Remarks: P'76? but at Norwich Victoria till '78.

| Numbers | Year | Type | Built | Diag | Lot | Location |
|---------|------|------|-------|------|-----|----------|
| 798 | 1941 | ROY | Wolverton | 2054 | 1167 | * Glasgow |

Remarks: 12-wheel King's Saloon, the armoured replacement for 800. P'77, restored by BREL Wolverton in LMS livery '78 & at York till moved to Kelvin Hall '87

| Numbers | Year | Type | Built | Diag | Lot | Location |
|---------|------|------|-------|------|-----|----------|
| 799 | 1941 | ROY | Wolverton | 2054 | 1168 | * NRM |

Remarks. 12-wheel Queen's Saloon, the armoured replacement for 801. P'77, restored by BREL Wolverton in BR livery '78 then displayed at York. To 'NRM On Tour' exhibition at Swindon '90-1

| Numbers | Year | Type | Built | Diag | Lot | Location |
|---------|------|------|-------|------|-----|----------|
| 1371 | 1924 | TK | Derby | 1695 | 71 | ? |
| 1295 | 1933 | | | | | |
| DM395498 | 1959 | | | | | |

Remarks: P'91 by A Vigar

| Numbers | Year | Type | Built | Diag | Lot | Location |
|---------|------|------|-------|------|-----|----------|
| 1535 | 1933 | TK | Wolverton | 1860 | 695 | Swanage |
| DM395832 | 1963 | | | | | |

Remarks: P'88

| Numbers | Year | Type | Built | Diag | Lot | Location |
|---------|------|------|-------|------|-----|----------|
| 1782 | 1934 | TK | Wolverton | 1899 | 801 | N Yorks Moors |
| DM395911 | 1965 | | | | | |

Remarks: P'79, used as a dormitory coach.

1805 – see Midland Ry

| Numbers | Year | Type | Built | Diag | Lot | Location |
|---------|------|------|-------|------|-----|----------|
| 2300 | 1946 | TK | Derby | 2119 | 1407 | Severn Valley |

Remarks: P'78 ex Bass at Tavistock Jn Plymouth

| Numbers | Year | Type | Built | Diag | Lot | Location |
|---------|------|------|-------|------|-----|----------|
| 2884 | 1932 | BGZ | Wolverton | 1796 | 664 | Bulmers |
| 32918 | 1933 | | | | | |

Remarks: P'?? by Princess Elizabeth Loco Soc

| Numbers | Year | Type | Built | Diag | Lot | Location |
|---------|------|------|-------|------|-----|----------|
| 2886 | 1932 | BGZ | Wolverton | 1796 | 664 | Severn Valley |
| 32919 | 1933 | | | | | |

Remarks: P'70, on Dart Valley till '72

| Numbers | Year | Type | Built | Diag | Lot | Location |
|---------|------|------|-------|------|-----|----------|
| 3030 | 1930 | TK | Derby | 1782 | 551 | Bitton |
| 1501 | 1933 | | | | | |
| DM395801 | | | | | | |

Remarks: P'80 by London Midland Soc, on Mid-Hants till '86

| Numbers | Year | Type | Built | Diag | Lot | Location |
|---|---|---|---|---|---|---|
| 3286 | 1924 | RK | Derby | 1697 | 65 | Mid-Hants |
| 30005 | 1933 | | | | | |
| DM395223 | 1956 | | | | | |

*Remarks:* Latterly Track Recording Coach. P'89

| Numbers | Year | Type | Built | Diag | Lot | Location |
|---|---|---|---|---|---|---|
| ? | 1929 | TO | Derby | | | E Somerset |
| ? | 1933 | | | | | |
| Army 3322 | | | | | | |

*Remarks:* Converted for Ambulance Train use c1939 & 'captured' by German forces in France; repatriated at end of war. P'70 while at Longmoor, stored at Eastleigh '71-3 then Cranmore. Presented to National Army Museum '90

| Numbers | Year | Type | Built | Diag | Lot | Location |
|---|---|---|---|---|---|---|
| 4700 | 1927 | CCT | Derby | 1882 | 308 | Foxfield |
| 37518 | 1933 | | | | | |

*Remarks:* Scenery van. P'68

| Numbers | Year | Type | Built | Diag | Lot | Location |
|---|---|---|---|---|---|---|
| 4714 | 1927 | CCT | Derby | 1882 | 308 | Foxfield |
| 37519 | 1933 | | | | | |

*Remarks:* Scenery van. P'68

| Numbers | Year | Type | Built | Diag | Lot | Location |
|---|---|---|---|---|---|---|
| 5622 | 1926 | CCTZ | Wolverton | 1871 | 123 | Pitsford |
| 35062 | 1933 | | | | | |
| DM395492 | 1958 | | | | | |

*Remarks:* Latterly Cell Truck. P'90

| Numbers | Year | Type | Built | Diag | Lot | Location |
|---|---|---|---|---|---|---|
| 5682 | 1926 | TO | Metro C&W | 1745 | 185 | Midland |
| 7991 | 1933 | | | | | |
| MSC 3 | 1958 | | | | | |

*Remarks:* Sold to Manchester Ship Canal Co. 1958. P'72 by HRSG, on Severn Valley till '80.

| Numbers | Year | Type | Built | Diag | Lot | Location |
|---|---|---|---|---|---|---|
| 5734 | 1935 | BTK | Wolverton | 1905 | 859 | Midland |
| DM395898 | 1965 | | | | | |

*Remarks:* P'87 from Crewe Heritage Centre by David Smith

| Numbers | Year | Type | Built | Diag | Lot | Location |
|---|---|---|---|---|---|---|
| 5793 | 1936 | BTK | Derby | 1905 | 898 | E Kent |
| DM395903 | 1965 | | | | | |

*Remarks:* P'84, on Mid-Hants till '88, at Knebworth till '89, then Mangapps Farm till '91. Whilst LMS Book says this Lot built at Derby, coach carries a Wolverton plate

| Numbers | Year | Type | Built | Diag | Lot | Location |
|---|---|---|---|---|---|---|
| 5806 | 1926 | TO | Metro C&W | 1745 | 185 | E Lancs |
| 8000 | 1933 | | | | | |
| 44404 | 1960 | Spec | | | | |

*Remarks:* Latterly Boiler Van. P'89

| Numbers | Year | Type | Built | Diag | Lot | Location |
|---|---|---|---|---|---|---|
| 5861 | 1924 | TO | Derby | 1353 | 94 | Midland |
| 7816 | 1933 | | | | | |
| DM395519 | 1959 | | | | | |

*Remarks:* P'82 by Dawn Smith

| Numbers | Year | Type | Built | Diag | Lot | Location |
|---|---|---|---|---|---|---|
| 5913 | 1924 | TO | Derby | 1353 | 94 | Quainton |
| 7820 | 1933 | | | | | |
| DM395344 | 1962 | | | | | |

*Remarks:* W'62, converted for the LMR Control Train. P'80

| 5939 | 1926 | TO | Metro C&W | 1745 | 185 | E Lancs |
|---|---|---|---|---|---|---|
| 8023 | 1933 | | | | | |
| 44414 | 1960 | Spec | | | | |

*Remarks:* Latterly Boiler Van. P'89

| 5987 | 1937 | BTK | Derby | 1968 | 1035 | * NRM |
|---|---|---|---|---|---|---|

*Remarks:* P'?? by Princess Elizabeth Loco Soc, at Ashchurch till '77, then moved to Hereford? Sold to NRM in October '77

| 6039 | 1926 | TO | Metro C&W | 1745 | 185 | N Yorks Moors |
|---|---|---|---|---|---|---|
| 8044 | 1933 | | | | | |
| 44408 | 1960 | Spec | | | | |

*Remarks:* Latterly Boiler Van. P'87

Pictured gleaming following its refurbishment at Pickering is 1926-built Third Open No 44408. However, as can be seen, it is obviously nowadays no longer a TO, having been converted by BR in 1960 to become a Boiler Van. It ended its BR days at Marylebone. *Murray Brown*

88

| Numbers | Year | Type | Built | Diag | Lot | Location |
|---------|------|------|-------|------|-----|----------|
| ? <br> ? <br> 44415 <br> DM395939 | 1926 <br> 1933 <br> 1960 | TO <br> <br> Spec | Metro C&W | 1745 | 185 | * NRM |

*Remarks:* Latterly Boiler Van.

| | | | | | | |
|---------|------|------|-------|------|-----|----------|
| 6839 <br> DS70244 | 1935 <br> 1966 | BCK | Wolverton <br> Stewarts Lane | 1932 | 861 | Bitton |

*Remarks:* P'88

| | | | | | | |
|---------|------|------|-------|------|-----|----------|
| 7511 <br> 38740 <br> CTL 1N | 1934 <br> 196x <br> 196x | RFO | Wolverton | 1902 | 734 | Severn Valley |

*Remarks:* Interior gutted for use as an Exhibition coach. P'69, used as a dormitory coach till '88

| | | | | | | |
|---------|------|------|-------|------|-----|----------|
| 7571 | 1939 | RFO | Wolverton | 1902 | 1187 | - |

*Remarks:* W'65, body grounded at Parkfields School Derby to provide temporary accommodation. P'75, moved to Butterley & used as Cafeteria till '86. Too far gone for restoration & dismantled '87, providing parts for 7511 (qv).

| | | | | | | |
|---------|------|------|-------|------|-----|----------|
| 7878 <br> 8192 <br> DM395680 | 1927 <br> 1933 <br> 1960 | TO | Derby | 1692 | 343 | N Yorks Moors |

*Remarks:* P'91

| | | | | | | |
|---------|------|------|-------|------|-----|----------|
| 8188 <br> 35054 <br> DM395489 | 1926 <br> 1933 <br> 1958 | CCTZ | Wolverton | 1871 | 111 | W Somerset |

*Remarks:* Sold to V Berry '86, its u'frame scrapped but the body later grounded at Minehead

| | | | | | | |
|---------|------|------|-------|------|-----|----------|
| 8761 <br> 3515 <br> DM395470 | 1924 <br> 1933 | CK | Wolverton | 1694 | 30 | Worth Valley ? |

*Remarks:* Ex-WW2 Ambulance? P'82, at Northwich till '87, then Dinting till '90

| | | | | | | |
|---------|------|------|-------|------|-----|----------|
| 9125 <br> DM395892 | 1935 <br> 1964 | TO | Wolverton | 1915 | 897 | Steamtown |

*Remarks:* P'85 by D Smith, in store till '??

| | | | | | | |
|---------|------|------|-------|------|-----|----------|
| 9205 <br> DM395923 | 1936 <br> 1965 | TO | Derby | 1915 | 894 | Darley Dale |

*Remarks:* P'89 by Peak Rail, stored on BR till '90

| | | | | | | |
|---------|------|------|-------|------|-----|----------|
| 9229 <br> 3565 <br> DM395776 | 1925 <br> 1933 <br> 1961 | CK | Wolverton | 1694 | 120 | Aylesbury |

*Remarks:* P'84 by BR(LMR) Staff Association

| Numbers | Year | Type | Built | Diag | Lot | Location |
|---------|------|------|-------|------|-----|----------|
| 9355 | 1936 | TO | B R C W | 1915 | 954 | Severn Valley |
| CTL 2S | 196x | | | | | |
| 9355 | 1977 | RB | S V R | | | |
| 149 | 1987 | RB S | V R | 1948 | (902) | |

Remarks: P'71 with interior gutted. Restored as a Buffet Car, then rebuilt 1986/7 to resemble LMS Buffet Car No.131 & given fictitious number

| | | | | | | |
|---------|------|------|-------|------|-----|----------|
| 9864 | 1929 | BCK | Wolverton | 1704 | 454 | Midland |
| 6720 | 1933 | | | | | |
| DM395845 | 1965 | | | | | |

Remarks: P'89

| | | | | | | |
|---------|------|------|-------|------|-----|----------|
| 9884 | 1924 | BCK | Wolverton | 1754 | 31 | Southall |
| 6618 | 1933 | | | | | |
| DM395476 | 1959 | | | | | |

Remarks: P'88 by GW Pres Grp

| | | | | | | |
|---------|------|------|-------|------|-----|----------|
| 10257 | 1930 | sRFO | Derby | 1719 | 488 | Midland |
| 1030 | 1933 | | | | | |
| DM395222 | 1956 | Insp | Wolverton | | | |

Remarks: W'55, converted to an Inspection Saloon. P'72, stored at Derby till '75

| | | | | | | |
|---------|------|------|-------|------|-----|----------|
| 11937 | 1937 | T | Wolverton | 1906A | 1043 | South Shields |
| DM395887 | 1964 | | | | | |

Remarks: P'86 as 'Marsden Rattler' restaurant

| | | | | | | |
|---------|------|------|-------|------|-----|----------|
| 12059 | 1930 | T | Derby | 1784 | 523 | Bo'ness |
| 11406 | 1933 | | | | | |
| DM395918 | 1965 | | | | | |

Remarks: P'86 by SRPS, at Falkirk till '88 then Perth till '91

| | | | | | | |
|---------|------|------|-------|------|-----|----------|
| 12066 | 1938 | T | Wolverton | 1906A | 1094 | Worth Valley |
| K&WVR 6 | 1968 | | | | | |

Remarks: P'68

| | | | | | | |
|---------|------|------|-------|------|-----|----------|
| 12244 | 1951 | T | Wolverton | 2124 | 1633 | Padiham |
| DM395928 | | | | | | |
| | 1983 | DTT | Steamport | | | |

Remarks: P' ?, converted to driving trailer '83 for push/pull use on site, & at Steamport till '90

| | | | | | | |
|---------|------|------|-------|------|-----|----------|
| 12992 | 1949 | TK | B R C W | 2119 | 1484 | Severn Valley |

Remarks: P'72

| | | | | | | |
|---------|------|------|-------|------|-----|----------|
| 13045 | 1950 | TK | B R C W | 2119 | 1484 | - |

Remarks: P'72 on Severn Valley, broken up for spares in '80.

| | | | | | | |
|---------|------|------|-------|------|-----|----------|
| 14187 | 1927 | TO | Derby | 1692 | 343 | Southport |
| 8200 | 1933 | | | | | |

| Numbers | Year | Type | Built | Diag | Lot | Location |
|---------|------|------|-------|------|-----|----------|
| 14241<br>516<br>DM395777 | 1928<br>1933 | SLT | Derby | 1709 | 418 | * NRM |

*Remarks:* P'77, restored by BREL Wolverton '78. To Swindon 'NRM On Tour' exhibition '90, returned to York 4/91

| Numbers | Year | Type | Built | Diag | Lot | Location |
|---------|------|------|-------|------|-----|----------|
| 14256<br>1428<br>DM395798 | 1928<br>1933<br>1962 | TK | Wolverton | 1695 | 388 | Pitsford |

*Remarks:* P'89

| Numbers | Year | Type | Built | Diag | Lot | Location |
|---------|------|------|-------|------|-----|----------|
| 14281<br>1451<br>DM395799 | 1928<br>1933<br>1962 | TK | Wolverton | 1695 | 388 | Midland |

*Remarks:* P'87 as PW Dept dormitory coach

| Numbers | Year | Type | Built | Diag | Lot | Location |
|---------|------|------|-------|------|-----|----------|
| 14425<br>531<br>DM395778<br>SR 177 | 1928<br>1933 | SLT | Derby | 1709 | 428 | Strathspey |

| Numbers | Year | Type | Built | Diag | Lot | Location |
|---------|------|------|-------|------|-----|----------|
| 14718<br>8207 | 1927<br>1933 | TO | Derby | 1692 | 343 | * NRM |

*Remarks:* P pre'74, loaned to Princess Elizabeth Loco Soc. at Ashchurch till '77, then at Hereford?

| Numbers | Year | Type | Built | Diag | Lot | Location |
|---------|------|------|-------|------|-----|----------|
| 15412<br>1023<br>DM395205 | 1928<br>1933<br>1957 | sRFO | Derby | 1707 | 379 | E Lancs |

*Remarks:* P'89, briefly at Crewe Heritage Centre

| Numbers | Year | Type | Built | Diag | Lot | Location |
|---------|------|------|-------|------|-----|----------|
| 15486<br>10959<br>DM395645 | 1926<br>1933<br>1960 | T | Newton Heath | 1700 | 231 | Castle Ashby |

*Remarks:* P'84 by J Dunkley at Castle Ashby Stn., Northants, adapted as Cocktail Lounge

| Numbers | Year | Type | Built | Diag | Lot | Location |
|---------|------|------|-------|------|-----|----------|
| 16122<br>7828<br>DM395345 | 1925<br>1933<br>1962 | TO | Derby | 1692 | 154 | * NRM |

*Remarks:* Mess & Staff car in LMR Control Train. P'80

| Numbers | Year | Type | Built | Diag | Lot | Location |
|---------|------|------|-------|------|-----|----------|
| 15509<br>3820<br>DM395815 | 1931<br>1933<br>1962 | CK | Wolverton | 1791 | 531 | Mid-Hants |

*Remarks:* P'91

| Numbers | Year | Type | Built | Diag | Lot | Location |
|---------|------|------|-------|------|-----|----------|
| 16232<br>20165 | 1927<br>1933 | BT | Derby | 1703 | 141 | Ravenglass |

*Remarks:* P'??, used as dormitory for volunteers

| Numbers | Year | Type | Built | Diag | Lot | Location |
|---|---|---|---|---|---|---|
| 16243 | 1925 | TK | Derby | 1695 | 95 | Steamtown |
| 1307 | 1933 | | | | | |
| DM395812 | 1962 | | | | | |

Remarks: P'91

| 16411 | 1926 | BCK | Wolverton | 1755 | 208 | Llangollen |
|---|---|---|---|---|---|---|
| 6650 | 1933 | | | | | |
| DM395754 | 1961 | | | | | |

Remarks: P'87

| 16553 | 1925 | TO | Derby | 1692 | 154 | * NRM |
|---|---|---|---|---|---|---|
| 7863 | 1933 | | | | | |
| DM395346 | 1962 | | | | | |

Remarks: Mess & Staff car in LMR Control Train. P'80

| 16696 | 1925 | TO | Derby | 1692 | 154 | Swanage |
|---|---|---|---|---|---|---|
| 7868 | 1933 | | | | | |
| DM395347 | 1962 | | | | | |

Remarks: Mess & Staff car in LMR Control Train. P'80 by LMSSPG, not arriving at Swanage till '81

| 16782 | 1924 | TK | Derby | 1695 | 9 | Bluebell |
|---|---|---|---|---|---|---|
| 1272 | 1933 | | | | | |
| DM395584 | | | | | | |

Remarks: P'71, used as dormitory for volunteers.

| 18017 | 1927 | BCK | Wolverton | 1755 | 320 | Nene Valley |
|---|---|---|---|---|---|---|
| 6678 | 1933 | | | | | |
| DM395758 | | | | | | |

| 24617 | 1949 | CK | Derby | 2159 | 1500 | Severn Valley |
|---|---|---|---|---|---|---|

Remarks: P'68

| 24725 | 1950 | CK | Derby | 2159 | 1586 | Bo'ness |
|---|---|---|---|---|---|---|
| 99804 plated | | | | | | |

Remarks: P'?? by SRPS, at Falkirk till Dec'87

| 26668 | 1950 | BTK | Derby | 2161 | 1501 | - |
|---|---|---|---|---|---|---|

Remarks: P'?? on Severn Valley, broken up for spares in '75.

| 26680 | 1950 | BTK | Derby | 2161 | 1501 | Severn Valley |
|---|---|---|---|---|---|---|
| DM395979 | | | | | | |

Remarks: P'73

| 26921 | 1950 | BTK | Wolverton | 2161 | 1506 | Severn Valley |
|---|---|---|---|---|---|---|

Remarks: P'68

| Numbers | Year | Type | Built | Diag | Lot | Location |
|---------|------|------|-------|------|-----|----------|
| 26986 | 1950 | BTK | Wolverton | 2161 | 1506 | Severn Valley |

*Remarks:* P'71

| 27001 | 1950 | BTK | Wolverton | 2161 | 1506 | Great Central |

*Remarks:* P'?? by 71000 Loco Trust, but stored at Stanstead Abbots till '83

| 27023 | 1950 | BTK | Derby | 2161 | 1575 | - |

*Remarks:* P'?? on Severn Valley, broken up for spares in '75.

| 27043 SR 128 | 1951 | BTK | Derby | 2161 | 1575 | Strathspey |

| 27093 | 1951 | BTK | Wolverton | 2161 | 1597 | * NRM |

*Remarks:* W'62, allocated to 2nd WR Control Train without being renumbered. P'80

| 27109 65830 | 1945 | TO | Wolverton | 1999 | 1400 | Steamtown |

*Remarks:* P'84, reportedly by Severn Valley

| 27162 38746 | 1945 196x | TO | Wolverton | 1999 | 1401 | Quainton |

*Remarks:* Latterly Exhibition van. P'78 by GCR Coach Group

| 27218 | 1945 | TO | Wolverton | 1999 | 1401 | Severn Valley |

*Remarks:* P'68 by Warwickshire Railway Soc.

| 27220 | 1945 | TO | Wolverton | 1999 | 1401 | Severn Valley |

*Remarks:* P'68

| 27234 38742 SR 129 | 1945 196x | TO | Wolverton | 1999 | 1401 | Strathspey |

*Remarks:* Latterly Exhibition van.

| 27249 | 1945 | TO | Wolverton | 1999 | 1401 | Foxfield |

*Remarks:* P'67

| 27270 | 1947 | TO | Wolverton | 1999 | 1402 | Severn Valley |

*Remarks:* P'68

| 27389 99808 plated | 1947 | TO | Wolverton | 1999 | 1438 | Bo'ness |

*Remarks:* P' ? by SRPS, at Falkirk till '88

| Numbers | Year | Type | Built | Diag | Lot | Location |
|---------|------|------|-------|------|-----|----------|
| 27407 99805 plated | 1947 | TO | Wolverton | 1999 | 1438 | Bo'ness |

Remarks: P' ? by SRPS, at Falkirk till '88

| Numbers | Year | Type | Built | Diag | Lot | Location |
|---------|------|------|-------|------|-----|----------|
| 28361 | 1939 | DMBTO | Derby | 2012 | 1073 | * Steamport |

Remarks: EMU. P'80

| Numbers | Year | Type | Built | Diag | Lot | Location |
|---------|------|------|-------|------|-----|----------|
| 29896 | 1939 | DTC | Derby | 2013 | 1075 | * Steamport |

Remarks: EMU. P'80

| Numbers | Year | Type | Built | Diag | Lot | Location |
|---------|------|------|-------|------|-----|----------|
| 30088 DM395279 | 1936 1958 | RK | Gloucester | 1912 | 956 | Rowden Mill |

Remarks: P'88

| Numbers | Year | Type | Built | Diag | Lot | Location |
|---------|------|------|-------|------|-----|----------|
| 30225 | 1939 | POS | Wolverton | ?043 | 1238 | Midland |

Remarks: P'74

| Numbers | Year | Type | Built | Diag | Lot | Location |
|---------|------|------|-------|------|-----|----------|
| 30272 | 1950 | POS | Wolverton | 2167 | 1559 | * Tyseley |

Remarks: P'74, stored at Brighton till '77 & at NRM York till '84

There are still several lines where you can travel in LMS-designed post-war austerity vehicles — basic, but functional. Nowadays, however, they have a charisma of their own and an ability to transport you to another age. One such place is the Strathspey Railway where TO No 27234 awaits you. This coach is viewed at Boat of Garten in March 1987. *Hugh Madgin*

| Numbers | Year | Type | Built | Diag | Lot | Location |
|---|---|---|---|---|---|---|
| 30976 DB975562 | 1938 1976 | BG | Wolverton | 2007 | 1096 | Llangollen |

*Remarks:* P'89, the first vehicle at Ruabon

| 31036 (095001) | 1939 1974 | BG | Wolverton | 2007 | 1198 | Bo'ness |

*Remarks:* P'84 by SRPS, at Falkirk till Dec'87 (to be grounded as store? bogies being kept as spares?)

| 31082 K&WVR 111 | 1940 1980 | BG | Wolverton | 2007 | 1261 | Worth Valley |

*Remarks:* P'80

| 31129 | 1940 | BG | Derby | 2007 | 1304 | Steamtown |

*Remarks:* P'79?

| 31148 | 1940 | BG | Derby | 2007 | 1304 | Steamtown |

*Remarks:* P'79?

| 31209 2910 | 1941 1983 | Spec | Wolverton | 2056 | 1229 | - |

*Remarks:* 12-wheel Power Brake & Staff Sleeper from Royal Train. P'89 by Vic Berry, but scrappped '91.

| 31217 | 1941 | BG | Wolverton | 2007 | 1357 | Manchester |

*Remarks:* P'88? at L'pool Rd Stn

| 31225 041896 | •1941 1986 | BG | Wolverton | 2007 | 1357 | Great Central |

*Remarks:* Body P'?

| 31244 | •1941 | BG | Wolverton | 2007 | 1357 | Tyseley |

*Remarks:* P'83

| 31274 | •1941 | BG | Wolverton | 2007 | 1357 | - |

*Remarks:* Pc'82 for 'Western Lady', at Horwich till '83 then Steamport; fire damaged there, moved to Bodmin then swopped for BR GUV 86568 during '89 & body since scrapped.

| 31281 | •1941 | BG | Wolverton | 2007 | 1357 | Colne Valley |

*Remarks:* P'83?

| 31299 | •1941 | BG | Wolverton | 2007 | 1357 | Midland |

*Remarks:* P'81 by Mansfield Steam Railway Soc.

• Lot built from 1941, but the build plates on those so marked are dated 1944

| 31343 | 1947 | BG | Wolverton | 2007 | 1444 | Mid-Hants |

*Remarks:* P'80

| Numbers | Year | Type | Built | Diag | Lot | Location |
|---------|------|------|-------|------|-----|----------|
| 31352 | 1949 | BG | Wolverton | 2171 | 1508 | Southall |
| 31359<br>DB975986 | 1949<br>1980 | BG | Wolverton | 2171 | 1508 | Market Bosworth |

*Remarks:* P'90?

| 31361<br>DB977031 | 1949<br>1981 | BG | Wolverton | 2171 | 1508 | Steamtown |

*Remarks:* P'87 by R Edmondson

| 31370<br>DB975944 | 1949<br>1980 | BG | Wolverton | 2171 | 1508 | Great Central |

*Remarks:* Body P'84 ex Marple & Gillott, grounded at Loughborough

| 31384<br>DB977032 | 1949<br>1981 | BG | Derby | 2171 | 1563 | Middleton |

*Remarks:* P'91 by R Walton

| 31385<br>DB977024<br>31402 | 1949<br>1982<br>1983 | BG | Derby | 2171 | 1563 | E Lancs |

*Remarks:* When 31402 became the replacement DB977024 31385 assumed its number, clearly visible under the paint!

| 31387<br>DB977034 | 1949<br>1981 | BG | Derby | 2171 | 1563 | E Lancs |

*Remarks:* P'87 by Class 40 Pres Soc

| 31406 | 1950 | BG | Derby | 2171 | 1579 | Dean Forest |

*Remarks:* P'81

| 31407<br>DB977037 | 1950 | BG | Derby | 2171 | 1579 | Steamtown |

*Remarks:* P'87 by R Edmondson

| 31926 | 1944 | BG | Wolverton | 2100 | 1359 | Pitsford |

*Remarks:* P'87

| 31927 | 1944 | BG | Wolverton | 2100 | 1359 | S Devon |

*Remarks:* P'80? by DVR Association

| 31930 | 1944 | BG | Wolverton | 2100 | 1359 | Steamtown |

*Remarks:* P'79? by Mr Peakman

| 32975 | 1938 | BGZ | Wolverton | 2000 | 1091 | Bluebell |

*Remarks:* P'79

| Numbers | Year | Type | Built | Diag | Lot | Location |
|---------|------|------|-------|------|-----|----------|
| 32978 | 1938 | BGZ | Wolverton | 2000 | 1091 | Coleford ? |

*Remarks:* P'81? at Dean Forest; not found by '89 & reported at GW Museum (Gloucs)

| Numbers | Year | Type | Built | Diag | Lot | Location |
|---------|------|------|-------|------|-----|----------|
| 32988 SR 154 | 1938 | BGZ | Wolverton | 2000 | 1091 | Strathspey |

| Numbers | Year | Type | Built | Diag | Lot | Location |
|---------|------|------|-------|------|-----|----------|
| 32990 | 1938 | BGZ | Wolverton | 2000 | 1091 | Swanage |

*Remarks:* P'78, on Mid-Hants till '8?

| Numbers | Year | Type | Built | Diag | Lot | Location |
|---------|------|------|-------|------|-----|----------|
| 32994 | 1938 | BGZ | Wolverton | 2000 | 1091 | N Staffs |

*Remarks:* P'76 by S&DR Trust, on W Somerset till '89

| Numbers | Year | Type | Built | Diag | Lot | Location |
|---------|------|------|-------|------|-----|----------|
| 32998 DB975249 | 1938 | BGZ | Wolverton | 2000 | 1091 | Midland |

*Remarks:* P'84

| Numbers | Year | Type | Built | Diag | Lot | Location |
|---------|------|------|-------|------|-----|----------|
| 33002 | 1940 | BGZ | Wolverton | 2000 | 1262 | Didcot |

*Remarks:* P'?? by GWS, the body grounded as a store by '82 (its underframe was saved, reportedly for a replica of a broad-gauge coach)

One of the last six-wheeled vehicles to remain in operation with BR was this BGZ No DB975249, alias No 32998. It ended its days at Tinsley Traction Maintenance Depot where it had survived in departmental use far longer than its revenue-earning sisters and was bought by a locomotive owner at Butterley on the Midland Railway Centre's line. It has not yet been restored to original condition. *Murray Brown*

| Numbers | Year | Type | Built | Diag | Lot | Location |
|---------|------|------|-------|------|-----|----------|
| 33003 SR 153 | 1940 | BGZ | Wolverton | 2000 | 1262 | Strathspey |
| 33007 | 1940 | BGZ | Wolverton | 2000 | 1262 | Southport |
| 33014 | 1940 | BGZ | Wolverton | 2000 | 1262 | Quainton |
| 33016 | 1940 | BGZ | Wolverton | 2000 | 1262 | Betws-y-Coed |

*Remarks:* P' ? by Conwy Valley Railway Mus

| Numbers | Year | Type | Built | Diag | Lot | Location |
|---------|------|------|-------|------|-----|----------|
| 37011 | 1938 | CCTY | Metro-Cammell | 2026 | 1154 | Preston Park |

*Remarks:* P'85, on Nene Valley till '??

| Numbers | Year | Type | Built | Diag | Lot | Location |
|---------|------|------|-------|------|-----|----------|
| 37066 | 1938 | CCTY | Metro-Cammell | 2026 | 1154 | Nene Valley |

*Remarks:* P'85

| Numbers | Year | Type | Built | Diag | Lot | Location |
|---------|------|------|-------|------|-----|----------|
| 37071 | 1938 | CCTY | Metro-Cammell | 2026 | 1154 | Nene Valley |

*Remarks:* P'85

| Numbers | Year | Type | Built | Diag | Lot | Location |
|---------|------|------|-------|------|-----|----------|
| 37096 | 1938 | CCTY | Metro-Cammell | 2026 | 1154 | Nene Valley |

*Remarks:* P'85

| Numbers | Year | Type | Built | Diag | Lot | Location |
|---------|------|------|-------|------|-----|----------|
| 37103 DM396003 | 1938 | CCTY | Metro-Cammell | 2026 | 1154 | W Somerset |

*Remarks:* P'76 by S&DR Trust

| Numbers | Year | Type | Built | Diag | Lot | Location |
|---------|------|------|-------|------|-----|----------|
| 37141 | 1938 | CCTY | Metro-Cammell | 2026 | 1154 | Nene Valley |

*Remarks:* P'85

| Numbers | Year | Type | Built | Diag | Lot | Location |
|---------|------|------|-------|------|-----|----------|
| 37207 | 1956 | CCTY | Swindon | 2026 | GW1770 | Dean Forest |
| 37224 K&WVR 109 | 1956 | CCTY | Swindon | 2026 | GW1770 | Worth Valley |
| 37225 | 1956 | CCTY | Swindon | 2026 | GW1770 | Blunsdon |

*Remarks:* P'86? at Toddington, to Blunsdon by '88

| Numbers | Year | Type | Built | Diag | Lot | Location |
|---------|------|------|-------|------|-----|----------|
| 37306 | 1952 | CCTY | Earlestown | 2026 | 1636 | Tanfield |

*Remarks:* P'76, but soon grounded; u/frame used to carry body of NER TY 1056 (qv)

| Numbers | Year | Type | Built | Diag | Lot | Location |
|---------|------|------|-------|------|-----|----------|
| 37308 | 1952 | CCTY | Earlestown | 2026 | 1636 | Tanfield |

*Remarks:* P'76, but soon grounded; u/frame used to carry body of NER BTY 831 (qv)

| Numbers | Year | Type | Built | Diag | Lot | Location |
|---------|------|------|-------|------|-----|----------|
| 37311 K&WVR 110 | 1952 | CCTY | Earlestown | 2026 | 1636 | Worth Valley |

| Numbers | Year | Type | Built | Diag | Lot | Location |
|---|---|---|---|---|---|---|
| 37325 | 1952 | CCTY | Earlestown | 2026 | 1636 | Blunsdon |

*Remarks:* P'??, grounded as store

| Numbers | Year | Type | Built | Diag | Lot | Location |
|---|---|---|---|---|---|---|
| 37326 | 1952 | CCTY | Earlestown | 2026 | 1636 | Pitsford |

*Remarks:* P'87

| Numbers | Year | Type | Built | Diag | Lot | Location |
|---|---|---|---|---|---|---|
| 37817 (DB975229) | 1935 | CCT | Derby | 1870 | 848 | Bo'ness |

*Remarks:* P'84 by SRPS, at Falkirk till '88 (for conversion to a crane runner)

| Numbers | Year | Type | Built | Diag | Lot | Location |
|---|---|---|---|---|---|---|
| 37909 DB975560 | 1937 1976 | CCT | Wolverton | 1870 | 1050 | Brechin |

*Remarks:* P'91

| Numbers | Year | Type | Built | Diag | Lot | Location |
|---|---|---|---|---|---|---|
| 40226 | 1946 | FVZ | Wolverton | 2115 | 1428 | Bo'ness |

*Remarks:* P'?? by SRPS

| Numbers | Year | Type | Built | Diag | Lot | Location |
|---|---|---|---|---|---|---|
| 40252 | 1949 | FVZ | Wolverton | 2115 | 1445 | Darley Dale |

*Remarks:* P'83 by TFP as a store, at Midland till pre'87 then Buxton till '90

| Numbers | Year | Type | Built | Diag | Lot | Location |
|---|---|---|---|---|---|---|
| 40284 | 1949 | FVZ | Wolverton | 2115 | 1445 | Nene Valley |

*Remarks:* P pre'77

| Numbers | Year | Type | Built | Diag | Lot | Location |
|---|---|---|---|---|---|---|
| 40288 | 1949 | FVZ | Wolverton | 2115 | 1445 | Murton |

*Remarks:* Body P'?? by GYRPS, at Starbeck till moved to Yorks Farm Museum in '90

| Numbers | Year | Type | Built | Diag | Lot | Location |
|---|---|---|---|---|---|---|
| 40294 | 1949 | FVZ | Wolverton | 2115 | 1445 | Darley Dale |

*Remarks:* P'84 by Rowsley Loco Trust, at Buxton till '89

| Numbers | Year | Type | Built | Diag | Lot | Location |
|---|---|---|---|---|---|---|
| 40311 | 1949 | FVZ | Wolverton | 2115 | 1509 | Murton |

*Remarks:* Body P'?? by GYRPS, at Starbeck till moved to Yorks Farm Museum in '90

| Numbers | Year | Type | Built | Diag | Lot | Location |
|---|---|---|---|---|---|---|
| 40320 | 1949 | FVZ | Wolverton | 2115 | 1509 | Southall |

*Remarks:* P'85

| Numbers | Year | Type | Built | Diag | Lot | Location |
|---|---|---|---|---|---|---|
| 42608 | 1948 | HBY | Derby | 2125 | 1534 | Midland |

*Remarks:* P'71 by Derby Corp

| Numbers | Year | Type | Built | Diag | Lot | Location |
|---|---|---|---|---|---|---|
| 44057 | 1937 | MTZ | Derby | 1994 | 1067 | * NRM |

| Numbers | Year | Type | Built | Diag | Lot | Location |
|---|---|---|---|---|---|---|
| 45005 | 1942 | Spec | Wolverton | 2066 | 1323 | Steamtown |
| 99064 plated | 1948 | ROY | Wolverton | 2136 | | |

*Remarks:* Chairman's Saloon, built on the underframe of a war-damaged coach; altered to a Royal Saloon in 1948.

| Numbers | Year | Type | Built | Diag | Lot | Location |
|---------|------|------|-------|------|-----|----------|
| 45006 | 1942 | Spec | Wolverton | 2066 | 1331 | - |
|  | 1948 | ROY | Wolverton | 2137 |  |  |
| 2912 | 1983 |  |  |  |  |  |

*Remarks:* Chairman's Saloon, built on the underframe of a war-damaged coach; altered to a Royal Saloon in 1948. P'89 by Vic Berry, but scrapped '91.

| Numbers | Year | Type | Built | Diag | Lot | Location |
|---------|------|------|-------|------|-----|----------|
| 45021 | 1944 | Insp | Wolverton | 2046 | 1356 | Strathspey |
| SR 130 |  |  |  |  |  |  |

*Remarks:* P'72, on Severn Valley till '75, then in store till '??

| Numbers | Year | Type | Built | Diag | Lot | Location |
|---------|------|------|-------|------|-----|----------|
| 45036 | 1947 | Insp | Wolverton | 2046 | 1432 | Chinnor |

*Remarks:* P'89, stored at Tinsley, reportedly for Llangollen, but moved to Chinnor in '91

| Numbers | Year | Type | Built | Diag | Lot | Location |
|---------|------|------|-------|------|-----|----------|
| 45045 | 1940 | Insp | Wolverton | 2046 | 1221 | Chester |

*Remarks:* P'89 by Llangollen R S, restored at Chester goods shed

| Numbers | Year | Type | Built | Diag | Lot | Location |
|---------|------|------|-------|------|-----|----------|
| 45047 | 1941 | Insp | Wolverton | 2046 | 1264 | Midland |

*Remarks:* P'86 by 7F Pres Grp, after use in SAS training at MOD Moreton-on-Lugg

| Numbers | Year | Type | Built | Diag | Lot | Location |
|---------|------|------|-------|------|-----|----------|
| 45048 | 1941 | Insp | Wolverton | 2046 | 1264 | Gloucs-Warks |

*Remarks:* P'81, at Steamport till '83.

| Numbers | Year | Type | Built | Diag | Lot | Location |
|---------|------|------|-------|------|-----|----------|
| 45049 | 1949 | Spec |  |  |  | * NRM |
| Car No.3 |  |  |  |  |  |  |

*Remarks:* Dynamometer Car

| Numbers | Year | Type | Built | Diag | Lot | Location |
|---------|------|------|-------|------|-----|----------|
| 45053 | 1938 | Spec |  |  |  | * NRM |
| Test Unit No.1 |  |  |  |  |  |  |

*Remarks:* Mobile Test Unit

| Numbers | Year | Type | Built | Diag | Lot | Location |
|---------|------|------|-------|------|-----|----------|
| DB999502 | 1959 | Insp | Wolverton | 2046 | 3093 | Brechin |

*Remarks:* P'82

*Others:*
An unidentified BTK at Steamtown, owned by D Smith & painted pale green (30T, 57'0" x 9'3") [5734 perhaps?]
An unidentified 6-wheel 'Scenery Van' P'82 at Telford
An unidentified 6-wheel CCT at Rutland
Body of an unidentified postwar built Horse box at Bo'ness, P'85 by SRPS & at Falkirk till '88

The following survived into preservation as underframes only:
An unidentified former Ambulance coach at Steamtown, carrying Army No. 80.082
An unidentified 6-wheel Brake from Lot 1091, used in restoration of GER CZ 197 (qv) on Kent & E Sussex
6-wheel Milk Tank 6093 (built Derby 1931 to D1994 Lot 631, later 44180 & DM395780) was the crane runner that accompanied the Cowans Steam Breakdown crane P'80 at Midland Railway Centre
6-wheel Insulated Milk Van 3826 (built Wolverton 1926 to D1873 Lot 233, later 40070 & DM395663) was P'78 at Strathspey & has since been purchased to replace 6093 (above) as crane runner at Midland Ry Centre

# THE LONDON & NORTH EASTERN RAILWAY GROUP

Prefix numerals applied after Grouping:
NER - 2  NBR - 3  GNR - 4  GCR - 5  GER - 6  GNSR - 7
H&BR - 5000 added when merged with NER, then prefixed as NER stock (net effect - 25000 added)

| Numbers | Year | Type | Built | Diag | Lot | Location |
|---------|------|------|-------|------|-----|----------|

## EAST COAST JOINT STOCK

[Diagrams per 1909 Diagram Book]

| Numbers | Year | Type | Built | Diag | Lot | Location |
|---------|------|------|-------|------|-----|----------|
| 12 | 1898 | TK | York | 14 | | * NRM |
| 41805 | 1925 | | | | | |

*Remarks:* NER Clerestory design. W'52, still with gas lighting!, & stored at Hellifield & Brighton till '78. Restored at Steamtown '85-6

| 82 | 1908 | BG | Doncaster | 38 | | * NRM |
| 109 | 1927 | | | | | |

*Remarks:* GNR design. Used in ECJS Royal Train. P'c76, restored at BREL Doncaster, to 'NRM On Tour' display at Swindon '90, returned to York 5/91

| 107 | 1901 | SLC | York | 70 | | Woolwich |

*Remarks:* NER 12-wheel Clerestory design. W'27, body grounded near Easingwold Stn. P'81 by Resco

| 377 | 1907 | TK | Doncaster | 22 | | Colne Valley |
| 1377 | 1925 | | | | | |
| 52055 | 1929 | | | | | |
| DE320444 | 1957 | | | | | |

*Remarks:* P'91, part fire damaged

| 395 | 1908 | ROY | Doncaster | 81 | | * NRM |
| | | | | 81A | | |

*Remarks:* 12-wheel. King's Saloon until 1925, then Queen's Saloon after conversion for day-use only. P'77 but stored at Wolverton till '79

| Numbers | Year | Type | Built | Diag | Lot | Location |
|---------|------|------|-------|------|-----|----------|
| 396 | 1908 | ROY | York | 82 | | * Bressingham |

*Remarks:* 12-wheel. Queen's Saloon until converted for day-use only in 1925; since used by both Monarch & Consort. P'77, but stored at Wolverton till '79

## EASTERN COUNTIES RAILWAY

| | | | | | | |
|---------|------|------|-------|------|-----|----------|
| 1 | c1855 | FY | | | | * NRM |

*Remarks:* It's believed this vehicle was assembled by the GER about 1895, using the underframe from FY 63 of 1851 & body from FY 64 of 1852. Stored at Stratford till '??, then at Bressingham till '84/5

## GREAT CENTRAL RAILWAY

| | | | | | | |
|---------|------|------|-------|------|-----|----------|
| 228 | 1910 | TO | Dukinfield | 5C1 | 5067 | Banbury |
| 5228 | | | | | | |

*Remarks:* 'Barnum' Body grounded at Hull docks, as a greenhouse latterly, till P'89 by GCR Coach Grp

| | | | | | | |
|---------|------|------|-------|------|-----|----------|
| 652 | 1916 | BT | Dukinfield | 3B5 | 5038 | Banbury |
| 5652 | 1925 | | | | | |
| DB320603(sic) | | | | | | |

*Remarks:* P'81 by GCR Coach Group, at Aylesbury till '8?

| | | | | | | |
|---------|------|------|-------|------|-----|----------|
| 664 | 1910 | TO | Dukinfield | 5C1 | 5067 | Great Central |
| 5664 | 1925 | | | | | |
| DE320540 | 1957 | | | | | |

*Remarks:* 'Barnum' P'71, on Severn Valley till sold to MLST '79. Restored by MSC team in workshop at Nuneaton during '85

| | | | | | | |
|---------|------|------|-------|------|-----|----------|
| 666 | 1910 | TO | Dukinfield | 5C1 | 5067 | * Great Central |
| 5666 | 1925 | | | | | |
| DE320709 | 1958 | | | | | |

*Remarks:* 'Barnum' Latterly a Mess van. P'83 from a length of isolated track at Barnetby

| | | | | | | |
|---------|------|------|-------|------|-----|----------|
| 695 | 1911 | BTO | Dukinfield | 5E1 | 5112 | N Yorks Moors |
| 5695 | 1925 | | | | | |
| DE320528 | 1957 | | | | | |

*Remarks:* 'Barnum' P'70 by Barnum Coach Trust

| | | | | | | |
|---------|------|------|-------|------|-----|----------|
| 799 | 1905 | T | Gorton | 3B4 | | Banbury |
| 5799 | 1925 | | | | | |

*Remarks:* P'84 by GCR Coach Grp

| | | | | | | |
|---------|------|------|-------|------|-----|----------|
| 793 | 1905 | T | B R C W | | | Great Central |
| 5793 | 1925 | | | | | |
| 040451 | | | | | | |

*Remarks:* W'55, at Hull Docks till P'88

| Numbers | Year | Type | Built | Diag | Lot | Location |
|---------|------|------|-------|------|-----|----------|
| 957 | 1906 | F | Metro C&W | 3Q1 | 5013 | Banbury |
| 5957 | 1925 | | | | | |
| | 1930 | | | 3L8 | 5125 | |
| DE320179 | 1953 | | | | | |

*Remarks:* P'71 by GCR Coach Group member, stored till '74, then at Quainton till '83

| | | | | | | |
|---------|------|------|-------|------|-----|----------|
| 1663 | 1903 | BCL | Gorton? | | | Banbury |

*Remarks:* Clerestory. W'48, body grounded within a stand at Hull Kingston Rovers' ground with two other bodies (both dismantled for parts; GCR T 224? by GCRCG, M&NB BTK 118 by Midland Ry Trust). P'89 by GCRCG

*Others:*
Possibly a body at Bo'ness (see remarks at end of NBR section)

The Great Central Railway did things in style and their coaches were no exception. The 'Barnum' coaches were held in high regard, their 10 ft 6 in wheelbase offering a good ride and their matchboard panelling, inward-opening doors and huge door grab handles adding considerable distinction and variation to contemporary vehicles. There are three complete 'Barnums' surviving and No 664 is well worth a visit — and ride in — on the Great Central Railway, Loughborough, where it is frequently used for special parties. *Murray Brown*

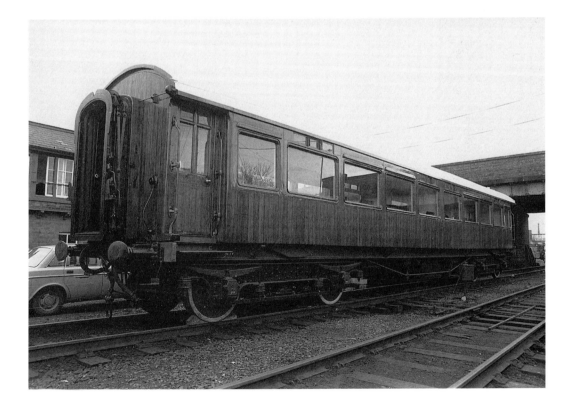

| Numbers | Year | Type | Built | Diag | Lot | Location |
|---------|------|------|-------|------|-----|----------|

# GREAT EASTERN RAILWAY

[Diagrams per PRO Diagram Book]

| Numbers | Year | Type | Built | Diag | Lot | Location |
|---------|------|------|-------|------|-----|----------|
| 1 | 1920 | Spec | Stratford | 34 | | Steamtown |
| 61 | 1925 | | | 34E | | |
| DE962450 | 1948 | | | | | |
| 99050 plated | | | | | | |

*Remarks:* Directors', then General Manager's Saloon, its Gresley bogies replaced by GER pattern in 1934. P'71 by W H McAlpine

| 3 | 1912 | FO | Stratford | | | K&ESR |
| 63 | 1924 | Insp | | 29 | | |
| 21870 | 1927 | | | | | |
| DE900271 | | | | | | |
| 62429 | 1977 | | | | | |

*Remarks:* P'?? by W H McAlpine, & for filming in '77 had an incorrect number painted on (1946 number of GER BTK). Sold to Resco c1980, but remained at Steamtown till '89

| 5 | 1898 | ROY | Stratford | 5 | | Lakeside |
| 65 | 1925 | | | 5E | | |
| DE960900 | c1946 | | | | | |
| (L&HR 61) | | | | | | |

*Remarks:* Royal Saloon. Downgraded to CCE's Saloon after Grouping, given Gresley bogies in '44 & became mobile office in '72. P'?? by W H McAlpine, later sold to A Maher but at Steamtown till '89

| 14 | 1889 | Spec | | 11 | | Rutland |
| 68 | 1925 | | | | | |
| DE960903 | | | | | | |

*Remarks:* 6-wheel Engineer's Saloon, latterly a Mess van at Doncaster. P'73 by W McAlpine, stored on his private railway at Fawley, near Henley, till '83

| 16 | | FY | | | | N Norfolk |

*Remarks:* 4-comp't body P'90 from site at Hevingham

| 19 | 1878 | FY | B R C W | 103 | | Chappel |

*Remarks:* Widened in 1903, W'13 & body grounded as a dwelling at Felixstowe. P'71, mounted onto a replacement underframe in '78

| 23 | 1872 | BTY | | 501? | | Chappel |

*Remarks:* Body P' ? from Storey Bros at Manningtree

| 37 | 1897 | SOZ | | 16 | | Chappel |
| | | TOY | | | | |
| 629 | 1925 | | | | | |

*Remarks:* Family Saloon. W'39, body grounded. P'68 by Saffron Walden Model Railway Club & at Audley End, Essex till '81

| Numbers | Year | Type | Built | Diag | Lot | Location |
|---|---|---|---|---|---|---|
| 44 | 1894 | BZ | | 506 | | Chasewater |

*Remarks:* Still in use beyond 30/4/25. P'60 by RPS

| | | | | | | |
|---|---|---|---|---|---|---|
| 197 | 1887 | CZ | | 219 | | K&ESR |
| c63293-379 | 1925 | | | 219E | | |
| K&ESR 81 | | | | | | |

*Remarks:* W'28, body grounded at Wisbech as chalet. P'79? by Resco at Plumstead premises, restoration begun '81 by K&ESR Thameside Group. Donated to K&ESR '83, moved to Tenterden '84 & mounted on u'frame from LMS BGZ of Lot 1091

| | | | | | | |
|---|---|---|---|---|---|---|
| 252 | 188x | SY | | 301 | | N Norfolk |
| 252E | 1923 | | | | | |

*Remarks:* Widened in 1890's; grounded c1925 at North Walsham & pres'd after 50 years use as a garden shed

| | | | | | | |
|---|---|---|---|---|---|---|
| 295 | 1907 | BTK | Stratford | 527 | | N Norfolk |
| 62377 | 1925 | | | | | |
| DE320325 | | | | | | |

*Remarks:* P'67 by M&GNJRS

| | | | | | | |
|---|---|---|---|---|---|---|
| 347 | 1864 | SY | Metro C&W | | | Burnham-on-Crouch |

*Remarks:* Body P'?? at Mangapps Farm

| | | | | | | |
|---|---|---|---|---|---|---|
| 352 | 1886 | CLZ? | | 203? | | Fulstow |

*Remarks:* W'24, body grounded at Ely as fruit shed till '26 then made into dwelling with 355 below. P'85 by GER Coach Grp, taken to Waltham for restoration (using plate wagon chassis purchased '89)

| | | | | | | |
|---|---|---|---|---|---|---|
| 355 | 1886 | CZ? | | 219? | | Fulstow |

*Remarks:* W'24, body grounded at Ely as fruit shed till '26 then made into dwelling with 352 above. P'85 by GER Coach Grp

| | | | | | | |
|---|---|---|---|---|---|---|
| 553 | 1890 | BZ | Stratford | 513 | | Chappel |
| 63761 | 1925 | | | | | |
| Dep'tl No? | | | | | | |

*Remarks:* W'34 for use as Tool van. P' ? by GER Group, dismantled for restoration in '87

| | | | | | | |
|---|---|---|---|---|---|---|
| 704 | 1891 | TZ? | | | | Chappel |
| 60704 | 1925 | | | | | |

*Remarks:* W'35, grounded at Homersfield (nr Bungay)

| | | | | | | |
|---|---|---|---|---|---|---|
| 928 | 1885 | TZ | Stratford | 403 | 20M47 | Chappel |

*Remarks:* W'21, body grounded '24 at Wickham Bishops (nr Maldon). Found near derelict & P'76

| | | | | | | |
|---|---|---|---|---|---|---|
| 1019 | 1920 | BTK | Midland C&W | 547 | | N Woolwich |
| 62482 | 1925 | | | | | |
| DE320610 | 1958 | | | | | |

*Remarks:* P'85

| Numbers | Year | Type | Built | Diag | Lot | Location |
|---------|------|------|-------|------|-----|----------|
| 1361 | | TY? | | | | N Norfolk |

*Remarks:* 5-comp't body P'90 from site at Hevingham

| Numbers | Year | Type | Built | Diag | Lot | Location |
|---------|------|------|-------|------|-----|----------|
| 1521 | | TY | | 424 | | N Norfolk |
| 1521E | 1923 | | | | | |

*Remarks:* W pre'18

| Numbers | Year | Type | Built | Diag | Lot | Location |
|---------|------|------|-------|------|-----|----------|
| 1600 | | TY? | | | | N Norfolk |

*Remarks:* 5-comp't body

| Numbers | Year | Type | Built | Diag | Lot | Location |
|---------|------|------|-------|------|-----|----------|
| 2155? | 1921 | TK | | 438 | | Chappel |
| 61533 | 1925 | | | | | |
| DE320731 | | | | | | |
| 041418 | 1978 | | | | | |

*Remarks:* P'88

| Numbers | Year | Type | Built | Diag | Lot | Location |
|---------|------|------|-------|------|-----|----------|
| ? | 1887 | TZ | | | | Rutland |
| ? | | | | | | |
| 60741 | 1946 | | | | | |

*Remarks:* Body P'82 from Boston

*Others:*
Unidentified body from 1880's BTY P'80 at Chappel, formerly grounded as workshop at Witnesham
2 bodies at N Norfolk, No.1201 P'90 & an unidentified 4 comp't TY? used as carpenters' workshop
Unidentified 1892 built body P'85 at N Woolwich
2 unidentified bodies P pre'77 at S Cams
Underframe of BT (DE320725) pres'd by S Yorks RPS (body destroyed by fire at Starbeck c'85)
Body P'91 at Mid-Suffolk

# GREAT NORTH OF SCOTLAND RAILWAY

| Numbers | Year | Type | Built | Diag | Lot | Location |
|---------|------|------|-------|------|-----|----------|
| 1 | 1898 | FO | Inverurie | | | Bo'ness |
| DE982002 | 1924 | | | | | |
| 99801 plated | | | | | | |

*Remarks:* Clerestory. Used as the Royal Saloon from 1901-10 & W'24. Sold for scrap in '65 but pres'd by SRPS in the nick of time, at Falkirk till Dec'87

| Numbers | Year | Type | Built | Diag | Lot | Location |
|---------|------|------|-------|------|-----|----------|
| 34 | 1896 | CZ | | | | Strathspey |
| DE970204 | | | | | | |
| SR 127 | | | | | | |

*Remarks:* P'74

| Numbers | Year | Type | Built | Diag | Lot | Location |
|---------|------|------|-------|------|-----|----------|
| 68 | 1898 | BZ | Cowlairs | | | |
| 749 | 1925 | | | | | |
| DE320010 | 1950 | | | | | |
| SR 152 | | | | | | |

*Remarks:* Body P'74 on Strathspey Rly but destroyed by fire in suspected arson attack 17/4/91.

| Numbers | Year | Type | Built | Diag | Lot | Location |
|---------|------|------|-------|------|-----|----------|

*Others:*
Body of a BZ (?) P'85 at Lochty
Underframe under LNWR Inspection Saloon at Quainton (qv)

# GREAT NORTHERN RAILWAY

| | | | | | | |
|---|---|---|---|---|---|---|
| 127 | 18xx | BCK | Doncaster | | | Woolwich |
| 4127 | 1925 | | | | | |

*Remarks:* 12-wheel Clerestory. W'c24, body grounded at Huntingdon. P'77 by Resco & at Tenterden till '??

| | | | | | | |
|---|---|---|---|---|---|---|
| 229 | 1912 | BCK | Doncaster | 218F | | Severn Valley |
| 4229 | 1925 | | | | | |
| DE320700 | | | | | | |

*Remarks:* P'77, used as a mess by 4150 Loco Fund, sold to LNER(SVR) Coach Fund in '86

| | | | | | | |
|---|---|---|---|---|---|---|
| 397 | 1912 | FO | Doncaster | 45D | | Jesmond |
| 4397 | 1925 | | | | | |
| DE320206 | | | | | | |

*Remarks:* P'75, at Steamtown till sold '81 & became 'The Carriage' Inn, Old Station House, Jesmond, Tyneside

One of only two Great North of Scotland Railway coaches surviving in preservation, Third No 34 owes its existence to being placed in the departmental fleet and thus lasting until the railway preservation era saw it plucked to safety in 1974. Boat of Garten is the location for this picture, taken in March 1987. *Hugh Madgin*

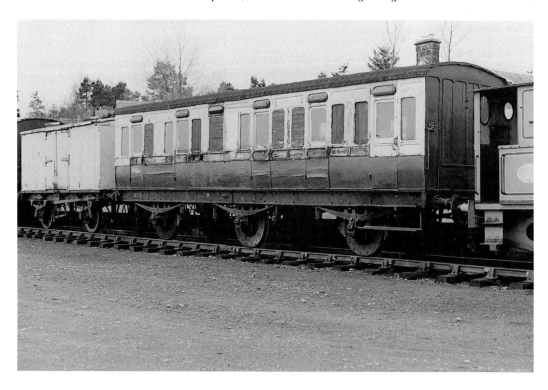

| Numbers | Year | Type | Built | Diag | Lot | Location |
|---------|------|------|-------|------|-----|----------|
| -459 | 1901 | TZ | Doncaster | 243 | | Quainton |
| 4459 ? | 1925 | | | | | |
| DE900178 | 1940 | | | | | |

Remarks: P'68 by NRM, 'released' from National Collection in '76

| | | | | | | |
|---------|------|------|-------|------|-----|----------|
| 706 | 1897 | Spec | Doncaster | | | Bluebell |
| 43909 | 1925 | | | | | |
| DE942090 | | | | | | |

Remarks: Clerestory Directors' Saloon. Mounted on Gresley bogies in ' ?. P'68, restored while in BR storage till '71

| | | | | | | |
|---------|------|------|-------|------|-----|----------|
| 807 | 1912 | FO | Doncaster | 45D | | St Leonards |
| 4807 | 1925 | | | | | |
| 99881 plated | | | | | | |

Remarks: P'76 by SVR member, stored in Gloucester till sold to Resco ' ?. Restored at Steamtown, leased to GS&WR for 'Royal Scotsman' till '89, then to abortive 'Queen of Scots'; at Steamtown till moved to storage '91

| | | | | | | |
|---------|------|------|-------|------|-----|----------|
| 836 | c1890 | TZ or CZ | | | | Tanfield |
| TR 2 | | | | | | |

Remarks: P pre'77 on Tanfield Railway, loaned to Knebworth '82-7 to house relics

| | | | | | | |
|---------|------|------|-------|------|-----|----------|
| 948 | 1887 | BZ | Doncaster | | | * NRM |

Remarks: Restored by BREL York '75

| | | | | | | |
|---------|------|------|-------|------|-----|----------|
| 1472 | 1889 | BTZ | Doncaster | | | Quainton |
| DE940460 | | | | | | |

Remarks: W'38 for dept'l use. P'69 but kept in store till donated to Quainton in '70

| | | | | | | |
|---------|------|------|-------|------|-----|----------|
| 1798 | 1906 | BTK | Doncaster | 258 | | Steamtown |
| 41798 ? | 1925 | | | | | |
| DE320145 | 1957 | | | | | |

Remarks: P'?? by Resco but stored at Nene Valley? till '83/4

| | | | | | | |
|---------|------|------|-------|------|-----|----------|
| 2440 ? | 1906 | TK | Doncaster? | 220? | | Colne Valley |
| 42440 | 1925 | | | | | |
| DE320154 | 1954 | | | | | |
| 041975 | 1988 | | | | | |

Remarks: P'90

| | | | | | | |
|---------|------|------|-------|------|-----|----------|
| 2856 | 1898 | BCL | Doncaster | 189 | | N Yorks Moors |
| 42856 | 1925 | | | | | |
| DE320051 | 1950 | | | | | |

Remarks: W'63, P'71 by the Newcastle Coach Group (renamed GNR Coach Group in '78) but stored at Heaton MPD till '73

| Numbers | Year | Type | Built | Diag | Lot | Location |
|---|---|---|---|---|---|---|
| 3013 | 1912 | PMV | Doncaster | 325A | | - |
| ? | 1925 | | | | | |
| 4151 | | | | | | |
| KWVR 100 (i) | | | | | | |

*Remarks:* Milk Van. P'67 on K&WVR, ex Chipman's weed-killing train; later the first of two vehicles to carry No.100, till scrapped '71 at Ingrow.

| | | | | | | |
|---|---|---|---|---|---|---|
| 3087 | 1909 | Spec | Doncaster | 10 | | Steamtown |
| 43087 | 1925 | | | | | |
| DE320042 | 1951? | | | | | |

*Remarks:* Invalid Saloon. P' ? by W H McAlpine

| | | | | | | |
|---|---|---|---|---|---|---|
| 3178 | 1910 | BFK | Doncaster | 97 | | Berwick area |
| 43178 | 1925 | | | | | |
| DE320651 | | | | | | |

*Remarks:* Latterly Packing van in Scunthorpe break-down train. P'74, at Radstock till '75, on W Somerset till sold to R Edmondson '85, then at Steamtown till resold '91 to 'Historic Buildings & Monuments'

| | | | | | | |
|---|---|---|---|---|---|---|
| 48941 | 1924 | BS | Doncaster | 68B | | N Norfolk |
| 48942 | | S | | 69 | | |
| 48943 | | C | | 70 | | |
| 48944 | | C | | 71 | | |
| 86272-5 | | LNER | | | | |
| 86762-5 | | BR | | | | |

*Remarks:* 'Quad-Art' four-car articulated Set No.74 P'67

| | | | | | | |
|---|---|---|---|---|---|---|
| ? | 1888 | BTZ | Doncaster | | | Worth Valley |
| DE940281 | | | | | | |

*Remarks:* P'66 by Vintage Carriage Trust

| | | | | | | |
|---|---|---|---|---|---|---|
| ? | 18xx | BZ | | | | Nene Valley |
| DE940400 | | | | | | |

*Remarks:* P pre'76

*Others:*
2 unidentified bodies on Tanfield (one of which P'76 from Consett Goods Yard)
Unidentified BZ of 1888 at S Cams, P pre'77

# HULL & BARNSLEY RAILWAY

[Diagrams per 1920 Diagram Book]

| | | | | | | |
|---|---|---|---|---|---|---|
| 1 | 1884 | BTY | Ashbury | | | Cardiff |
| 1A | 1919 | | | | | |
| 4257 | 1924 | | | | | |

*Remarks:* Sold to Neath & Brecon Rwy 1919. W'25 by GWR, body grounded '26? at The Narth, Monmouth (SO522063). P'86 by Welsh I & M Mus

| Numbers | Year | Type | Built | Diag | Lot | Location |
|---------|------|------|-------|------|-----|----------|
| 2 | 1907 | BT | Pickering | 7 | | N Yorks Moors |
| 40 | 1920 | | | | | |
| 5040 | 1922 | | | | | |
| 25040 | 1925 | | | | | |
| 23660 | | | | | | |
| DE320292 | 1955 | | | | | |

*Remarks:* P'70 from York by H&BR Stock Fund

| Numbers | Year | Type | Built | Diag | Lot | Location |
|---------|------|------|-------|------|-----|----------|
| 5 | 1908 | BTL | B R C W | 13 | | N Yorks Moors |
| 58 | 1920 | | | | | |
| 5058 | 1922 | | | | | |
| 25058 | 1925 | | | | | |
| DE320362 | 1956 | | | | | |

*Remarks:* P'68 from Springhead by H&BR Stock Fund

## LANCASHIRE, DERBYSHIRE & EAST COAST RAILWAY

| Numbers | Year | Type | Built | Diag | Lot | Location |
|---------|------|------|-------|------|-----|----------|
| 28 ? | 1896 | TZ | Ashbury | - | | Midland |
| 1808 | 1907 | | | | | |
| 51808 | 1925 | | | | | |
| DE950249 | 1938 | | | | | |

*Remarks:* P'73, stored in Derby till '75

## MANCHESTER, SHEFFIELD & LINCOLNSHIRE RAILWAY

| Numbers | Year | Type | Built | Diag | Lot | Location |
|---------|------|------|-------|------|-----|----------|
| 154 • | 1876 | CY | Gorton | | | Worth Valley |
| 154A • | by 1903 | | | | | |
| 1787c • | 1923 | | | | | |
| 5176 | 1925 | | • – Nos. 277, 277A & 1788c are possible, but less likely | | | |
| DE953003 | | | | | | |

*Remarks:* P'61 by VCT, but in store till '65 (original number listed as 103, incorrectly)

| Numbers | Year | Type | Built | Diag | Lot | Location |
|---------|------|------|-------|------|-----|----------|
| 373 | 1888 | TZ | Gorton | 2B8 | 5033 | Chappel |
| 5373 | 1925 | | | | | |
| CC.35 | 1934 | Camp | | | | |

*Remarks:* W'33, Camping Coach then Mess Van. P'71

| Numbers | Year | Type | Built | Diag | Lot | Location |
|---------|------|------|-------|------|-----|----------|
| 946 | 1888 | TZ | Gorton | 2B8 | 5033 | Quainton |
| 5946 | 1925 | | | | | |
| CC.15 | 1934 | Camp | | | | |
| DE320256 | 1954 | | | | | |

*Remarks:* Built for use on MSJ&AR. W'33, to Camper then to departmental use during WW2. P'71 by GCR Coach Grp member & presented to QRS '73 (original number listed as 1076, incorrectly)

| Numbers | Year | Type | Built | Diag | Lot | Location |
|---------|------|------|-------|------|-----|----------|
| 1470 | 1898 | BCZ | Gorton | 2A16 | 5078 | Chasewater |
| 51470 | 1925 | | | | | |

*Remarks:* W'43, sold to Easingwold Light Railway & in use till '56. P'59 by RPS, on Derwent Valley Ry till '68

| Numbers | Year | Type | Built | Diag | Lot | Location |
|---|---|---|---|---|---|---|

*Others:*
Unidentified TZ P pre'77 nr Royston (S Cams)

# MIDLAND & GREAT NORTHERN JOINT RAILWAY

| 129 | 188x | TZ | Doncaster | | | N Norfolk |

*Remarks:* Body P'90 from Gamston

# NORTH BRITISH RAILWAY

| 1 | 1856 | Tram | St Margarets | 117 | | * NRM |

*Remarks:* Horse-drawn 'Dandy Car'. Worked various branches (N Leith, & briefly N Berwick claimed) till moved to Port Carlisle branch 1859 & in use till 1914. Restored by NRM '75 & at York except for visit to Swindon '90-1

| ? | ? | FY | Ashbury | 115 | ? | Tanfield |

*Remarks:* Body P'91 (original No 73, 194, 220, 269 or 279)

| 461 | 1919 | Spec | Cowlairs | 152 | | Bo'ness |
| 32283 | 1925 | CK | | | | |
| DE320577 | 1951 | Insp | | | | |
| 99800 plated | | | | | | |

*Remarks:* Invalid Saloon. Classed as CK by LNER. Rebuilt as DE's Saloon in 1951. P' ? by SRPS, & at Falkirk till '81

| 467 | 1916 | BT | Cowlairs | | | Bo'ness |
| 3467 | 1925 | | | | | |
| DE320405 | | | | | | |

*Remarks:* P'?? by SRPS, at Falkirk till '88

| 565 | 1921 | TK | Cowlairs | 162 | | Bo'ness |
| 3565 | 1925 | | | | | |
| DE320401 | | | | | | |

*Remarks:* P'?? by SRPS, at Falkirk till '88

| 1184 | c1865 | SY | Ashbury | 103 | | Bo'ness |

*Remarks:* 4-comp't body P'91 by SRPS from farm near Pencaitland (E Lothian) traversed by line to E Saltoun. To be mounted on chassis from DE773090 below

| 1748 | 1905 | TL | Cowlairs | | | Strathspey |
| 31748 | 1925 | | | | | |
| DE970012 | 1947 | | | | | |
| SR 176 | | | | | | |

*Remarks:* Latterly Mess & Dormitory van. P'73

| ? | c1885 | TZ | | | | |
| DE773090 | | | | | | |

*Remarks:* 6-comp't coach P'74 by SRPS & at Falkirk till '88; since dismantled, chassis restored for 1184 (qv).

| Numbers | Year | Type | Built | Diag | Lot | Location |
|---------|------|------|-------|------|-----|----------|

*Others:*
Unidentified body P'88? by SRPS & grounded at Birkhill (former Ambulance Room at Portobello)
Unidentified body P'88? by SRPS & grounded at Bo'ness (former bothy at Paisley Canal Station), though could be GCR
Unidentified body at Brechin built c1880

# NORTH EASTERN RAILWAY

[Diagrams per 1914 Diagram Book]

| 41 | 1896 | Spec | York | B | | Matlock |
|----|------|------|------|---|---|---------|
| 241 | 1928 | | | | | |
| DE900269 | | | | | | |

*Remarks:* 6-wheel Officers' Saloon, latterly used as Tunnel Inspection van. P' ?, at Embsay till moved to Buxton by Peak Rail '87, & to Matlock '91

| 70 ? | c1870 | CLY | | | | Tanfield |
|------|-------|-----|---|---|---|----------|
| Dupl no? | 1899 | | | | | |

*Remarks:* Body grounded nr Chester-le-Street. P'76 & mounted on u'frame ex BR FVY 87937

| 100 | 1885 | FLOZ | | 75a | | Tanfield |
|-----|------|------|---|-----|---|----------|
| | 1902 | | | 4 | | |
| 2100 | | | | | | |

*Remarks:* W'33, body grounded near Withernsea. P'82 & mounted on 4-wheel van u'frame

**North Eastern Railway Saloon No 41 is one of four from that company to survive and is seen here at Peak Rail's Buxton site, having previously been a resident of the Yorkshire Dales Railway at Embsay.** *Hugh Madgin*

| Numbers | Year | Type | Built | Diag | Lot | Location |
|---|---|---|---|---|---|---|
| 118 | 1913 | T | York | 178 | | Beamish |
| 2118 | 1925 | | | | | |
| 9300/163 | 1955 | | | | | |

*Remarks:* Sold to NCB Nov'55. P'68 from Ashington Colliery, but at Templetown Works, Consett till Dec'73

| 305 | 1903 | Insp | York | 81 | | Steamtown |
| 2305 | 1926 | | | | | |
| DE902177 | | | | | | |
| 99051 plated | | | | | | |

*Remarks:* Clerestory Saloon. Restored by BREL York in '73, at Steamtown ever since except for brief resiting at Crewe Heritage Centre during '90

| 795 | ? | TY | | 58 | | Tanfield |

*Remarks:* W'09, body grounded as part of rifle range & clubroom at Gallows Close, Scarborough. P'76

| 818 | 1903 | C | York | 7 | | Beamish |
| 2818 | 1930 | T | | | | |
| 9300/159 | 1949 | | | | | |

*Remarks:* Clerestory; sold to NCB Oct'46. P'68 from Ashington Colliery, but stored at Templetown Works, Consett till Dec'73. (For restored coach with this number see 3071)

| 831 | ? | BTY | | 59 | | Tanfield |

*Remarks:* W'09, body grounded as part of rifle range & clubroom at Gallows Close, Scarborough. P'76 & mounted on underframe ex LMS CCTY 37308

| 853 | 1875 | Spec | | | | Tanfield |

*Remarks:* Officers' Saloon, modernised 1894. Body P'91 from an allotment at York

| 945 | 1924 | TO | York | 155 | | N Yorks Moors |
| 2945 | 1926 | | | | | |
| DE320716 | 1959 | | | | | |

*Remarks:* P'73 by NER Coach Group (Diag.Bk. says 1912 to D.158, but believed incorrect)

| 1056 | ? | TY | | 58 | | Tanfield |

*Remarks:* W'09, body grounded as part of rifle range & clubroom at Gallows Close, Scarborough. P'76 & mounted on underframe ex LMS CCTY 37306

| 1111 | 1890 | CZ | York | 9 | | N Yorks Moors |
| DE900192 | | | | | | |

*Remarks:* W'24 to become a Tool van, losing its centre wheelset. P'73 by NER Coach Group

| 1149 | 1900 | C | York | 7 | | |
| 21149 | 1927 | | | | | |
| | 1929 | T | | | | |
| 9300/153 | 1949 | | | | | |

*Remarks:* Clerestory; sold to NCB Nov'49. P'68 from Ashington Colliery, but stored at Templetown Works, Consett. One end fire damaged in '73, rest dismantled for spares.

| Numbers | Year | Type | Built | Diag | Lot | Location |
|---------|------|------|-------|------|-----|----------|
| 1173 | 1870 | FOY | York | 4 ? | | Worth Valley |
| | 1892 | Spec | | A | | |
| 21173 | 1925 | | | | | |
| DE900270 | | | | | | |

*Remarks:* Officers' Saloon from 1892, renovated 1924 & remained in use till P'67. On Derwent Valley a while?

| 1661 | 1904 | Insp | | H | | Worth Valley |
| 21661 | 1927 | | | C | | |
| DE902179 | | | | | | |
| 99750 plated | | | | | | |
| K&WVR 22 | | | | | | |

*Remarks:* Clerestory. Originally TZ built 1871 for Stockton & Darlington Railway, to NER 1876. Became Inspection Saloon from 1884, then rebuilt & mounted on bogies in 1904; W'69 (on loan to NRM 19??-?? & to NYMR '91)

| 1972 | 1911 | T | York | 178 | | Beamish |
| 21972 | 1927 | | | | | |
| 9300/164 | 1955 | | | | | |

*Remarks:* Sold to NCB Nov'55. P'68 from Ashington Colliery, but at Templetown Works, Consett till Dec'73

| 2118 | 1922 | RFO | York | 204 | | Great Central |
| 22118 | 1925 | | | | | |
| | 194x | RTO | | | | |
| 040877 | 196x | | | | | |

*Remarks:* Downgraded c1943-8. P'88

| 3071 | 1903 | C | York | 7 | | Beamish |
| 23071 | 1930 | T | | | | |
| 9300/152 | 1949 | | | | | |
| 818 | 1981 | | | | | |

*Remarks:* Clerestory; sold to NCB Nov'49. P'68 from Ashington Colliery, but stored at Templetown Works, Consett till Dec'73. Photographic evidence exists that it was this coach which was restored as NER 818 in error!

| 3267 | 1904 | DMPV | York | 100 | | * N Tyneside |
| 23267 | 1929 | | | | | |
| DE900730 | 1939 | | | | | |

*Remarks:* Clerestory Electric Parcels Van. W'38, latterly de-icing vehicle. P'??, at Monkwearmouth till '?? then to Middle Engine Lane

| 3453 | 1904 | T | York | 14 | | N Yorks Moors |
| | 1906 | DTBC | | 116 | | |
| | 1921 | BC | | | | |
| 23453 | 1928 | | | | | |
| DE320180 | 1952 | | | | | |

*Remarks:* Clerestory. Converted to driving trailer 1906 but control equipment removed 1921; mobile office 1952. P'71 by NER Coach Group, but restored at Hull till '78

| Numbers | Year | Type | Built | Diag | Lot | Location |
|---------|------|------|-------|------|-----|----------|
| 3591<br>23591<br>DE902502 | 1903<br>1928 | Spec | Darlington | 101a | | * NRM |

*Remarks:* Clerestory Dynamometer Car, most famous for the record-breaking run behind *Mallard*. Replacement finally delivered 1951, so honourably retired & preserved by BTC. (NER Carriage Register says built Mar.1906)

| | | | | | | |
|---------|------|------|-------|------|-----|----------|
| 5523<br>DE903004 | 1902 | Spec | | H2 | | Beamish |

*Remarks:* Stores Van, P'73

| | | | | | | |
|---------|------|------|-------|------|-----|----------|
| ? | c1860 | TY | | | | * Darlington |

*Remarks:* P' ? at N Road Museum

*Others:*
Unidentified bogie van at Dairycoates, built c1904, latterly 041273 & P'74 from Springhill

## STOCKTON & DARLINGTON RAILWAY

| | | | | | | |
|---------|------|------|-------|------|-----|----------|
| 31 | 1846 | CY | Horner & Wilkinson | | | * Darlington |

*Remarks:* Displayed at Stockton Station 1925-70

| | | | | | | |
|---------|------|------|-------|------|-----|----------|
| 59 | 1846 | CY | Tweeddale & Barton | | | * Swindon |

*Remarks:* On display at Queen Street Museum, York from ?-?. At NRM till '90

| | | | | | | |
|---------|------|------|-------|------|-----|----------|
| 179 | 1867 | TY | Darlington | | | * Shildon |

*Remarks:* W'1884, sold to Forcett Railway & in use till ' ?. At York Museum till ' ?, Beamish till post'81, restored at BREL Shildon then at the Hackworth Museum

see also NER 1661

## WISBECH & UPWELL TRAMWAY

| | | | | | | |
|---------|------|------|-------|------|-----|----------|
| 7<br>60461 | 1884<br>192x | C<br>T | | GE602 | | Rutland |

*Remarks:* W'50, body used as an onion store till '73 then stored at Cambridge Museum of Technology till '83

## LONDON & NORTH EASTERN RAILWAY

| | | | | | | |
|---------|------|------|-------|------|-----|----------|
| 14<br>DB975316 | 1948 | BG | York | 344 | | ˗ |

*Remarks:* P'84 by Sea Containers as a store & at Steamtown till late'80s (presumed scrapped)

| | | | | | | |
|---------|------|------|-------|------|-----|----------|
| 100 | 1948 | BG | York | 344 | 1180 | ˗ |

*Remarks:* P'71 on Worth Valley; broken up at Ingrow in '82.

| | | | | | | |
|---------|------|------|-------|------|-----|----------|
| 104 | 1948 | BG | York | 344 | | ?, USA |

*Remarks:* To USA '69 with 'Flying Scotsman' (fate unknown, but see 'Others' at end)

| Numbers | Year | Type | Built | Diag | Lot | Location |
|---------|------|------|-------|------|-----|----------|
| 109 – see ECJS 82 | | | | | | |
| 110 NYMR 17 | 1948 | BG | York | 344 | 1180 | N Yorks Moors |

*Remarks:* P'74, sold to LNERCA c'84

| 145 041402 | 1950 | BG | York | 344 | | - |

*Remarks:* P'84 by Sea Containers & at Steamtown till late'80s (presumed scrapped)

| 641 9129 | 1937 1946 | RB | York | 167 | | N Yorks Moors |

*Remarks:* P'74, on Dart Valley till sold to LNERCA member in '83

| 642 9130 DB975079 | 1937 1946 | RB | York | 167 | | - |

*Remarks:* P'83 at Steamtown for spare parts, then broken up in '84.

One of the best-known light railways in the country was the Wisbech & Upwell Tramway. Passenger services ceased on 2 January 1928 but freight continued into the diesel era. This is the sole coaching stock survivor — Composite No 7 — and historians and appreciators of this famous railway can see it at the Rutland Railway Museum where it was pictured in March 1991. *Hugh Madgin*

| Numbers | Year | Type | Built | Diag | Lot | Location |
|---|---|---|---|---|---|---|
| 643 | 1937 | RB | York | 167 | | Severn Valley |
| 9131 | 1946 | | | | | |

*Remarks:* P'77 by Gardner-Shaw (Minerals) Ltd

| Numbers | Year | Type | Built | Diag | Lot | Location |
|---|---|---|---|---|---|---|
| 644 | 1937 | RB | York | 167 | | Bo'ness |
| 9132 | 1946 | | | | | |
| 99806 plated | | | | | | |

*Remarks:* P'77 by SRPS, at Falkirk till Dec'87

| Numbers | Year | Type | Built | Diag | Lot | Location |
|---|---|---|---|---|---|---|
| 649 | 1937 | RB | York | 167 | | N Yorks Moors |
| 9134 | 1946 | | | | | |
| NYMR 2 | | | | | | |

*Remarks:* P'69

Thompson BG No 110 is the last example of its type in this country, although one may survive in America. No 110 was sold for £1 by the North Yorkshire Moors Railway's governing Council to the LNER Coach Association, following the railway management's wish to dispose of the vehicle. Restoration has started — a new roof canvas has been fitted and this picture shows the first section of the new panelling fitted in April 1991. The whole of this side has now been reclad. **Murray Brown**

| Numbers | Year | Type | Built | Diag | Lot | Location |
|---------|------|------|-------|------|-----|----------|
| 650 | 1937 | RB | York | 167 | | * NRM |
| 9135 | 1946 | | | | | |

Remarks: P'76, restored by NRM York '79, to 'NRM On Tour' exhibition at Swindon '90, returned to York 4/91

| Numbers | Year | Type | Built | Diag | Lot | Location |
|---------|------|------|-------|------|-----|----------|
| 772 | 1929 | BY | Doncaster? | 120? | | N Norfolk |
| 70246 | 1946 | | | | | |
| 040923 | | | | | | |

Remarks: P'71

| Numbers | Year | Type | Built | Diag | Lot | Location |
|---------|------|------|-------|------|-----|----------|
| 957 | 1943 | BG | Doncaster | 260 | | (Stewarts Lane) |
| 70741 | 1946 | | | | | |
| Baggage Car No.7 | 1981 | | | | | |
| 99533 plated | | | | | | |

Remarks: P' ? by Sea Containers for VSOE

1008 – see 10023

| Numbers | Year | Type | Built | Diag | Lot | Location |
|---------|------|------|-------|------|-----|----------|
| 1052 | 1925 | TK | York | 23 | | S Devon |
| 4474 | 193x | | | | | |
| 12048 | 1946 | | | | | |
| DE320744 | | | | | | |

Remarks: Former WW2 Ambulance Train coach. P'73 by David & Charles, at Newton Abbot till presented to S Devon Ry by Readers Digest & moved to Buckfastleigh 4/91

| Numbers | Year | Type | Built | Diag | Lot | Location |
|---------|------|------|-------|------|-----|----------|
| 1065 | 1924 | CK | York | 7 | | Great Central |
| 7781 | 193x | | | | | |
| 18033 | 1946 | | | | | |
| DE320741 | | | | | | |

Remarks: Became Mess & Tool van, its Gresley bogies replaced by GER type. P'73 by RVP, stored in Hertford till '75, then at Chappel till '81. Re-shod with Gresley bogies in ' ?. Now owned by 61'6" Fund

| Numbers | Year | Type | Built | Diag | Lot | Location |
|---------|------|------|-------|------|-----|----------|
| 1186 | 1932 | SLT | Doncaster | 162 | | * NRM |

Remarks: Half of an articulated twin. Part-body P'62 by NRM, the rest broken up; at Clapham till '75, one compartment sectioned for museum display as per original

| Numbers | Year | Type | Built | Diag | Lot | Location |
|---------|------|------|-------|------|-----|----------|
| 1211 | 1935 | SLF | Doncaster | 157 | | Strathspey |
| SR 178 | | | | | | |

Remarks: W'72 as the last wooden-bodied Sleeper in service

| Numbers | Year | Type | Built | Diag | Lot | Location |
|---------|------|------|-------|------|-----|----------|
| 1222 | 1929 | RF | Doncaster | 10C | | Great Central |
| 651 | | | | | | |
| 9019 | 1946 | | | | | |
| DE320907 | 1961 | | | | | |

Remarks: P'91 by RVP

| Numbers | Year | Type | Built | Diag | Lot | Location |
|---------|------|------|-------|------|-----|----------|
| 1249 | 1939 | CCTY | York | Y006 | | ? |

Remarks: Reportedly to Severn Valley but never seen

| Numbers | Year | Type | Built | Diag | Lot | Location |
|---------|------|------|-------|------|-----|----------|
| 1259<br>NYMR 100 | 1950 | SLF | Doncaster | 359 | | ˶ |

Remarks: P'68 on N Yorks Moors, burnt out during asbestos removal by contractors '88 & scrapped.

| 1260 | 1950 | SLF | Doncaster | 359 | | ˶ |

Remarks: Pres'd at Welshpool for use as volunteers' accommodation, till replaced by BR 2536.

| 1296 | 1939 | CCTY | York | Y006 | | ? |

Remarks: Reportedly to Severn Valley but never seen

| 1298 | 1939 | CCTY | York | Y006 | | Monkwearmouth |

Remarks: Car Van.

| 1299<br>DE320931 | 1930<br>1962 | SLT | York | 109 | | N Yorks Moors |

Remarks: P'82 by LNERCA member

| 1322<br>DB975792 | 1950<br>1978 | CCTY | Darlington | Y006 | 1223 | N Yorks Moors |

Remarks: P'81

| 1334<br>KWVR 108 | 1950 | CCTY | York | Y006 | 1223 | Worth Valley |

Remarks: P' ?

| 1345 | 1950 | CCTY | York | Y006 | | Southall |

Remarks: P'?? by GW Pres Grp

| 1370 | 1950 | CCT | York | Y006 | 1224 | Betws-y-Coed |

Remarks: P' ? by Conwy Valley Railway Museum

| 1531<br>DE902260<br>1999 'Lochaber'<br>99131 plated | 1945<br><br>1980 | FK<br>Insp<br>Obs | Doncaster<br>York | 334 | <br>1116 | (Craigentinny) |

Remarks: Prototype Thompson FK, later converted to Inspection Saloon; returned to Capital stock 1980 for use as Observation Car on W Highland line. P'84 by FSE, loaned to Crewe Her Cr '88, sold to GS&WR '89 for new 'Royal Scotsman' & named 'Victory' for '90

| 1591 | 1936 | SLF | Doncaster | 157 | | Wisconsin, USA |

Remarks: Part of General Eisenhower's HQ Train during 1944. P'69 & exported to the NRM at Green Bay

| 1592 | 1936 | SLF | Doncaster | 157 | | Wisconsin, USA |

Remarks: As 1591 above

| Numbers | Year | Type | Built | Diag | Lot | Location |
|---|---|---|---|---|---|---|
| 1623￼DE321133 | 1950 | TK | York | 329 | | N Yorks Moors |

*Remarks:* P'83 by LNERCA member

| 1706￼DB975882 | 1948￼1979 | RB | Doncaster | 352 | 1197 | Llangollen |

*Remarks:* P'81 by Sea Containers, resold in '83 but at Steamtown till Dec'85

| 1719 | 1937￼1959 | Spec | Doncaster￼Cowlairs | 232 | | Lochty |

*Remarks:* 'Beavertail' Observation Car from the 'Coronation' set. P'68

| 1729￼KWVR 23 | 1937￼1959￼198? | Spec | Doncaster￼Cowlairs￼Steamtown | 232 | | Steamtown |

*Remarks:* 'Beavertail' Observation Car from the 'Coronation' set. P'67 by Gresley Soc, at Worth Valley till '74, Ashford till '78 then stored at BNF Sellafield till '??. Being rebuilt to original design

| 1767 | 1951 | SLT | Doncaster | 369 | | E Somerset |

*Remarks:* P' ?, at Eastleigh till '73 then Cranmore. Intended to be dismantled as asbestos filled?

This historic coach — No 1592 — was rebuilt in 1944 for the personal use of General Eisenhower in the SHAEF train. Six of the berths were replaced by a saloon room and a personal compartment for the General. It was also armour plated and weighed 51 tonnes. It was withdrawn in 1966 and following restoration was shipped to the USA where it — and another Sleeper No 1591 — can be seen at Green Bay, Wisconsin. *BR*

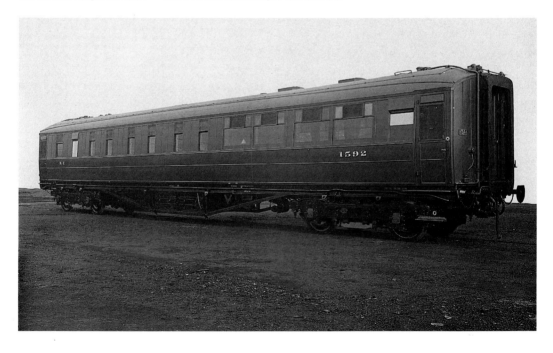

| Numbers | Year | Type | Built | Diag | Lot | Location |
|---------|------|------|-------|------|-----|----------|
| 1769 KWVR 104 | 1951 | SLT | Doncaster | 369 | | ˌ |

*Remarks:* P'72 on Worth Valley for accommodation at Haworth. Broken up at Ingrow in '84.

| 1770 KWVR 103 | 1951 | SLT | Doncaster | 369 | | ˌ |

*Remarks:* P'71 on Worth Valley for accommodation at Haworth. Broken up at Ingrow in '84.

| 1852 KWVR 21 | 1938 | RB | Doncaster | 258 | | Great Central |

*Remarks:* Built for the 'Flying Scotsman' set; rebuilt in 1959. P'66 by Gresley Society, on Worth Valley till '74 then at Ashford till '78

| 1866 DE321120 99300 plated | 1950 | BTK | Doncaster | 346 | | ICI Wilton |

*Remarks:* P pre'77 as Support Coach for *Blue Peter* & at Dinting till '86

1998 – see 900580

1999 – see 1531

| 2441 70294 | 1937 1946 | POS | York | 164 | | Great Central |

*Remarks:* P'74 by RVP, stored at Hertford till '78 then at Chappel till '81

| 2459 | 1954 | HBY | Earlestown | 9 | LM1662 | Southport |

| 3107 86072 DE320759 | 1926 1946 1959 | BT | York | 65 | | Bere Ferrers |

*Remarks:* P'90 by Kingsgrove Developments Ltd at the Station Museum

| 3188 12934 | 1934 1946 1961 | TK | York Cowlairs | 155 | | Quainton |

*Remarks:* W'61 for ScR Control Train; P'80 but in store at MOD Bicester till '82

| 3291 12481 DE321007 | 1931 1946 1963 | TK | Metro-Cammell York | 115 | | N Yorks Moors |

*Remarks:* W'61 for ER Control Train. P'80 by Resco, stored in Doncaster till '84 then at Steamtown till sold to LNERCA '88, restored at Starbeck till '90

| Numbers | Year | Type | Built | Diag | Lot | Location |
|---------|------|------|-------|------|-----|----------|
| 3374 ? | 1931 | TK | Metro-Cammell | 115 | | Bere Ferrers |
| 12466 | 1946 | | | | | |
| DE320894 | 1961 | | | | | |

Remarks: P'90 by Kingsgrove Developments Ltd at the Station Museum (original number per 'Platform 5' but suspect)

| Numbers | Year | Type | Built | Diag | Lot | Location |
|---------|------|------|-------|------|-----|----------|
| 3395 | 1931 | TK | Metro-Cammell | 115 | | N Norfolk |
| 12493 | 1946 | | | | | |
| DE320877 | | | | | | |

Remarks: P'76 by M&GNJRS, partly restored at Norwich Victoria till '79

| Numbers | Year | Type | Built | Diag | Lot | Location |
|---------|------|------|-------|------|-----|----------|
| 3641 | 1926 | BT | Clayton | 64 | | Burnham-on-Crouch |
| 86056 | 1946 | | | | | |
| DE320779 | 1959 | | | | | |

Remarks: P'81 by LNERCA member & on N Yorks Moors till sold to Mangapps Farm '91

| Numbers | Year | Type | Built | Diag | Lot | Location |
|---------|------|------|-------|------|-----|----------|
| 3669 | 1930 | BTK | B R C W | 114 | | Embsay |
| 16335 | 1946 | | | | | |
| DE320984 | | | | | | |

Remarks: P'80

| Numbers | Year | Type | Built | Diag | Lot | Location |
|---------|------|------|-------|------|-----|----------|
| 4050 | 1941 | BGP | York | 245 | 1017 | Great Central |
| 70427 | 1946 | | | | | |

Remarks: P'76 by RVP, stored at Hertford till '78 then at Chappel till '81

| Numbers | Year | Type | Built | Diag | Lot | Location |
|---------|------|------|-------|------|-----|----------|
| 4052 | 1941 | BGP | York | 245 | | Worth Valley |
| 70442 | 1946 | | | | | |
| KWVR 105 | | | | | | |

Remarks: P'71

| Numbers | Year | Type | Built | Diag | Lot | Location |
|---------|------|------|-------|------|-----|----------|
| 4149 | 1936 | BG | York | 198 | | Lakeside |
| 70361 | 1946 | | | | | |
| L&HR 71 | | | | | | |

Remarks: P'70

| Numbers | Year | Type | Built | Diag | Lot | Location |
|---------|------|------|-------|------|-----|----------|
| 4163 | 1928 | BFK | York | 136 | | N Tyneside |
| 11047 | 1946 | | | | | |
| DE320797 | 1960 | | | | | |

| Numbers | Year | Type | Built | Diag | Lot | Location |
|---------|------|------|-------|------|-----|----------|
| 4236 | 1938 | BGP | York | 245 | | Steamtown ? |
| 70459 | 1946 | | | | | |

Remarks: P'75 by EMF member, on Severn Valley till c'81; not found in recent years

| Numbers | Year | Type | Built | Diag | Lot | Location |
|---------|------|------|-------|------|-----|----------|
| 4237 | 1938 | BGP | York | 245 | | Steamtown |
| 70460 | 1946 | | | | | |
| DB975242 | | | | | | |

Remarks: P'80, body grounded as polishers' store, bogies for VSOE & now only fit for scrap

| Numbers | Year | Type | Built | Diag | Lot | Location |
|---------|------|------|-------|------|-----|----------|
| 4238<br>70461<br>DB975318 | 1938<br>1946 | BGP | York | 245 | | ｡ |

*Remarks:* P'84 by Sea Containers & broken up for spares at Steamtown the same year.

| 4247<br>70470<br>KWVR 106 | 1938<br>1946 | BGP | York | 245 | | Worth Valley |

*Remarks:* P'70?

| 4268<br>70491<br>MM3023<br>M99628<br>DB975399 | 1940<br>1946 | BGP | York | 245 | 983 | Bulmers |

*Remarks:* P'81 by MNLPS, body grounded as a store and workshop

| 4271<br>70494 | 1940<br>1946 | BGP | York | 245 | 983 | Bo'ness |

*Remarks:* P' ? by SRPS, at Falkirk till '88, Perth till '91

| 4274<br>70497 | 1940<br>1946 | BGP | York | 245 | | ?, USA |

*Remarks:* To USA '69 with 'Flying Scotsman' (fate unknown, but see 'Others' at end)

4474 – see 1052

| 5280<br>70505<br>041501 | 1939<br>1946 | BGP | York | 245 | | ｡ |

*Remarks:* P'84 by Sea Containers & broken up for spares at Steamtown the same year.

| 5283<br>70508<br>041435 | 1939<br>1946 | BGP | York | 245 | | ｡ |

*Remarks:* P'84 at Steamtown, broken up for spares the same year.

| 5527<br>12134<br>041305 | 1925<br>1946<br>1976 | TO | Dukinfield | 27 | | ｡ |

*Remarks:* P'89 by LNERCA on N Yorks Moors for spares

| 6118<br>12190<br>DE320897 | 1931<br>1946<br>1960 | RTO | Doncaster | 27A | | Steamtown |

*Remarks:* P'?? by Resco but stored till '83/4

| Numbers | Year | Type | Built | Diag | Lot | Location |
|---------|------|------|-------|------|-----|----------|
| 6777 | 1931 | BP | Dukinfield | 129 | | Great Central |
| 70268 | 1946 | | | | | |
| | 195x | POT | | | | |

*Remarks:* Converted to Post Office Tender in late 50's, its Gresley bogies replaced by GER type at the same time; W'68. P'73 by RVP, stored at Hertford till '75 then at Chappel till '81

| 6854 | 1930 | BYP | York? | 120 | | Llangollen |
| 776 | | | | | | |
| 70250 | 1946 | | | | | |
| | 1983 | BSODY | Llangollen | | | |

*Remarks:* W' ?, on Derwent Valley till P'79. Converted '83 to a 'Sunshine Coach' for disabled passengers, sponsored by Variety Club of GB

| 6866 | 1941 | BG | York | 260 | | - |
| 70548 | 1946 | | | | | |
| 041403 | | | | | | |

*Remarks:* P'84 by Sea Containers as a store? & at Steamtown till late'80s (presumed scrapped)

| 7960 | 1936 | RC | Doncaster | 187 | | Severn Valley |
| 9162 | 1946 | | | | | |
| DE321021 | | | | | | |

*Remarks:* P'81

| 10023 • | 1924 | TK | York | 23 | | Bo'ness |
| 1008 • | 1925 | | | | | |
| 4464 | 193x | | | | | |
| 12041 | 1946 | | | | | |
| DE320874 | 1963 | | | | | |

*Remarks:* P'71 by SRPS, at Falkirk till '88 (• No.1002 has been quoted in press)

(10161 – mistakenly attributed to SRPS Falkirk)

| 10178 | 1924 | BCK | York | 34 | | N Yorks Moors |
| 1077 | 1925 | | | | | |
| 52181 | 1936? | | | | | |
| 10021 | 1946 | | | | | |
| DE320427 | 1958 | | | | | |
| 041469 | 1979 | | | | | |

*Remarks:* P'79

| 13803 | 1947 | TO | York | 330 | | Bo'ness |

*Remarks:* Body grounded as bothy at Bellahouston. P'77 by SRPS, restored at Falkirk till Dec'87

| 18477 | 1950 | CK | York | 328 | | N Yorks Moors |
| NYMR 6 | | | | | | |

*Remarks:* P'69 by LNERCA member

| Numbers | Year | Type | Built | Diag | Lot | Location |
|---------|------|------|-------|------|-----|----------|
| 21772 | 1927 | TO | Dukinfield | 27 | | - |
| 12128 | 1946 | | | | | |
| DE320679 | | | | | | |

*Remarks:* P'77 by Engineering Services, for Nene Valley, but later scrapped by Resco at Woolwich.

| | | | | | | |
|---------|------|------|-------|------|-----|----------|
| 22219 | 1925 | T | Metro C&W | 56 | | Quainton |
| 61857 | | | | | | |
| 82145 | 1946 | | | | | |
| DE320832 | 1959 | | | | | |

*Remarks:* P'82, reaching Quainton in '83

| | | | | | | |
|---------|------|------|-------|------|-----|----------|
| 22255 | 1925 | TK | York | 23 | | nr Heanor |
| 12013 | 1946 | | | | | |
| 155 | 1958 | Camp | | | | |
| DE321089 | | | | | | |
| 041593 | 1981 | | | | | |

*Remarks:* P'88 by W Hall, at Swineshead Br (Lincs) till May'89, then stored; resold '91 to Stoneyford Lodge Hotel (Derbys)

| | | | | | | |
|---------|------|------|-------|------|-----|----------|
| 23834 ? | 1935 | BTO | York | 196 | | - |
| 16600 | 1946 | | | | | |
| DE320942 | | | | | | |

*Remarks:* P'77 on Severn Valley, found to be in much worse condition than expected; broken up in 1980.

| | | | | | | |
|---------|------|------|-------|------|-----|----------|
| 23890 | 1935 | TK | B R C W | 115 | | (Craigentinny) |
| 12322 | 1946 | | | | | |
| DE320959 | 1963 | | Doncaster | | | |
| 99960 plated | 1990 | RF | H L P G | | | |

*Remarks:* W'61 for ER Control Train. P'80, sold to GS&WR '89 & rebuilt with kitchen by '90 for 'Royal Scotsman'

| | | | | | | |
|---------|------|------|-------|------|-----|----------|
| 23896 | 1935 | TK | B R C W | 115 | | Steamtown |
| 12328 | 1946 | | | | | |
| DE321008 | 1963 | | York | | | |

*Remarks:* W'61 for ER Control Train. P'80 by Resco but stored in Doncaster till '84

| | | | | | | |
|---------|------|------|-------|------|-----|----------|
| 23953 | 1936 | TO | BRCW or M-C? | 186 | | * NRM |
| 13251 | 1946 | | | | | |
| | 1963 | | Cowlairs | | | |

*Remarks:* W'61 for ScR Control Train. P'80

| | | | | | | |
|---------|------|------|-------|------|-----|----------|
| 23956 | 1936 | TO | BRCW or M-C? | 186 | | * NRM |
| 13254 | 1946 | | | | | |
| | 1963 | | Cowlairs | | | |

*Remarks:* W'61 for ScR Control Train. P'80

| Numbers | Year | Type | Built | Diag | Lot | Location |
|---------|------|------|-------|------|-----|----------|
| 24068 | 1937 | BCK | York | 175 | | Severn Valley |
| 10078 | 1946 | | | | | |

Remarks: P'72

| Numbers | Year | Type | Built | Diag | Lot | Location |
|---------|------|------|-------|------|-----|----------|
| 24079 | 1936 | RB | York | 167 | | Bulmers |
| 9115 | 1946 | | | | | |
| ? plated | | | | | | |

Remarks: P'77 by 6000 Loco Assoc

| Numbers | Year | Type | Built | Diag | Lot | Location |
|---------|------|------|-------|------|-----|----------|
| 24082 | 1936 | RB | York | 167 | | Chappel |
| 9118 | 1946 | | | | | |

| Numbers | Year | Type | Built | Diag | Lot | Location |
|---------|------|------|-------|------|-----|----------|
| 24105 | 1936 | TO | B R C W | 186 | | Severn Valley |
| 13317 | 1946 | | | | | |
| DE320957 | 1963 | | Doncaster | | | |
| | 199x | TOD | Severn Valley | 186A | | |

Remarks: W'61 for ER Control Train. P'80 by EMF

| Numbers | Year | Type | Built | Diag | Lot | Location |
|---------|------|------|-------|------|-----|----------|
| 24109 | 1936 | TO | York | 186 | | N Yorks Moors |
| 13320 | 1946 | | | | | |
| DE320956 | 1963 | | Doncaster | | | |

Remarks: W'61 for ER Control Train as Office Coach. P'80 by LNERCA member

| Numbers | Year | Type | Built | Diag | Lot | Location |
|---------|------|------|-------|------|-----|----------|
| 24278 | 1937 | RB | York | 167 | | Great Central |
| 9122 | 1946 | | | | | |

Remarks: P'73 by RVP, stored at Hertford till '78 then at Chappel till moved to Loughborough in '81; sold to Great Central in '83

| Numbers | Year | Type | Built | Diag | Lot | Location |
|---------|------|------|-------|------|-----|----------|
| 24279 | 1937 | RB | York | 167 | | Tyseley |
| 9123 | 1946 | | | | | |

Remarks: P'??, here in '78 (in BR use till early 70's)

| Numbers | Year | Type | Built | Diag | Lot | Location |
|---------|------|------|-------|------|-----|----------|
| 24280 | 1937 | RB | York | 167 | | Great Central |
| 9124 | 1946 | | | | | |

Remarks: P'75

| Numbers | Year | Type | Built | Diag | Lot | Location |
|---------|------|------|-------|------|-----|----------|
| 24287 | 1939 | RB | Dukinfield | 275 | | Steamtown |
| 9195 | 1946 | | | | | |
| 99054 plated | | | | | | |

Remarks: P'?? by W H McAlpine

| Numbers | Year | Type | Built | Diag | Lot | Location |
|---------|------|------|-------|------|-----|----------|
| 32455 | 1930 | CL | Dukinfield | 50 | | Starbeck |
| 88026 | 1946 | | | | | |
| DE321015 | 1963 | | | | | |

Remarks: P'85 by S Yorks RPS, to Chapeltown '86; sold to Gt Yorks RPS c'88 & to Starbeck

| Numbers | Year | Type | Built | Diag | Lot | Location |
|---------|------|------|-------|------|-----|----------|
| 41384 | 1938 | BTK | Doncaster | 37A | | Quainton |
| 16076 | 1946 | | | | | |
| DE321058 | 1966 | | | | | |

Remarks: P'70

| | | | | | | |
|---------|------|------|-------|------|-----|----------|
| 42969 | 1929 | RF | Doncaster | 10C | | N Woolwich |
| 9007 | 1946 | | | | | |
| DE320947 | 1963 | | | | | |

Remarks: P'86

| | | | | | | |
|---------|------|------|-------|------|-----|----------|
| 42972 | 1928 | TOP | York | 112 | | Steamtown |
| 9066 | 1946 | | | | | |
| DE320927 | 1961 | | | | | |

Remarks: Pantry Third; P' ? by Resco but stored at Nene Valley? till '83/4

| | | | | | | |
|---------|------|------|-------|------|-----|----------|
| 43556 | 1938 | BTO | Cravens | 196 | | Chappel |
| 16631 | 1946 | | | | | |

| | | | | | | |
|---------|------|------|-------|------|-----|----------|
| 43567 | 1934 | BTO | York | 191 | | N Yorks Moors |
| 16547 | 1946 | | | | | |

Remarks: W'60, at Tees Dock till P'74. Now owned by LNERCA

| | | | | | | |
|---------|------|------|-------|------|-----|----------|
| 43571 | 1935 | BTO | York | 191 | | Colne Valley |
| 16551 | 1946 | | | | | |
| DE320995 | 1963 | | | | | |
| | 1988 | Bar | CVR | | | |

Remarks: Latterly BR Weedkiller Spray coach. P'86, restored as First Class Bar for Conference Train

| | | | | | | |
|---------|------|------|-------|------|-----|----------|
| 43600 | 1934 | TO | York | 186 | | Severn Valley |
| 13354 | 1946 | | | | | |
| DE320960 | 1963 | | | | | |

Remarks: W'61 for ER Control Train as Office Coach. P'80

| | | | | | | |
|---------|------|------|-------|------|-----|----------|
| 43612 | 1934 | TO | York | 186 | | Severn Valley |
| 13366 | 1946 | | | | | |
| 042197 | | | | | | |

Remarks: P'79 by Gardner-Shaw (Minerals) Ltd

| | | | | | | |
|---------|------|------|-------|------|-----|----------|
| 43632 | 1935 | TO | Doncaster | 186 | | Embsay |
| 13385 | 1946 | | | | | |
| DE321006 | 1963 | | York | | | |

Remarks: W'61 for ER Control Train as Control & Apparatus Coach. P'80

| | | | | | | |
|---------|------|------|-------|------|-----|----------|
| 43654 | 1935 | TO | Doncaster | 186 | | Embsay |
| 13407 | 1946 | | | | | |
| DE321001 | 1963 | | York | | | |

Remarks: W'61 for ER Control Train as Office Coach. P'80

| Numbers | Year | Type | Built | Diag | Lot | Location |
|---------|------|------|-------|------|-----|----------|
| 51769 | 1937 | RB | York | 167 | | N Norfolk |
| 9128 | 1946 | | | | | |

*Remarks:* P'77 by M&GNJRS, partially restored at Norwich Victoria till '79

| 51773 | 1929 | RF | Doncaster | 10C | | Market Bosworth |
| 9012 | 1946 | | | | | |
| DE320921 | | | | | | |

*Remarks:* P'89, its interior restoration revealing strong evidence of RF origin; conjecture says that TK 61703 & this coach got departmental numbers opposite way round to official records (see *Steam Railway* No 112 or *Rail* No 138)

| 52255 | 1935 | TO | York | 186 | | Severn Valley |
| 13547 | 1946 | | | | | |
| DE321005 | 1963 | | York | | | |

*Remarks:* W'61 for ER Control Train as Office Coach. P'80

| 52256 | 1935 | TO | York | 186 | | Embsay |
| 13548 | 1946 | | | | | |
| DE321002 | 1963 | | York | | | |

*Remarks:* W'61 for ER Control Train as Control & Apparatus Coach. P'80

| 56856 | 1938 | TO | Metro-Cammell | 186 | | N Yorks Moors |
| 13577 | 1946 | | | | | |
| DE321108 | | | | | | |

*Remarks:* MO's Saloon P'81 by Resco, stored at ? till sold to LNERCA '88, restored at Starbeck till '90

| 57451 | 1939 | BTK | York | 178 | | Great Central |
| 16520 | 1946 | | | | | |
| KWVR 11 | | | | | | |

*Remarks:* P'65 by Gresley Society, on Worth Valley till '75

| 59404 | 1954 | DMBSO | Metro-Cammell | | | Midland |
| 59504 | 1954 | TSO | Metro-Cammell | | | Midland |
| 59604 | 1954 | DTSO | B R C W | | | Midland |

*Remarks:* EMU. P'85 by W Yorks Transport Museum Trust, kept briefly at Dinting then stored at Bradford Hammerton St till '89 (may move to Bury '91)

| 60505 | 1936 | TTO | York | 216 | | Berwick area |
| DE321048 | 1964 | | | | | |

*Remarks:* P'91 by Historical Buildings & Monuments

| 61634 | 1926 | TK | Stratford | 25 | | Nene Valley |
| DE320904 | | | | | | |

*Remarks:* P'??, at Dairycoates till '91

| Numbers | Year | Type | Built | Diag | Lot | Location |
|---|---|---|---|---|---|---|
| 61684 | 1927 | T | Cravens | 57 | | Burnham |
| 82347 | 1947 | | | | | |
| DE320803 | 1960 | | | | | |

*Remarks:* P'89 at Mangapps Farm

61703 – see 51773

| 62515 | 1924 | BTK | Stratford | 38 | | Bo'ness |
| 4930 | 1925? | | | | | |
| 16122 | 1946 | | | | | |
| DE320680 | | | Cowlairs | | | |

*Remarks:* P'81 by SRPS, at Falkirk till Dec'87

| 62565 | 1927 | BTK | York | 41 | | Great Central |
| DE320746 | | | | | | |

*Remarks:* P'75 by RVP, on Nene Valley till '76 then stored at Hertford till '78. At Chappel 1978-81 (DE320783 wrongly quoted at times)

| 65217 | 1949 | DMSO | Metro-Cammell | | | BR Ilford |
| 65417 | 1949 | TBSO | Metro-Cammell | | | BR Ilford |
| 65617 | 1949 | DTSO | B R C W | | | BR Ilford |

*Remarks:* EMU, Set 306.017. P'88 by BR

| 70592 | 1945 | BG | York | 327 | 1123 | - |
| MM3021 | | | | | | |
| M99626 | | | | | | |
| DB975400 | | | | | | |

*Remarks:* P'81 at Steamtown, its bogies swopped with those from Pullman Car 'Audrey'. Body broken up in late'80s but underframe still extant '90 as flatbed wagon (mounted on Pullman bogies built Metro CW&F 1923)

| 70621 | 1945 | BG | York | 327 | 1123 | N Norfolk |

*Remarks:* P'78 by M&GNJRS

| 70630 | 1946 | BG | York | 327 | | Steamtown |
| MM3022 | | | | | | |
| M99627 | | | | | | |
| DB975401 | | | | | | |

*Remarks:* P'81, used as a source of spares; by '90 it had lost one headstock & was mounted on LMS freight type bogies

| 70632 | 1946 | BG | York | 327 | | ?, USA |

*Remarks:* To USA '69 with 'Flying Scotsman' (fate unknown, but see 'Others' at end)

| 70636 | 1946 | BG | York | 327 | | ?, USA |

*Remarks:* To USA '69 with 'Flying Scotsman' (fate unknown, but see 'Others' at end)

| 70654 | 1950 | BZ | Stratford | 358 | 1284 | Great Central |

| Numbers | Year | Type | Built | Diag | Lot | Location |
|---|---|---|---|---|---|---|
| 70668 | 1950 | BZ | Stratford | 358 | 1284 | Great Central |

*Remarks:* Body P'?

| 70687 | 1950 | BZ | Stratford | 358 | 1284 | N Yorks Moors |

*Remarks:* P'76

| 70692 | 1950 | BZ | Stratford | 358 | 1284 | Mid-Hants |

*Remarks:* P'78 by Steam & Diesel Publications of Yateley, resold '82 to a group of M-H members

| 70754 041366 | 1943 1977 | BGP | York | 245 | 1073 | N Tyneside |

*Remarks:* P'91

| 70758 | 1943 | BGP | York | 245 | 1073 | ?, USA |

*Remarks:* To USA '69 with 'Flying Scotsman' (fate unknown, but see 'Others' at end)

For many years, this Gresley BGP (Brake Guard Pigeon) lay dumped at Heaton depot, carrying internal user No 041366. It was, despite being derailed and derelict, practically intact, even still having its gangway connections. It nearly yielded parts for other preserved Gresley vehicles, but in 1991 the North Tyneside Railway, literally just down the road, saved it from oblivion. All's well that ends well! *Peter J. Robinson*

| Numbers | Year | Type | Built | Diag | Lot | Location |
|---------|------|------|-------|------|-----|----------|
| 70759 | 1943 | BGP | York | 245 | 1073 | S Devon |

*Remarks:* P'73 by David & Charles, at Newton Abbot till presented to S Devon Rly by Readers Digest & moved to Buckfastleigh 4/91

| | | | | | | |
|---------|------|------|-------|------|-----|----------|
| 75169 041255 | 1950? | FVY? | | 214? | | Great Central |

| | | | | | | |
|---------|------|------|-------|------|-----|----------|
| 80417 99807 plated | 1952 | BC | Pickering | 360 | | Bo'ness |

*Remarks:* P'?? by SRPS, at Falkirk till '81

| | | | | | | |
|---------|------|------|-------|------|-----|----------|
| 88339 NYMR 5 | 1947 | CL | Cravens | 338 | | N Yorks Moors |

*Remarks:* W'67, P'70

| | | | | | | |
|---------|------|------|-------|------|-----|----------|
| DE900580 1998 'Loch Eil' 99065 plated | 1936 1983 | Insp Obs | Doncaster | - | | Steamtown |

*Remarks:* Taken into Capital stock in 1982, for use as an Observation Saloon on the West Highland line. P'84 by FSE (subject to a lease-back agreement with BR) & restored during '85

DE902260 – see 1531

*Others:*
3 unidentified Gresley vehicles at 'Victoria Station' restaurant, Universal Studios, Los Angeles, which may be ex 'Flying Scotsman' tour BGs listed in text

*Underframe only:*
That of a CCTY (latterly 064809) P'75 on W Somerset; its body was promptly pulled off by the GWR Pannier tank & destroyed, but the underframe wasn't converted to a sleeper wagon till Oct'90
That of 32480 (CL built Dukinfield 1930 to D50, later 88030) used to build BR GUV 96202 (qv)

# BRITISH RAILWAYS

| Numbers | Year | Type | Built | Diag | Lot | Location |
|---------|------|------|-------|------|-----|----------|
| 301 | 1952 | RF | Doncaster | 16 | 30013 | Market Bosworth |
| 1104 | 1965 | RE | | 31 | | |
| 'Jessie' | 1982 | | | | | |

*Remarks*: P'82

| | | | | | | |
|---------|------|------|-------|------|-----|----------|
| 302 | 1952 | RF | Doncaster | 16 | 30013 | Mid-Hants |
| 1105 | 1965 | RE | | 31 | | |
| (DB975878) | | | | | | |

*Remarks*: P'82

| | | | | | | |
|---------|------|------|-------|------|-----|----------|
| 324 | 1960 | RF | Swindon | 17 | 30633 | N Yorks Moors |

*Remarks*: P'83

| | | | | | | |
|---------|------|------|-------|------|-----|----------|
| 334 | 1961 | RF | Swindon | 17 | 30633 | Midland |
| 1779 | 1969 | RBK | Wolverton | 26 | | |

*Remarks*: W'81, P'83, then sold to MR Trust in '85

| | | | | | | |
|---------|------|------|-------|------|-----|----------|
| 504 'Ullswater' | 1966 | PK | Derby | 15 | 30755 | Crewe |

*Remarks*: P'91 by Manchester Pullman Co & named 'The White Rose'

| | | | | | | |
|---------|------|------|-------|------|-----|----------|
| 506 'Windermere' | 1966 | PK | Derby | 15 | 30755 | Crewe |

*Remarks*: P'91 by MPC (as above) & named 'The Red Rose'

| | | | | | | |
|---------|------|------|-------|------|-----|----------|
| 546 'Coniston Water' | 1966 | PC | Derby | 78 | 30754 | Crewe |
| 99670 plated | | | | | | |

*Remarks*: P'91 by MPC & named 'City of Manchester'

| | | | | | | |
|---------|------|------|-------|------|-----|----------|
| 548 'Grasmere' | 1966 | PC | Derby | 78 | 30754 | Crewe |
| 99671 plated | | | | | | |

*Remarks*: P'91 by MPC & named 'Elizabethan'

| Numbers | Year | Type | Built | Diag | Lot | Location |
|---------|------|------|-------|------|-----|----------|
| 549 'Bassenthwaite' 1966<br>99672 plated | | PC | Derby | 78 | 30754 | Crewe |

*Remarks:* P'91 by MPC & named 'Prince Rupert'

| 550 'Rydal Water' 1966<br>99673 plated | | PC | Derby | 78 | 30754 | Crewe |
|---------|------|------|-------|------|-----|----------|

*Remarks:* P'91 by MPC & named 'Golden Arrow'

| 551 'Buttermere' 1966<br>99674 plated | | PC | Derby | 78 | 30754 | Crewe |
|---------|------|------|-------|------|-----|----------|

*Remarks:* P'91 by MPC & named 'Caledonian'

| 552 'Ennerdale W' 1966<br>99675 plated | | PC | Derby | 78 | 30754 | Crewe |
|---------|------|------|-------|------|-----|----------|

*Remarks:* P'91 by MPC & named 'Southern Belle'

| 553 'Crummock W' 1966<br>99676 plated | | PC | Derby | 78 | 30754 | Crewe |
|---------|------|------|-------|------|-----|----------|

*Remarks:* P'91 by MPC & named 'King Arthur'

The last genuine Pullmans built were those in 1966 for the Manchester Pullman. Survivors eventually passed into BR InterCity's Charter Train Unit and were finally sold as a complete set to the Manchester Executive Railway Company Ltd who were contractually obliged to remove any vestiges of InterCity livery. They re-appeared as a private rake in 1991 adorned in a glorious colour scheme of claret and gold. This picture shows the Pullman set on its inaugural run as the Lakeland Pullman (all vehicles were then named after Lake District locations) at Oxenholme on 20 May 1987. *Eddie Bellass*

| Numbers | Year | Type | Built | Diag | Lot | Location |
|---------|------|------|-------|------|-----|----------|
| 586 'Derwent Water' 1966<br>99677 plated | | PB | Derby | 85 | 30753 | Crewe |

*Remarks:* P'91 by MPC & named 'Talisman'

| Numbers | Year | Type | Built | Diag | Lot | Location |
|---------|------|------|-------|------|-----|----------|
| DS70200<br>1000 | 1962<br>1963 | S | Lancing | | | E Somerset |

*Remarks:* Experimental GRP body mounted on u'frame from Mk.1 TSO 4377 (wrecked in 1957 Lewisham accident), each compartment with a different decor. In Lancing Works train July '63, then capital stock. W'67 & stored at Micheldever. P'73, briefly at Eastleigh then to Cranmore

| Numbers | Year | Type | Built | Diag | Lot | Location |
|---------|------|------|-------|------|-----|----------|
| 1012<br>DW150353 | 1951<br>1963 | RSO<br>Spec | York | 56 | 30014 | Great Central |

*Remarks:* Latterly Cinema Coach. P'90

| Numbers | Year | Type | Built | Diag | Lot | Location |
|---------|------|------|-------|------|-----|----------|
| 1013<br>TDB975323<br>KWVR 35 | 1951<br>1973 | RSO | York | 56 | 30014 | Worth Valley |

*Remarks:* P'85, restored with seats from TSO 4524

| Numbers | Year | Type | Built | Diag | Lot | Location |
|---------|------|------|-------|------|-----|----------|
| 1100<br>95404 plated | 1960 | RE | Eastleigh | 30 | 30637 | * NRM |

*Remarks:* Prototype Griddle Car, P'77 & restored by BREL Glasgow

| Numbers | Year | Type | Built | Diag | Lot | Location |
|---------|------|------|-------|------|-----|----------|
| 1102 | 1960 | RE | Eastleigh | 30 | 30637 | Great Central |

*Remarks:* P'81?

1104 – see 301

1105 – see 302

| Numbers | Year | Type | Built | Diag | Lot | Location |
|---------|------|------|-------|------|-----|----------|
| 1106 | 1968 | RE | Derby | 32 | 30783 | Gwili |

*Remarks:* The solitary 'Booth Car'; P'80

1513 – only leased from BR

| Numbers | Year | Type | Built | Diag | Lot | Location |
|---------|------|------|-------|------|-----|----------|
| 1525 | 1960 | RKB | Cravens | 25 | 30514 | Great Central |

*Remarks:* P'83

| Numbers | Year | Type | Built | Diag | Lot | Location |
|---------|------|------|-------|------|-----|----------|
| 1526 | 1960 | RKB | Cravens | 25 | 30514 | Great Central |

*Remarks:* Used in 'Centenary of Catering' train '78. P'83 by NYMR & in Pickering's cafeteria complex till '85

| Numbers | Year | Type | Built | Diag | Lot | Location |
|---------|------|------|-------|------|-----|----------|
| 1555 | 1961 | RKB | Cravens | 25 | 30624 | Mid-Hants |

*Remarks:* P'90 from Mayer Newman, moved to V Berry's for asbestos removal

| Numbers | Year | Type | Built | Diag | Lot | Location |
|---------|------|------|-------|------|-----|----------|
| 1566 | 1961 | RKB | Cravens | 25 | 30624 | Bluebell |

*Remarks:* P'82, at Steamtown till '86

| Numbers | Year | Type | Built | Diag | Lot | Location |
|---------|------|------|-------|------|-----|----------|
| 1569 | 1961 | RKB | Cravens | 25 | 30624 | Blunsdon |
| Remarks: P'82, at Steamtown till '86 | | | | | | |
| 1657 | 1960 | RB | Pressed Steel | 24 | 30628 | Llangollen |
| Remarks: P'91 | | | | | | |
| 1665 | 1961 | RB | Pressed Steel | 24 | 30628 | Llangollen |
| Remarks: P'91 | | | | | | |
| 1668 | 1960 | RB | Pressed Steel | 24 | 30628 | Mid-Hants |
| Remarks: P'81 | | | | | | |
| 1682 | 1961 | RB | Pressed Steel | 24 | 30628 | Severn Valley |
| Remarks: P'81 | | | | | | |
| 1694 | 1961 | RB | Pressed Steel | 24 | 30628 | Torbay |
| Remarks: P'91, renovated at Wolverton | | | | | | |
| 1703 | 1960 | RB | B R C W | 24 | 30512 | E Lancs |
| Remarks: P'83 | | | | | | |
| 1705 | 1960 | RB | B R C W | 24 | 30512 | Llangollen |
| Remarks: P'90 | | | | | | |
| 1730 99818 plated | 1960 | RB | B R C W | 24 | 30512 | Bo'ness |
| Remarks: P'88 by SRPS, at Perth till '90 | | | | | | |
| 1802 | 1957 | RMB | York | 97 | 30485 | Midland |
| Remarks: P'80 | | | | | | |
| 1803 | 1957 | RMB | York | 97 | 30485 | Dean Forest |
| Remarks: P'83, at Blunsdon till '87 | | | | | | |
| 1804 'Aries' | 1957 1986 | RMB | York | 97 | 30485 | W Somerset |
| Remarks: P'82 | | | | | | |
| 1806 | 1957 | RMB | York | 97 | 30485 | Mid-Hants |
| Remarks: P'82 | | | | | | |
| 1807 | 1957 | RMB | York | 97 | 30485 | Mid-Hants |
| Remarks: P'82 | | | | | | |

| Numbers | Year | Type | Built | Diag | Lot | Location |
|---------|------|------|-------|------|-----|----------|
| 1808 | 1957 | RMB | York | 97 | 30485 | Gloucs-Warks |
| *Remarks:* P'82 | | | | | | |
| 1809 | 1957 | RMB | York | 97 | 30485 | Colne Valley |
| *Remarks:* P'81 | | | | | | |
| 1811 | 1957 | RMB | York | 97 | 30485 | Gloucs-Warks |
| *Remarks:* P'83 | | | | | | |
| 1812 L&HR 60 | 1957 | RMB | York | 97 | 30485 | Lakeside |
| *Remarks:* P'83 | | | | | | |
| 1815 | 1960 | RMB | Wolverton | 99 | 30520 | Bere Ferrers |
| *Remarks:* P'90 by Kingsgrove Developments Ltd at Station Museum | | | | | | |
| 1818 | 1960 | RMB | Wolverton | 99 | 30520 | Bluebell |
| *Remarks:* P'83 | | | | | | |
| 1823 | 1960 | RMB | Wolverton | 99 | 30520 | N Yorks Moors |
| *Remarks:* P'84 | | | | | | |
| 1824 | 1960 | RMB | Wolverton | 99 | 30520 | Worth Valley |
| *Remarks:* P'84 | | | | | | |
| 1826 YDR 2 | 1960 | RMB | Wolverton | 99 | 30520 | Embsay |
| *Remarks:* P'83 | | | | | | |
| 1829 DB977098 | 1960 1982 | RMB | Wolverton | 99 | 30520 | Llangollen |
| *Remarks:* P'89, restored at Chester till '90 | | | | | | |
| 1835 DB977186 | 1960 1983 | RMB | Wolverton | 99 | 30520 | Darley Dale |
| *Remarks:* P'88 by Peak Rail, delivered '90 | | | | | | |
| 1836 | 1960 | RMB | Wolverton | 99 | 30520 | Worth Valley |
| *Remarks:* P'84 | | | | | | |
| 1837 | 1960 | RMB | Wolverton | 99 | 30520 | E Lancs |
| *Remarks:* P'82 | | | | | | |
| 1838 | 1960 | RMB | Wolverton | 98 | 30507 | Bluebell |
| *Remarks:* P'91 | | | | | | |

| Numbers | Year | Type | Built | Diag | Lot | Location |
|---------|------|------|-------|------|-----|----------|
| 1839 | 1960 | RMB | Wolverton | 98 | 30507 | Southport |
| Remarks: P'82 | | | | | | |
| 1840 | 1960 | RMB | Wolverton | 98 | 30507 | Mid-Hants |
| Remarks: P'83 | | | | | | |
| 1851 | 1960 | RMB | Wolverton | 98 | 30507 | Mid-Hants |
| Remarks: P'82 | | | | | | |
| 1852 | 1960 | RMB | Wolverton | 98 | 30507 | Great Central |
| Remarks: P'83 | | | | | | |
| 1855 | 1961 | RMB | Wolverton | 99 | 30670 | Severn Valley |
| Remarks: P'83 | | | | | | |
| 1856 | 1961 | RMB | Wolverton | 99 | 30670 | Severn Valley |
| Remarks: P'89 | | | | | | |

A highly sought-after Mk 1 coach on private railways is the Restaurant Miniature Buffet (RMB), as catering forms an intrinsic part of revenue on these volunteer-orientated lines. As a result, and partly because for many years BR did not release any for sale, prices paid for RMBs reached ludicrous levels. This one, No 1823, was bought in terrible condition from March depot and has now been returned to traffic on the North Yorkshire Moors Railway. *Murray Brown*

| Numbers | Year | Type | Built | Diag | Lot | Location |
|---------|------|------|-------|------|-----|----------|
| 1859 | 1961 | RMB | Wolverton | 99 | 30670 | Bo'ness |

*Remarks:* P'89 by SRPS post-lease, at Perth till '91

| Numbers | Year | Type | Built | Diag | Lot | Location |
|---------|------|------|-------|------|-----|----------|
| 1861<br>99132 plated | 1961 | RMB | Wolverton | 99 | 30670 | (Bounds Green) |

*Remarks:* P'89 by FSS for Pullman Rail stock

| Numbers | Year | Type | Built | Diag | Lot | Location |
|---------|------|------|-------|------|-----|----------|
| 1862<br>99305 plated<br>'Wyvern Bar' | 1961<br><br>1988 | RMB | Wolverton | 99 | 30670 | Midland |

*Remarks:* P'84 by TFP, sold to MRT in '86

| Numbers | Year | Type | Built | Diag | Lot | Location |
|---------|------|------|-------|------|-----|----------|
| 1866<br>'Maclays'<br>99811 plated | 1961<br>1984 | RMB | Wolverton | 99 | 30702 | Bo'ness |

*Remarks:* P'83 by SRPS, at Falkirk till '88 then at Perth till '90

| Numbers | Year | Type | Built | Diag | Lot | Location |
|---------|------|------|-------|------|-----|----------|
| 1872 | 1961 | RMB | Wolverton | 99 | 30702 | Nene Valley |

*Remarks:* Worked with SR EMU's. P'88

| Numbers | Year | Type | Built | Diag | Lot | Location |
|---------|------|------|-------|------|-----|----------|
| 1873 | 1961 | RMB | Wolverton | 99 | 30702 | Bodmin |

*Remarks:* Worked with SR EMU's. P'88

| Numbers | Year | Type | Built | Diag | Lot | Location |
|---------|------|------|-------|------|-----|----------|
| 1874 | 1961 | RMB | Wolverton | 99 | 30702 | Swanage |

*Remarks:* P'89 by SST

| Numbers | Year | Type | Built | Diag | Lot | Location |
|---------|------|------|-------|------|-----|----------|
| 1879 | 1962 | RMB | Wolverton | 99 | 30702 | ? |

*Remarks:* P'91 by LMS Trust

| Numbers | Year | Type | Built | Diag | Lot | Location |
|---------|------|------|-------|------|-----|----------|
| 1882 | 1962 | RMB | Wolverton | 99 | 30702 | Steamtown |

*Remarks:* P'91

| Numbers | Year | Type | Built | Diag | Lot | Location |
|---------|------|------|-------|------|-----|----------|
| 1883<br>'Leslie' | 1968<br>1989 | Bar | Derby | 100 | 30784 | Severn Valley |

*Remarks:* Built on u'frame of former RK No 80021 (C Roberts 1962 to Diag.701 Lot 30524). P'81, at Chappel till '84 then Isfield till '90

1885 – see 3764

1886 – see 3058

| Numbers | Year | Type | Built | Diag | Lot | Location |
|---------|------|------|-------|------|-----|----------|
| 1908 | 1957 | RU | Swindon | 23 | 30401 | Swanage |

*Remarks:* P'80

| Numbers | Year | Type | Built | Diag | Lot | Location |
|---------|------|------|-------|------|-----|----------|
| 1909 | 1957 | RU RUB | Swindon | 23 29 | 30401 | W Somerset |
| 'Orion' | 1986 | | | | | |

Remarks: P'81

| 1917 | 1958 | RU RUB | Swindon | 23 29 | 30476 | Dean Forest |

Remarks: P'81

| 1926 | 1959 | RU | B R C W | 23 | 30513 | Steamtown |

Remarks: P'76?, grounded as joiners' wood store

| 1928 | 1959 | RU RB | B R C W | 23 27 | 30513 | Strathspey |
| SR 109 | | | | | | |

Remarks: P'80

| 1929 | 1959 | RU | B R C W | 23 | 30513 | Steamtown |

Remarks: P'78?, an ideal body for grounding as a workshop for French-polishing

| 1933 | 1959 | RU RUB | B R C W | 23 29 | 30513 | Bitton |

Remarks: P'81?

| 1936 | 1959 | RU | B R C W | 23 | 30513 | Strathspey |
| SR 110 | | | | | | |

Remarks: P'80, as built with Gresley bogies

| 1949 | 1960 | RU | Swindon | 23 | 30575 | Steamtown |

Remarks: P'81

| 1955 | 1960 | RU | Swindon | 23 | 30575 | K&ESR |
| K&ESR 69 'Diana' | 1981 | | | | | |

Remarks: P'79, given Pullman livery in '81 & named in honour of the Princess of Wales.

| 1963 | 1960 | RU | Swindon | 23 | 30632 | Worth Valley |
| DB975948 | 1981 | | | | | |
| Test Car 11 | | | | | | |

Remarks: P'87, rebuilt '89

| 1973 | 1961 | RU | Eastleigh | 23 | 30632 | Mid-Hants |

Remarks: P'91

| 2013 | 1958 | SLF | Wolverton | 1 | 30159 | Steamtown |
| 2908 | 1982 | | | | | |

Remarks: P'84 by FSE, ex Royal Train

| Numbers | Year | Type | Built | Diag | Lot | Location |
|---|---|---|---|---|---|---|
| 2080 | 1959 | SLF | Metro-Cammell | 1 | 30490 | Darley Dale |

*Remarks:* P'83, on Dart Valley till '88

| 2108<br>99883 plated | 1960 | SLF | Metro-Cammell | 1 | 30590 | (Steamtown) |

*Remarks:* P'84 by R Edmondson, refurbished & leased to GS&WR as 'Sleeper 3' in 'Royal Scotsman' 1985-9; from '90 became 'State Car 83' in 'Queen of Scots'

| 2110<br>99885 plated | 1960 | SLF | Metro-Cammell | 1 | 30590 | (Steamtown) |

*Remarks:* P'84 by R Edmondson, refurbished & leased to GS&WR as 'Sleeper 1' in 'Royal Scotsman' 1985-9; from '90 became 'State Car 85' in 'Queen of Scots'

| 2127<br>99360 plated<br>99887 plated | 1961<br>1983<br>1988 | SLF | Wolverton | 1 | 30687 | (Craigentinny) |

*Remarks:* P'83 by SLOA, sold to GS&WR '87 & used in the 'Royal Scotsman' rake

| 2131 | 1962 | SLF | Wolverton | 1 | 30722 | ? |

*Remarks:* P'84 by A4 Loco Soc, at Steamtown till sold '90 in appalling condition (Pullman bogies with cut spring hangers & asbestos bared within) - appeared briefly on W Somerset in October

| 2132 | 1962 | SLF | Wolverton | 1 | 30722 | Llangollen |

*Remarks:* P'84, at Steamtown till '87

| 2442<br>99888 plated | 1961 | SLC | Wolverton | 5 | 30688 | (Steamtown) |

*Remarks:* P'84, later sold to R Edmondson & became 'Service Car 2' in 'Queen of Scots' from '90

| 2500<br>2909 | 1957<br>1982 | SLSTP | Doncaster | 10 | 30036 | Steamtown |

*Remarks:* P'84 by FSE, ex Royal Train

| 2521 | 1957 | SLSTP | Doncaster | 10 | 30036 | Worth Valley |

*Remarks:* P'83?

| 2536<br>2815 | 1957<br>1971 | SLSTP<br>SLEP | Doncaster | 10<br>14 | 30245 | Welshpool |

*Remarks:* P'84

| 2538 | 1958 | SLSTP | Doncaster | 10 | 30379 | Brechin |

*Remarks:* Sold to Fulmar Services, Invergordon '83. P'85, then grounded

| 2563<br>2808 | 1958<br>1971 | SLSTP<br>SLEP | Doncaster | 10<br>14 | 30379 | Gloucs-Warks |

*Remarks:* P'89

| Numbers | Year | Type | Built | Diag | Lot | Location |
|---------|------|------|-------|------|-----|----------|
| 2564 | 1958 | SLSTP | Doncaster | 10 | 30379 | Swanage |

*Remarks:* P'81 by Southern Steam Trust

| Numbers | Year | Type | Built | Diag | Lot | Location |
|---------|------|------|-------|------|-----|----------|
| 2573 | 1958 | SLSTP | Doncaster | 10 | 30379 | Embsay |

*Remarks:* P'83

| 2574 | 1959 | SLSTP | Metro-Cammell | 10 | 30491 | Llangollen |

*Remarks:* P'83, on Dart Valley till '86

| 2583 | 1959 | SLSTP | Wolverton | 10 | 30529 | Worth Valley |

*Remarks:* P'83?

| 2586 | 1959 | SLSTP | Wolverton | 10 | 30529 | E Lancs |

*Remarks:* P'83

| 2588 | 1959 | SLSTP | Wolverton | 10 | 30529 | Buxton |
| 2801 | 1971 | SLEP | | 14 | | |

*Remarks:* P'83, on Dart Valley till '86

| 2592 | 1959 | SLSTP | Wolverton | 10 | 30529 | Bisley Stn |

*Remarks:* Sold to Lloyds Bank Rifle Club '84.

| 2599 | 1959 | SLSTP | Wolverton | 10 | 30529 | Bitton |

*Remarks:* P'83, on Dart Valley till '86?

| 2612 | 1960 | SLSTP | Wolverton | 10 | 30586 | Bo'ness |
| 2821 | 1971 | SLEP | | 14 | | |

*Remarks:* Sold to Fulmar Services, Invergordon '83. P'84 by SRPS, at Falkirk till '88 then Perth till '91

| 2613 | 1960 | SLSTP | Wolverton | 10 | 30586 | Bo'ness |
| 2822 | 1971 | SLEP | | 14 | | |

*Remarks:* Sold to Fulmar Services, Invergordon '83. P'84 by SRPS, at Falkirk till '88

| 3014 | 1954 | FO | B R C W | 72 | 30008 | Steamtown |
| DB975658 | 1977 | | | | | |
| (6336) | 1989 | | | | | |

*Remarks:* P'90

| 3016 | 1954 | FO | B R C W | 72 | 30008 | Steamtown |
| DB975650 | 1977 | | | | | |
| 6331 | 1989 | | | | | |

*Remarks:* P'90 by Mr Oakley

| 3042 | 1954 | FO | Doncaster | 73 | 30091 | Great Central |
| | | RFO | Great Central | | | |

*Remarks:* P'77

| Numbers | Year | Type | Built | Diag | Lot | Location |
|---------|------|------|-------|------|-----|----------|
| 3043 | 1954 | FO | Doncaster | 73 | 30091 | Mid-Hants |

Remarks: P'77

| 3045 | 1954 | FO | Doncaster | 73 | 30091 | Tyseley |

Remarks: P'90 by B'ham Ry Mus Trust

| 3051 | 1954 | FO | Doncaster | 73 | 30091 | Long Marston |
| DB977492 | | | | | | |

Remarks: P'91 by Avon Valley member

| 3058 | 1955 | FO | Doncaster | 73 | 30169 | W Somerset |
| DB975313 | 1973 | | | | | |
| 1886 | 1990 | RMB | | | | |

Remarks: P'83 by 5542 Group, conv'd to RMB during restoration as 'Taunton Cider Bar' 1989-90

| 3060 | 1955 | FO | Doncaster | 73 | 30169 | Gwili |
| DB975314 | 1973 | | | | | |

Remarks: P'79 (now a Buffet?)

| 3063 | 1955 | FO | Doncaster | 73 | 30169 | Stewarts Lane |

Remarks: P'87 by VSOE

| 3064 | 1955 | FO | Doncaster | 73 | 30169 | Stewarts Lane? |
| DB975607 | 1977 | | | | | |
| 'Test Car 7' | | | | | | |

Remarks: P'90 by VSOE

| 3065 | 1955 | FO | Doncaster | 73 | 30169 | Mid-Hants |
| 'Orchid' | 1988 | | | | | |

Remarks: P'82

| 3066 | 1955 | FO | Doncaster | 73 | 30169 | Stewarts Lane |

Remarks: P'83 by VSOE

| 3067 | 1955 | FO | Doncaster | 73 | 30169 | Mid-Hants |

Remarks: P'82

| 3068 | 1955 | FO | Doncaster | 73 | 30169 | Stewarts Lane |
| DB975606 | 1977 | | | | | |
| Lab 2 'Electra' | | | | | | |

Remarks: P'88 by VSOE

| 3069 | 1955 | FO | Doncaster | 73 | 30169 | (Stewarts Lane) |
| 99540 plated | | | | | | |

Remarks: P'83 by VSOE, became 'Saloon Car No.1'

| Numbers | Year | Type | Built | Diag | Lot | Location |
|---------|------|------|-------|------|-----|----------|
| 3070 'Fern' | 1955 1988 | FO | Doncaster | 73 | 30169 | Mid-Hants |
| Remarks: P'82 | | | | | | |
| 3079 TDB975315 | 1956 1973 | FO | Doncaster | 73 | 30242 | Great Central |
| Remarks: P'87 | | | | | | |
| 3081 | 1957 | FO | B R C W | 77 | 30359 | Dart Valley |
| Remarks: Experimental. P pre'77, sold '91 | | | | | | |
| 3083 | 1957 | FO | Doncaster | 74 | 30372 | Severn Valley |
| Remarks: Experimental. P'72 | | | | | | |
| 3084 99601 plated | 1957 1972 | FO Disco | Doncaster Dart Valley | 75 | 30373 | Dart Valley |
| Remarks: Experimental. P pre'77, sold '91 | | | | | | |
| 3090 | 1959 | FO | B R C W | 73 | 30472 | Hoddesdon |
| Remarks: P'89 by SST for Swanage, stored in Essex | | | | | | |
| 3092 | 1959 | FO | B R C W | 73 | 30576 | Great Central |
| Remarks: P'87 | | | | | | |
| 3095 | 1959 | FO | B R C W | 73 | 30576 | Great Central |
| Remarks: P'87 | | | | | | |
| 3096 99827 plated | 1959 | FO | B R C W | 73 | 30576 | Bo'ness |
| Remarks: P'90 by SRPS | | | | | | |
| 3098/100 – only leased from BR | | | | | | |
| 3103 | 1961 | FO | Wolverton | 73 | 30648 | Severn Valley |
| Remarks: P'84 | | | | | | |
| 3105 99121 plated 'Julia' | 1962 1984 1986 | FO | Swindon | 73 | 30697 | Steamtown |
| Remarks: P'84 by Pullman-Rail, based at Bounds Green till '90 | | | | | | |
| 3106 99122 plated 'Helen' | 1962 1984 1986 | FO | Swindon | 73 | 30697 | (Bounds Green) |
| Remarks: P'84 by Pullman-Rail | | | | | | |

| Numbers | Year | Type | Built | Diag | Lot | Location |
|---------|------|------|-------|------|-----|----------|
| 3108<br>99358 plated | 1962 | FO | Swindon | 73 | 30697 | W Somerset |

*Remarks:* P'84 by Pullman-Rail; used in Pullman rake except for lease to Bluebell '90-1, then sold

| Numbers | Year | Type | Built | Diag | Lot | Location |
|---------|------|------|-------|------|-----|----------|
| 3109<br>99123 plated<br>'Grace' | 1962<br>1984<br>1986 | FO | Swindon | 73 | 30697 | (Bounds Green) |

*Remarks:* P'84 by Pullman-Rail

| Numbers | Year | Type | Built | Diag | Lot | Location |
|---------|------|------|-------|------|-----|----------|
| 3110<br>99124 plated<br>'Frances' | 1962<br>1984<br>1986 | FO | Swindon | 73 | 30697 | (Bounds Green) |

*Remarks:* P'84 by Pullman-Rail

| Numbers | Year | Type | Built | Diag | Lot | Location |
|---------|------|------|-------|------|-----|----------|
| 3112<br>99357 plated | 1962 | FO | Swindon | 73 | 30697 | (Bounds Green) |

*Remarks:* P'82 by SLOA, to Pullman-Rail in '84

| Numbers | Year | Type | Built | Diag | Lot | Location |
|---------|------|------|-------|------|-----|----------|
| 3113<br>99125 plated<br>'Eileen' | 1962<br>1984<br>1986 | FO | Swindon | 73 | 30697 | (Bounds Green) |

*Remarks:* P'84 by Pullman-Rail; used in maroon rake except for lease to Bluebell '90-1

| Numbers | Year | Type | Built | Diag | Lot | Location |
|---------|------|------|-------|------|-----|----------|
| 3116<br>99358 plated<br>99126 plated<br>'Diane' | 1962<br>1982<br>1984<br>1986 | FO | Swindon | 73 | 30697 | Bluebell |

*Remarks:* P'82 by Pullman-Rail; used in Pullman rake till '84, then maroon rake till leased to Bluebell '90, sold '91

| Numbers | Year | Type | Built | Diag | Lot | Location |
|---------|------|------|-------|------|-----|----------|
| 3117<br>99127 plated<br>'Cheryl'<br>'Carol' | 1962<br>1984<br>1986<br>1987 | FO | Swindon | 73 | 30697 | (Bounds Green) |

*Remarks:* P'84 by Pullman-Rail; used in maroon rake except for lease to Bluebell '90-1

| Numbers | Year | Type | Built | Diag | Lot | Location |
|---------|------|------|-------|------|-----|----------|
| 3125<br>'Mandy' | 1963<br>1989 | FO | Swindon | 73 | 30697 | Isfield |

*Remarks:* P'81, at Chappel till '84

| Numbers | Year | Type | Built | Diag | Lot | Location |
|---------|------|------|-------|------|-----|----------|
| 3126 | 1963 | FO | Swindon | 73 | 30697 | Great Central |

*Remarks:* P'82

| Numbers | Year | Type | Built | Diag | Lot | Location |
|---------|------|------|-------|------|-----|----------|
| 3128<br>1058<br>3600<br>99371 plated | 1963<br>1976<br>1981 | FO<br>RSO<br>SO | Swindon | 73 | 30697 | (Aberdeen) |

*Remarks:* P'87 by Grampian Railtours

| Numbers | Year | Type | Built | Diag | Lot | Location |
|---------|------|------|-------|------|-----|----------|
| 3130<br>99128 plated<br>'Beryl' | 1963<br>1984<br>1986 | FO | Swindon | 73 | 30717 | (Bounds Green) |

Remarks: P'84 by Pullman-Rail; used in maroon rake except for lease to Bluebell '90-1

| | | | | | | |
|---------|------|------|-------|------|-----|----------|
| 3138<br>1061<br>3607 | 1963<br>1976<br>1982 | FO<br>RSO<br>SO | Swindon | 73 | 30717 | Llangollen |

Remarks: P'89

| | | | | | | |
|---------|------|------|-------|------|-----|----------|
| 3167<br>6400 | 1970<br>1982 | FO<br>SO | Derby | 80 | 30810 | N Yorks Moors |

Remarks: Mk.2c. P'91

| | | | | | | |
|---------|------|------|-------|------|-----|----------|
| 3168<br>6412 | 1970<br>1983 | FO<br>SO | Derby | 80 | 30810 | Midland |

Remarks: Mk.2c. P'90 as Swanwick Buffet

| | | | | | | |
|---------|------|------|-------|------|-----|----------|
| 3727 | 1954 | SO | Derby | 94 | 30031 | Gloucs-Warks |

Remarks: P'90

| | | | | | | |
|---------|------|------|-------|------|-----|----------|
| 3733 | 1954 | SO | Derby | 94 | 30031 | BC, Canada |

Remarks: P'69 by Fort Steele Historical Museum

| | | | | | | |
|---------|------|------|-------|------|-----|----------|
| 3736 | 1953 | TSO | Doncaster | 93 | 30043 | Tyseley |

Remarks: P'83

| | | | | | | |
|---------|------|------|-------|------|-----|----------|
| 3738 | 1953 | TSO | Doncaster | 93 | 30043 | Mid-Hants |

Remarks: P'88 by VSOE but promptly resold

| | | | | | | |
|---------|------|------|-------|------|-----|----------|
| 3743 | 1953 | TSO | Doncaster | 93 | 30043 | South Shields |

Remarks: P'86, part of 'Marsden Rattler' restaurant

| | | | | | | |
|---------|------|------|-------|------|-----|----------|
| 3745 | 1953 | TSO | Doncaster | 93 | 30043 | Bitton |

Remarks: P'89

| | | | | | | |
|---------|------|------|-------|------|-----|----------|
| 3746 | 1953 | TSO | Doncaster | 93 | 30043 | Andover |

Remarks: P'88 (damaged) by SST, for Swanage

| | | | | | | |
|---------|------|------|-------|------|-----|----------|
| 3748 | 1953 | TSO | Doncaster | 93 | 30043 | Mid-Hants |

Remarks: P'89

| | | | | | | |
|---------|------|------|-------|------|-----|----------|
| 3749<br>(DB977623) | 1953 | TSO | Doncaster | 93 | 30043 | Long Marston |

Remarks: P'91 by Avon Valley member

| Numbers | Year | Type | Built | Diag | Lot | Location |
|---------|------|------|-------|------|-----|----------|
| 3753 | 1953 | TSO | Doncaster | 93 | 30043 | K&ESR |
| KESR 64 | 1977 | | | | | |

*Remarks:* P'77

| Numbers | Year | Type | Built | Diag | Lot | Location |
|---------|------|------|-------|------|-----|----------|
| 3764 | 1953 | TSO | York | 93 | 30079 | Rye House |
| 1885 | 1991 | RMB | | | | |

*Remarks:* P'87 by SST, converted to RMB before going to Swanage

| Numbers | Year | Type | Built | Diag | Lot | Location |
|---------|------|------|-------|------|-----|----------|
| 3766 | 1953 | TSO | York | 93 | 30079 | Steamtown |
| 99317 plated | | | | | | |

*Remarks:* P'91, in D Smith's maroon rake

| Numbers | Year | Type | Built | Diag | Lot | Location |
|---------|------|------|-------|------|-----|----------|
| 3767 | 1953 | TSO | York | 93 | 30079 | Glenfinnan |

*Remarks:* P'91 for the Station Museum

| Numbers | Year | Type | Built | Diag | Lot | Location |
|---------|------|------|-------|------|-----|----------|
| 3779 | 1953 | TSO | Doncaster | 93 | 30043 | Chappel |

*Remarks:* P'81?

| Numbers | Year | Type | Built | Diag | Lot | Location |
|---------|------|------|-------|------|-----|----------|
| 3785 | 1953 | TSO | Doncaster | 93 | 30043 | Market Bosworth |
| | 1957 | SO | Doncaster | | | |

*Remarks:* Refurbished '57 as one of the experimental coaches. P'75 & on Severn Valley (called the 'York Buffet') till '79

| Numbers | Year | Type | Built | Diag | Lot | Location |
|---------|------|------|-------|------|-----|----------|
| 3798 | 1953 | TSO | York | 93 | 30079 | N Yorks Moors |
| NYMR 19 | | | | | | |

*Remarks:* P'77

| Numbers | Year | Type | Built | Diag | Lot | Location |
|---------|------|------|-------|------|-----|----------|
| 3801 | 1953 | TSO | York | 93 | 30079 | N Yorks Moors |

*Remarks:* P'81

| Numbers | Year | Type | Built | Diag | Lot | Location |
|---------|------|------|-------|------|-----|----------|
| 3805 | 1953 | TSO | York | 93 | 30079 | N Yorks Moors |

*Remarks:* P'82

| Numbers | Year | Type | Built | Diag | Lot | Location |
|---------|------|------|-------|------|-----|----------|
| 3809 | 1953 | TSO | York | 93 | 30079 | Midland |
| | 1987 | RSO | | | | |

*Remarks:* P'82

| Numbers | Year | Type | Built | Diag | Lot | Location |
|---------|------|------|-------|------|-----|----------|
| 3815 | 1953 | TSO | York | 93 | 30079 | Bitton |
| Army 3305 | | | | | | |

*Remarks:* P'89 ex Marchwood

| Numbers | Year | Type | Built | Diag | Lot | Location |
|---------|------|------|-------|------|-----|----------|
| 3825 | 1953 | TSO | Eastleigh | 93 | 30054 | Buxton |
| KWVR 14 | | | | | | |

*Remarks:* P pre'74, on Worth Valley till '87

| Numbers | Year | Type | Built | Diag | Lot | Location |
|---------|------|------|-------|------|-----|----------|
| 3836 | 1953 | TSO | Eastleigh | 93 | 30054 | N Norfolk |
| *Remarks:* P pre'74 | | | | | | |
| 3860<br>NYMR 8 | 1953 | TSO | York | 93 | 30080 | N Yorks Moors |
| *Remarks:* P'70 | | | | | | |
| 3866 | 1953 | TSO | York | 93 | 30080 | Delph |
| *Remarks:* P'76 at former Station | | | | | | |
| 3868 | 1953 | TSO | York | 93 | 30080 | N Norfolk |
| *Remarks:* P'69 | | | | | | |
| 3872 | 1953 | TSO | York | 93 | 30080 | N Yorks Moors |
| *Remarks:* P'83 | | | | | | |
| 3878 | 1953 | TSO | York | 93 | 30080 | N Yorks Moors ? |
| *Remarks:* P'89, but also reported scrapped by Birds | | | | | | |
| 3881<br>L&HR 48 | 1953 | TSO | York | 93 | 30080 | Lakeside |
| *Remarks:* P'83 | | | | | | |
| 3906 | 1954 | TSO | Eastleigh | 93 | 30086 | Mid-Hants |
| *Remarks:* P'82 | | | | | | |
| 3918 | 1954 | TSO | Eastleigh | 93 | 30086 | Rushden Stn |
| *Remarks:* P'89 by Rushden Historical Transport Soc | | | | | | |
| 3919<br>(DB977624) | 1954 | TSO | Eastleigh | 93 | 30086 | Pitsford |
| *Remarks:* P'90 | | | | | | |
| 3924<br>DB977626 | 1954 | TSO | Eastleigh | 93 | 30086 | Coventry |
| *Remarks:* P'90 by 1857 Soc, to be static buffet | | | | | | |
| 3925 | 1954 | TSO | Eastleigh | 93 | 30086 | Betws-y-Coed |
| *Remarks:* P pre'74 by Conwy Valley Railway Museum | | | | | | |
| 3948 | 1954 | TSO | Eastleigh | 93 | 30086 | N Yorks Moors |
| *Remarks:* P'89 | | | | | | |
| 3950 | 1955 | TSO | Eastleigh | 93 | 30086 | Llangollen |
| *Remarks:* P'91 | | | | | | |

| Numbers | Year | Type | Built | Diag | Lot | Location |
|---------|------|------|-------|------|-----|----------|
| 3962<br>L&HR 49 | 1954 | TSO | Eastleigh | 93 | 30086 | Lakeside |

*Remarks:* P'83

| 3984 | 1954 | TSO | York | 93 | 30090 | Audley End |

*Remarks:* P'83? by the miniature railway

| 3991<br>(DB977627) | 1954 | TSO | York | 93 | 30090 | Long Marston |

*Remarks:* P'91 by Avon Valley member

| 4035 | 1956 | TSO | Swindon | 93 | 30149 | Andover |

*Remarks:* P'89 by SST, for Swanage

| 4037<br>KESR 65 | 1956 | TSO | Swindon | 93 | 30149 | K&ESR |

*Remarks:* P'77

| 4039 | 1956 | TSO | Swindon | 93 | 30149 | W Somerset |

*Remarks:* P'77, used by Minehead MRC initially, then became Minehead Station Buffet

| 4046<br>99604 plated | 1956 | TSO | Swindon | 93 | 30149 | Blaenavon |

*Remarks:* P'70, on Dart Valley till '85

| 4054 | 1956 | TSO | Swindon | 93 | 30149 | - |

*Remarks:* P'77 on Severn Valley; W'87, broken up '89

| 4055 | 1956 | TSO | Swindon | 93 | 30149 | Andover |

*Remarks:* P'89 by SST, for Swanage

| 4058<br>(DB977629) | 1956 | TSO | Swindon | 93 | 30149 | Long Marston |

*Remarks:* P'91 by Avon Valley member

| 4074 | 1957 | TSO | Swindon | 93 | 30149 | Andover |

*Remarks:* P'89 by SST, for Swanage

| 4079 | 1957 | TSO | Swindon | 93 | 30149 | Strathspey |

*Remarks:* P'82

| 4081 | 1957 | TSO | Swindon | 93 | 30149 | Torbay |

*Remarks:* P'87

| Numbers | Year | Type | Built | Diag | Lot | Location |
|---------|------|------|-------|------|-----|----------|
| 4127<br>SR 103 | 1955 | TSO | York | 93 | 30171 | Strathspey |
| *Remarks:* P pre'74 | | | | | | |
| 4166 | 1956 | TSO | York | 93 | 30171 | - |
| *Remarks:* P'70 on Dart Valley; scrapped '90. | | | | | | |
| 4198 | 1956 | TSO | York | 93 | 30172 | N Yorks Moors |
| *Remarks:* P'82 | | | | | | |
| 4199 | 1956 | TSO | York | 93 | 30172 | E Lancs |
| *Remarks:* P'82 | | | | | | |
| 4200 | 1956 | TSO | York | 93 | 30172 | Nene Valley |
| *Remarks:* P'82 | | | | | | |
| 4205 | 1956 | TSO | York | 93 | 30172 | Torbay |
| *Remarks:* P'87 | | | | | | |
| 4207 | 1956 | TSO | York | 93 | 30172 | N Yorks Moors |
| *Remarks:* P'83 for Pickering catering complex | | | | | | |
| 4215<br>99810 plated | 1956 | TSO | York | 93 | 30172 | Bo'ness |
| *Remarks:* P'83 by SRPS, at Falkirk till '88 then at Perth till '90 | | | | | | |
| 4218 | 1956 | TSO | York | 93 | 30172 | Dean Forest |
| *Remarks:* P'83 | | | | | | |
| 4223 | 1956 | TSO | York | 93 | 30172 | Lochty |
| *Remarks:* P'83 | | | | | | |
| 4224<br>99813 plated | 1956 | TSO | York | 93 | 30172 | Bo'ness |
| *Remarks:* P'83 by SRPS, at Falkirk till '88 then at Perth till '90 | | | | | | |
| 4232 | 1956 | TSO | York | 93 | 30172 | E Lancs |
| *Remarks:* P'84? | | | | | | |
| 4233 | 1956 | TSO | York | 93 | 30172 | Torbay |
| *Remarks:* P'87 | | | | | | |
| 4236 | 1956 | TSO | York | 93 | 30172 | Llangollen |
| *Remarks:* P'86 | | | | | | |

| Numbers | Year | Type | Built | Diag | Lot | Location |
|---|---|---|---|---|---|---|
| 4243 | 1956 | TSO | York | 93 | 30172 | Llangollen |

*Remarks:* P'89 ex W Highland set

| 4249 | 1956 | TSO | York | 93 | 30172 | Brechin |

*Remarks:* P'83

| 4252 | 1956 | TSO | York | 93 | 30172 | N Yorks Moors |

*Remarks:* P'82

| 4255 L&HR 50 | 1956 | TSO | York | 93 | 30172 | Lakeside |

*Remarks:* P'83

4256 – see 4654

| 4260 | 1956 | TSO | B R C W | 93 | 30207 | W Somerset |

*Remarks:* P'83

| 4275 | 1956 | TSO | B R C W | 93 | 30207 | Woolacombe Stn |

*Remarks:* P'73 on Dart Valley; body sold in '84 to Watermouth Castle Estates & grounded at site of Woolacombe Station, near Ilfracombe in '85

| 4280 KWVR 13 | 1956 | TSO | B R C W | 93 | 30207 | - |

*Remarks:* P pre'74, on Worth Valley till sold to SRPS in ' ?, broken up for spares at Falkirk in '84.

| 4286 NRM 75 | 1956 | TSO | B R C W | 93 | 30207 | * NRM |

*Remarks:* P'74

| 4288 | 1956 | TSO | B R C W | 93 | 30207 | Woolacombe Stn |

*Remarks:* P'73 on Dart Valley; body grounded '85.

| 4289 | 1956 | TSO | B R C W | 93 | 30207 | Woolacombe Stn |

*Remarks:* P'73 on Dart Valley; body grounded '85.

| 4290 | 1956 | TSO | B R C W | 93 | 30207 | N Yorks Moors |

*Remarks:* P'81

| 4300 | 1956 | TSO | B R C W | 93 | 30207 | Dean Forest |

*Remarks:* P'87

(4305 – for Severn Valley but damaged en route & rejected)

| 4306 | 1956 | TSO | B R C W | 93 | 30207 | Worth Valley |

*Remarks:* P'88

| Numbers | Year | Type | Built | Diag | Lot | Location |
|---------|------|------|-------|------|-----|----------|
| 4316 | 1956 | TSO | B R C W | 93 | 30207 | Dean Forest |

Remarks: P'87

| 4317 99602 plated | 1956 | TSO | B R C W | 93 | 30207 | Woolacombe Stn |

Remarks: P'73 on Dart Valley; body grounded '85.

| 4325 | 1956 | TSO | B R C W | 93 | 30207 | Huddersfield Stn |

Remarks: P'84, grounded as children's play area

| 4328 | 1956 | TSO | B R C W | 93 | 30207 | Seaburn |

Remarks: P'81, at Steamtown till sold '?; part of 'Puffing Billy's' restaurant at Ocean Park (nr Sunderland)

| 4331 | 1956 | TSO | B R C W | 93 | 30207 | Buxton |

Remarks: P'88 as static restaurant 'The Palatine'

| 4332 | 1956 | TSO | B R C W | 93 | 30207 | Barwick in Elmet |

Remarks: P'84? as part of restaurant nr Leeds

| 4345 | 1956 | TSO | B R C W | 93 | 30207 | Severn Valley |

Remarks: P'88 ex GW150 set

| 4346 | 1956 | TSO | B R C W | 93 | 30207 | W Somerset |

Remarks: P'76. W'85, became Mess Coach at Minehead & provided parts for restoration of 3058 (qv)

| 4349 | 1956 | TSO | B R C W | 93 | 30207 | Swanage |

Remarks: P'81 by LMSSPG

| 4350 | 1956 | TSO | B R C W | 93 | 30207 | E Lancs |

Remarks: P pre'74

| 4354 | 1956 | TSO | B R C W | 93 | 30207 | Mid-Hants |

Remarks: P'88

| 4355 DB977412 | 1956 1986 | TSO | B R C W | 93 | 30207 | N Norfolk |

Remarks: Used for SAS training at Moreton-on-Lugg. P'88 by Avon Valley member & moved to Long Marston '90; due to go to N Norfolk '91 for 5-year loan

| 4362 | 1955 | SO | Eastleigh | 94 | 30067 | Great Central |

Remarks: P'87

| 4366 | 1955 | SO | Eastleigh | 94 | 30121 | Midland |

Remarks: P'91

| Numbers | Year | Type | Built | Diag | Lot | Location |
|---------|------|------|-------|------|-----|----------|
| 4371 | 1955 | SO | Eastleigh | 94 | 30121 | E Lancs |
| Remarks: P'88? | | | | | | |
| 4372 | 1955 | SO | Eastleigh | 94 | 30121 | Matlock |
| Remarks: P'89 | | | | | | |
| 4392 DB977632 | 1957 | TSO | Swindon | 93 | 30219 | N Staffs ? |
| Remarks: P'90 (may be incorrect) | | | | | | |
| 4399 | 1957 | TSO | Swindon | 93 | 30219 | Severn Valley |
| Remarks: P'83 | | | | | | |
| 4406 | 1957 | TSO | Swindon | 93 | 30219 | Embsay |
| Remarks: P'89 ex GW150 set | | | | | | |
| 4410 L&HR 51 | 1957 | TSO | Swindon | 93 | 30219 | Lakeside |
| Remarks: P'82 | | | | | | |
| 4416 | 1956 | TSO | B R C W | 93 | 30226 | Swanage |
| Remarks: P'86 | | | | | | |
| 4419 | 1956 | TSO | B R C W | 93 | 30226 | W Somerset |
| Remarks: P'91 | | | | | | |
| 4422 | 1956 | TSO | B R C W | 93 | 30226 | Bo'ness |
| Remarks: Leased by SRPS '87, at Falkirk till P'88 | | | | | | |
| 4423 | 1956 | TSO | B R C W | 93 | 30226 | Mid-Hants |
| Remarks: P'82 | | | | | | |
| 4424 | 1956 | TSO | B R C W | 93 | 30226 | Corton |
| Remarks: P'83, grounded at Pleasurewood Hills Pk | | | | | | |
| 4425 | 1956 | TSO | B R C W | 93 | 30226 | N Yorks Moors |
| Remarks: Leased by SRPS '87, at Falkirk then Perth. Ran hot Dec'88, lay OOU at Rugby & P'89 | | | | | | |
| 4427 | 1956 | TSO | B R C W | 93 | 30226 | W Linten, Peebles |
| Remarks: P'85 at 'Leadburn Inn' | | | | | | |
| 4440 DB977175 | 1957 1984 | TSO | B R C W | 93 | 30226 | Gloucs-Warks |
| Remarks: P'90 by A S Lear | | | | | | |

| Numbers | Year | Type | Built | Diag | Lot | Location |
|---------|------|------|-------|------|-----|----------|
| 4449<br>DB977413 | 1957<br>1986 | TSO | B R C W | 93 | 30226 | W Somerset |

Remarks: P'88 after used for SAS training at MOD Moreton-on-Lugg

| | | | | | | |
|---------|------|------|-------|------|-----|----------|
| 4455 | 1957 | TSO | B R C W | 93 | 30226 | N Yorks Moors |

Remarks: P'83

| | | | | | | |
|---------|------|------|-------|------|-----|----------|
| 4460<br>YDR 1 | 1957 | TSO | B R C W | 93 | 30226 | Embsay |

Remarks: P'83

| | | | | | | |
|---------|------|------|-------|------|-----|----------|
| 4466<br>99816 plated | 1957 | TSO | B R C W | 93 | 30226 | Bo'ness |

Remarks: P'86 by SRPS, at Falkirk till '88, Perth till '91

| | | | | | | |
|---------|------|------|-------|------|-----|----------|
| 4467<br>KWVR 34 | 1957 | TSO | B R C W | 93 | 30226 | Worth Valley |

Remarks: P'84?

| | | | | | | |
|---------|------|------|-------|------|-----|----------|
| 4472 | 1957 | TSO | B R C W | 93 | 30226 | Dean Forest |

Remarks: P'87

| | | | | | | |
|---------|------|------|-------|------|-----|----------|
| 4474 | 1957 | SO | B R C W | 94 | 30227 | Haverhill |

Remarks: P'88? by 'Trains of Thought'

| | | | | | | |
|---------|------|------|-------|------|-----|----------|
| 4476 | 1957 | SO | B R C W | 94 | 30227 | Matlock |

Remarks: P'89

| | | | | | | |
|---------|------|------|-------|------|-----|----------|
| 4477 | 1957 | SO | B R C W | 94 | 30227 | Strathspey |

Remarks: P'86

| | | | | | | |
|---------|------|------|-------|------|-----|----------|
| 4480 | 1957 | SO | B R C W | 94 | 30227 | Midland |

Remarks: P'89

| | | | | | | |
|---------|------|------|-------|------|-----|----------|
| 4481<br>NYMR 14 | 1957 | SO | B R C W | 94 | 30227 | N Yorks Moors |

Remarks: P'73, to Pickering for use in the static catering complex in '83

| | | | | | | |
|---------|------|------|-------|------|-----|----------|
| 4484 | 1957 | SO | B R C W | 94 | 30227 | Llangollen |

Remarks: P'90

| | | | | | | |
|---------|------|------|-------|------|-----|----------|
| 4489 | 1956 | TSO | York | 93 | 30243 | Mid-Hants |

Remarks: P'82, craned off rails '84 as Museum coach

| | | | | | | |
|---------|------|------|-------|------|-----|----------|
| 4493 | 1956 | TSO | York | 93 | 30243 | W Somerset |

Remarks: P'75, W'85 to be Mess coach at Williton

| Numbers | Year | Type | Built | Diag | Lot | Location |
|---------|------|------|-------|------|-----|----------|
| 4494 | 1956 | TSO | York | 93 | 30243 | Loch Awe ? |

*Remarks:* P'89? by Dalriada Stm Packet Co

| Numbers | Year | Type | Built | Diag | Lot | Location |
|---------|------|------|-------|------|-----|----------|
| 4495 | 1956 | TSO | York | 93 | 30243 | Brechin |

*Remarks:* Sold to Fulmar Services, Invergordon '83. P'85

| Numbers | Year | Type | Built | Diag | Lot | Location |
|---------|------|------|-------|------|-----|----------|
| 4496 | 1956 | TSO | York | 93 | 30243 | S Devon |

*Remarks:* P'73 by David & Charles, at Newton Abbot till presented to S Devon Rly by Readers Digest & moved to Buckfastleigh 4/91

| Numbers | Year | Type | Built | Diag | Lot | Location |
|---------|------|------|-------|------|-----|----------|
| 4503 | 1956 | TSO | York | 93 | 30243 | Llangollen |

*Remarks:* P'85

| Numbers | Year | Type | Built | Diag | Lot | Location |
|---------|------|------|-------|------|-----|----------|
| 4507<br>99609 plated | 1956 | TSO | York | 93 | 30243 | Torbay |

*Remarks:* P'73

| Numbers | Year | Type | Built | Diag | Lot | Location |
|---------|------|------|-------|------|-----|----------|
| 4508 | 1956 | TSO | York | 93 | 30243 | Steamtown ? |

*Remarks:* Reported P'88 at Tyseley, then P'90 here

| Numbers | Year | Type | Built | Diag | Lot | Location |
|---------|------|------|-------|------|-----|----------|
| 4509 | 1956 | TSO | York | 93 | 30243 | Severn Valley |

*Remarks:* P'82

| Numbers | Year | Type | Built | Diag | Lot | Location |
|---------|------|------|-------|------|-----|----------|
| 4512 | 1956 | TSO | York | 93 | 30243 | Colne Valley |

*Remarks:* P'87, end of static Restaurant set

| Numbers | Year | Type | Built | Diag | Lot | Location |
|---------|------|------|-------|------|-----|----------|
| 4521 | 1956 | TSO | York | 93 | 30243 | N Norfolk |
| 4529<br>99817 plated | 1956 | TSO | York | 93 | 30243 | Bo'ness |

*Remarks:* P'86 by SRPS, at Falkirk till '88 then at Perth till '90

| Numbers | Year | Type | Built | Diag | Lot | Location |
|---------|------|------|-------|------|-----|----------|
| 4534 | 1956<br>1988 | TSO<br>RMB | York<br>Midland | 93 | 30243 | Midland |

*Remarks:* P'86

| Numbers | Year | Type | Built | Diag | Lot | Location |
|---------|------|------|-------|------|-----|----------|
| 4537 | 1956 | TSO | York | 93 | 30243 | Midland |

*Remarks:* P'86

| Numbers | Year | Type | Built | Diag | Lot | Location |
|---------|------|------|-------|------|-----|----------|
| 4545 | 1956 | TSO | York | 93 | 30243 | Severn Valley |

*Remarks:* P'83

| Numbers | Year | Type | Built | Diag | Lot | Location |
|---------|------|------|-------|------|-----|----------|
| 4549 | 1956 | TSO | York | 93 | 30243 | Mid-Hants |

*Remarks:* P'76

| Numbers | Year | Type | Built | Diag | Lot | Location |
|---|---|---|---|---|---|---|
| 4550 | 1956 | TSO | York | 93 | 30243 | Severn Valley |

Remarks: P'82

| 4555 | 1956 | TSO | York | 93 | 30243 | - |
| KWVR 31 | | | | | | |

Remarks: P'76 on Worth Valley; broken up '83.

| 4562 | 1956 | TSO | York | 93 | 30243 | E Somerset |

Remarks: P'83

| 4575 | 1956 | TSO | York | 93 | 30243 | Embsay |

Remarks: P'89

| 4584 | 1956 | TSO | York | 93 | 30243 | Severn Valley |

Remarks: P'84

| 4588 | 1956 | TSO | York | 93 | 30243 | Worth Valley |
| KWVR 25 | 1977 | Bar | K&WVR | | | |
| 'Jubilee Bar | | | | | | |

Remarks: P'76, converted to a Bar Car, painted in Pullman livery, then named in honour of the Queen's Silver Jubilee

| 4593 | 1956 | TSO | York | 93 | 30243 | Severn Valley |

Remarks: P'88 ex GW150 set

| 4597 | 1956 | TSO | York | 93 | 30243 | N Yorks Moors |
| NYMR 13 | | | | | | |
| | 1989 | RMB | NYMR | | | |

Remarks: P'73, but OOU by '85 & part cannibalised. Converted at Goathland to RMB over period 1986-9

| 4599 | 1956 | TSO | York | 93 | 30243 | W Somerset |

Remarks: P'83

| 4600 | 1956 | TSO | York | 93 | 30243 | Mid-Hants |

Remarks: P'76

| 4602 | 1956 | TSO | York | 93 | 30243 | W Somerset |

Remarks: P'75. W'85, put on isolated track behind platform at Bishops Lydeard as station shop.

| 4606 | 1956 | TSO | York | 93 | 30243 | Bosham |

Remarks: P'82 at Mid-Hants, sold '84 to 'Cedar Tree' Inn & named 'Moonlight Express'

| 4610 | 1956 | TSO | York | 93 | 30243 | Great Central |

Remarks: P'89 ex W Highland set

| Numbers | Year | Type | Built | Diag | Lot | Location |
|---------|------|------|-------|------|-----|----------|
| 4614 | 1957 | TSO | York | 93 | 30243 | Dean Forest |
| Remarks: P'87 | | | | | | |
| 4615 | 1957 | TSO | York | 93 | 30243 | Nene Valley |
| Remarks: P'83 | | | | | | |
| 4623 | 1957 | TSO | York | 93 | 30243 | Matlock |
| Remarks: P'89 by Peak Rail | | | | | | |
| 4627 | 1957 | TSO | York | 93 | 30243 | Nene Valley |
| Remarks: P'83 | | | | | | |
| 4628 | 1957 | TSO | York | 93 | 30243 | Colne Valley |
| Remarks: P'82?, now static Restaurant Car | | | | | | |
| 4630 | 1957 | TSO | York | 93 | 30243 | Great Central |
| Remarks: P'83 | | | | | | |
| 4634 | 1957 | TSO | York | 93 | 30243 | Bo'ness |
| Remarks: P'90 by SRPS | | | | | | |
| 4635 | 1957 | TSO | York | 93 | 30243 | Nene Valley |
| Remarks: P'83, body grounded as office at Wansford. | | | | | | |
| 4640 KESR 85 | 1957 | TSO | York | 93 | 30375 | K&ESR |
| Remarks: P'86 | | | | | | |
| 4641 | 1957 | TSO | York | 93 | 30375 | E Somerset |
| Remarks: P'86 | | | | | | |
| 4642 'Nina' ? | 1957 1991 | TSO RSO | York | 93 | 30375 | Torbay |
| Remarks: P'87, converted for 'Devonian Pullman' set | | | | | | |
| 4643 | 1957 | TSO | York | 93 | 30375 | Llangollen |
| Remarks: P'89 ex W Highland set | | | | | | |
| 4647 | 1957 | TSO | York | 93 | 30375 | E Lancs |
| Remarks: P'82 | | | | | | |
| 4651 | 1957 | TSO | York | 93 | 30375 | N Norfolk |
| Remarks: P'82? | | | | | | |

| Numbers | Year | Type | Built | Diag | Lot | Location |
|---------|------|------|-------|------|-----|----------|
| 4654<br>4256<br>99606 plated | 1957<br>1973? | TSO | York | 93 | 30375 | Blaenavon |

Remarks: P'72, on Dart Valley till '85

| | | | | | | |
|---------|------|------|-------|------|-----|----------|
| 4656 | 1957 | TSO | York | 93 | 30375 | Mid-Hants |

Remarks: P'82

| | | | | | | |
|---------|------|------|-------|------|-----|----------|
| 4660 | 1957 | TSO | York | 93 | 30375 | W Somerset |

Remarks: P'83

| | | | | | | |
|---------|------|------|-------|------|-----|----------|
| 4662 | 1957 | TSO | York | 93 | 30375 | Great Central |

Remarks: P'83

| | | | | | | |
|---------|------|------|-------|------|-----|----------|
| 4663<br>'Natalie' | 1957<br>1985 | TSO | York | 93 | 30375 | N of York |

Remarks: Purchased by Bert Gemmell to form part of 'The Sidings' Hotel at Shipton-by-Beningborough. Body was grounded 17/3/85 as half of the Restaurant section.

| | | | | | | |
|---------|------|------|-------|------|-----|----------|
| 4665 | 1957 | TSO | York | 93 | 30375 | Torbay |

Remarks: P'87

| | | | | | | |
|---------|------|------|-------|------|-----|----------|
| 4666 | 1957 | TSO | York | 93 | 30375 | Embsay |

Remarks: P'89

| | | | | | | |
|---------|------|------|-------|------|-----|----------|
| 4667 | 1957 | TSO | York | 93 | 30375 | Nene Valley |

Remarks: P'83

| | | | | | | |
|---------|------|------|-------|------|-----|----------|
| 4668<br>'Natalie' | 1957<br>1989 | TSO | York | 93 | 30375 | Isfield |

Remarks: P'84

| | | | | | | |
|---------|------|------|-------|------|-----|----------|
| 4672 | 1957 | TSO | York | 93 | 30375 | Colwyn Bay |

Remarks: P'? as 'Platform 3' restaurant

| | | | | | | |
|---------|------|------|-------|------|-----|----------|
| 4676 | 1957 | TSO | York | 93 | 30375 | Brechin |

Remarks: Sold to Fulmar Services, Invergordon '83. P'85

| | | | | | | |
|---------|------|------|-------|------|-----|----------|
| 4677 | 1957 | TSO | York | 93 | 30375 | Blaenavon |

Remarks: P'83

| | | | | | | |
|---------|------|------|-------|------|-----|----------|
| 4686 | 1957 | TSO | York | 93 | 30375 | Nene Valley |

Remarks: P'83

| | | | | | | |
|---------|------|------|-------|------|-----|----------|
| 4690 | 1957 | TSO | York | 93 | 30375 | Severn Valley |

Remarks: P'82

| Numbers | Year | Type | Built | Diag | Lot | Location |
|---------|------|------|-------|------|-----|----------|
| 4702 | 1957 | TSO | York | 93 | 30375 | Llangollen |
| Remarks: P'86 | | | | | | |
| 4704 | 1957 | TSO | York | 93 | 30375 | - |
| Remarks: P'86 by SRPS at Falkirk; cut up in '87 | | | | | | |
| 4712 | 1957 | TSO | York | 93 | 30375 | Mid-Hants |
| Remarks: P'82 | | | | | | |
| 4728 | 1964 | TSO | Derby | 91 | 30739 | N Yorks Moors |
| Remarks: XP64 stock. P'81 by Diesel Traction Grp | | | | | | |
| 4729 | 1964 | TSO | Derby | 91 | 30739 | Dean Forest |
| Remarks: XP64 stock. P'81 | | | | | | |
| 4751 | 1957 | TSO | York | 93 | 30375 | South Shields |
| Remarks: P'85, part of 'Marsden Rattler' restaurant | | | | | | |
| 4755 | 1957 | TSO | York | 93 | 30375 | ? |
| Remarks: P'87 at Steamtown; not found '90 | | | | | | |
| 4756 | 1957 | TSO | York | 93 | 30375 | Torbay |
| Remarks: P'87 | | | | | | |
| 4758 | 1957 | TSO | York | 93 | 30375 | Great Central |
| Remarks: P'88 & at Steamtown till '90 | | | | | | |
| 4760 L&HR 52 | 1957 | TSO | York | 93 | 30375 | Lakeside |
| Remarks: P'83 | | | | | | |
| 4762 | 1957 | TSO | York | 93 | 30375 | E Lancs |
| Remarks: P'85? | | | | | | |
| 4763 | 1957 | TSO | York | 93 | 30375 | Torbay |
| Remarks: P'87 | | | | | | |
| 4764 | 1957 | TSO | York | 93 | 30375 | Blunsdon |
| Remarks: P'84 | | | | | | |
| 4766 | 1957 | TSO | York | 93 | 30375 | Blunsdon |
| Remarks: P'84 | | | | | | |
| 4767 | 1957 | TSO | York | 93 | 30375 | E Lancs |
| Remarks: P'86 | | | | | | |

| Numbers | Year | Type | Built | Diag | Lot | Location |
|---------|------|------|-------|------|-----|----------|
| 4772 | 1957 | TSO | York | 93 | 30375 | Torbay |
| Remarks: P'87 | | | | | | |
| 4774 | 1957 | TSO | York | 93 | 30375 | Worth Valley |
| Remarks: P'89 | | | | | | |
| 4779 | 1957 | SO | York | 94 | 30376 | Llangollen |
| Remarks: P'91 | | | | | | |
| 4784 | 1957 | SO | York | 94 | 30376 | E Lancs |
| Remarks: P'86 | | | | | | |
| 4785 | 1957 | SO | York | 94 | 30376 | Llangollen |
| Remarks: P'91 | | | | | | |
| 4786 99426 plated | 1957 | SO | York | 94 | 30376 | Dairycoates |
| Remarks: To be P'89 by Ridings Railtours, but after being vandalised was P'90 by HLPG | | | | | | |
| 4787 | 1957 | SO | York | 94 | 30376 | Gloucs-Warks |
| Remarks: P'90 | | | | | | |
| 4788 | 1957 | SO | York | 94 | 30376 | Great Central |
| Remarks: P'87 | | | | | | |
| 4789 | 1957 | SO | York | 94 | 30376 | Llangollen |
| Remarks: P'91 | | | | | | |
| 4790 | 1957 | SO | York | 94 | 30376 | Gloucs-Warks |
| Remarks: P'91 | | | | | | |
| 4794 | 1957 | SO | York | 94 | 30376 | Whittlesea |
| Remarks: P'87 as 'Railway Inn' restaurant | | | | | | |
| 4795 | 1957 | SO | York | 94 | 30376 | N Staffs |
| Remarks: P'91 | | | | | | |
| 4796 | 1957 | SO | York | 94 | 30376 | Llangollen |
| Remarks: To be P'89 by Ridings Railtours, but after being vandalised was P'90 | | | | | | |
| 4798 | 1957 | SO | York | 94 | 30376 | Gloucs-Warks |
| Remarks: P'91 for Llangollen, but promptly resold | | | | | | |
| 4799 | 1957 | SO | York | 94 | 30376 | Embsay |
| Remarks: P'89 | | | | | | |

| Numbers | Year | Type | Built | Diag | Lot | Location |
|---------|------|------|-------|------|-----|----------|
| 4802 | 1957 | SO | York | 94 | 30376 | S Devon |
| Remarks: P'91 | | | | | | |
| 4803 | 1957 | SO | York | 94 | 30376 | Swanage |
| Remarks: P'89 | | | | | | |
| 4804 | 1957 | SO | York | 94 | 30376 | Midland |
| Remarks: P'90 | | | | | | |
| 4805 | 1957 | SO | York | 94 | 30376 | Dairycoates |
| Remarks: P'90 by HLPG | | | | | | |
| 4806 | 1957 | SO | York | 94 | 30376 | Gloucs-Warks |
| Remarks: P'90 | | | | | | |
| 4808 | 1957 1991 | SO RFO | York | 94 | 30376 | Llangollen |
| Remarks: P'89 | | | | | | |
| 4810 | 1959 | SO | B R C W | 94 | 30473 | Colne Valley |
| Remarks: P'80 | | | | | | |
| 4814 | 1959 1981 1985 | SO RFB RMB | B R C W W Somerset | 94 | 30473 | W Somerset |
| Remarks: P'76, converted to First in winter '80/1 using seats removed from PSP's & reconverted to 'Whitbread Bar' with Buffet section in '85 | | | | | | |
| 4816 | 1959 | SO | B R C W | 94 | 30473 | Midland |
| Remarks: P'90 | | | | | | |
| 4817 | 1959 | SO | B R C W | 94 | 30473 | N Yorks Moors |
| Remarks: P'89 | | | | | | |
| 4822 99425 plated | 1959 | SO | B R C W | 94 | 30473 | Dairycoates |
| Remarks: P'90 by HLPG | | | | | | |
| 4823 99424 plated | 1959 | SO | B R C W | 94 | 30473 | Dairycoates |
| Remarks: P'90 by HLPG | | | | | | |
| 4824 | 1959 | SO | B R C W | 94 | 30473 | Market Bosworth |
| Remarks: P'91 | | | | | | |

| Numbers | Year | Type | Built | Diag | Lot | Location |
|---------|------|------|-------|------|-----|----------|
| 4828<br>99423 plated | 1959 | SO | B R C W | 94 | 30473 | Dairycoates |
| *Remarks:* P'90 by HLPG | | | | | | |
| 4831<br>99824 plated | 1959 | TSO | Wolverton | 89 | 30506 | Bo'ness |
| *Remarks:* P'91 by SRPS | | | | | | |
| 4832 | 1959 | TSO | Wolverton | 89 | 30506 | Bo'ness |
| *Remarks:* Leased by SRPS, P'89 & at Perth till '90 | | | | | | |
| 4836 | 1959 | TSO | Wolverton | 89 | 30506 | Bo'ness |
| *Remarks:* P'91 by SRPS | | | | | | |
| 4839 | 1959 | TSO | Wolverton | 89 | 30506 | N Yorks Moors |
| *Remarks:* P'87, stored till '89 | | | | | | |
| 4840 | 1959 | TSO | Wolverton | 89 | 30525 | Worth Valley |
| *Remarks:* P'82 | | | | | | |
| 4843 | 1959 | TSO | Wolverton | 89 | 30525 | Llangollen |
| *Remarks:* P'91 | | | | | | |
| 4844 | 1959 | TSO | Wolverton | 89 | 30525 | Bo'ness |
| *Remarks:* Leased by SRPS '87 at Falkirk. P'88, at Perth till '91 | | | | | | |
| 4857 | 1960 | TSO | Wolverton | 89 | 30525 | Great Central |
| *Remarks:* P'91 | | | | | | |
| 4871 | 1960 | TSO | Wolverton | 89 | 30525 | Bo'ness |
| *Remarks:* Leased by SRPS '87 at Falkirk. P'88, at Perth till '91 | | | | | | |
| 4885 | 1960 | TSO | Wolverton | 89 | 30525 | E Lancs |
| *Remarks:* P'91 | | | | | | |
| 4886 | 1960 | TSO | Wolverton | 89 | 30525 | Steamport |
| *Remarks:* P'91 | | | | | | |
| 4900 | 1961 | TSO | Wolverton | 89 | 30646 | Worth Valley |
| *Remarks:* P'91 | | | | | | |
| 4907 | 1961 | TSO | Wolverton | 89 | 30646 | E Somerset |
| *Remarks:* P'91 | | | | | | |

| Numbers | Year | Type | Built | Diag | Lot | Location |
|---------|------|------|-------|------|-----|----------|
| 4911 | 1961 | TSO | Wolverton | 89 | 30646 | W Somerset |
| *Remarks:* P'91 | | | | | | |
| 4912 | 1961 | TSO | Wolverton | 89 | 30646 | Steamtown |
| *Remarks:* P'91 | | | | | | |
| 4914 | 1961 | TSO | Wolverton | 89 | 30646 | Great Central |
| *Remarks:* P'77, on Nene Valley till '? | | | | | | |
| 4918 | 1962 | TSO | Wolverton | 89 | 30690 | Market Bosworth |
| *Remarks:* P'91 | | | | | | |
| 4921 99171 plated | 1962 1989 | TSO Spec | Wolverton | 89 | 30690 | (Cathays) |
| *Remarks:* P'89 by Travelling College (conv to classroom) | | | | | | |
| 4922 | 1962 | TSO | Wolverton | 89 | 30690 | Gloucs-Warks |
| *Remarks:* P'91 | | | | | | |
| 4937 | 1962 | TSO | Wolverton | 89 | 30690 | E Lancs |
| *Remarks:* P'91 | | | | | | |
| 4941 99169 plated | 1962 1989 | TSO Spec | Wolverton | 89 | 30690 | (Cathays) |
| *Remarks:* P'89 by Travelling College (conv to classroom) | | | | | | |
| 4947 | 1962 | TSO | Wolverton | 89 | 30690 | Dairycoates |
| *Remarks:* P'91 by HLPG | | | | | | |
| 4948 | 1962 | TSO | Wolverton | 89 | 30690 | Great Central |
| *Remarks:* P'91 | | | | | | |
| 4957 99170 plated | 1962 1989 | TSO Spec | Wolverton | 89 | 30690 | (Cathays) |
| *Remarks:* P'89 by Travelling College (conv to classroom) | | | | | | |
| 4965 | 1962 | TSO | Wolverton | 89 | 30690 | Great Central |
| *Remarks:* P'91 | | | | | | |
| 4981 | 1962 | TSO | Wolverton | 89 | 30690 | Dairycoates |
| *Remarks:* P'91 by HLPG | | | | | | |
| 4982 | 1962 | TSO | Wolverton | 89 | 30690 | Gloucs-Warks |
| *Remarks:* P'91 | | | | | | |

| Numbers | Year | Type | Built | Diag | Lot | Location |
|---------|------|------|-------|------|-----|----------|
| 4983 | 1962 | TSO | Wolverton | 89 | 30690 | Dairycoates |
| Remarks: P'91 by HLPG | | | | | | |
| 5034 | 1962 | TSO | Wolverton | 89 | 30690 | (Cathays) |
| 99165 plated | 1989 | Spec | | | | |
| Remarks: P'89 by Travelling College (conv to dormitory) | | | | | | |
| 5036 | 1962 | TSO | Wolverton | 89 | 30690 | Dairycoates |
| Remarks: P'91 by HLPG | | | | | | |
| 5045 | 1963 | TSO | York | 89 | 30724 | Midland |
| Remarks: P'83 by TFP, sold to MRT in '86 | | | | | | |
| 5049 | 1963 | TSO | York | 89 | 30724 | Dalmellington |
| Remarks: P'91 by Ayrshire RPS | | | | | | |
| 5053 | 1963 | TSO | York | 89 | 30724 | Strathspey |
| Remarks: P'91 | | | | | | |
| 5054 | 1963 | TSO | York | 89 | 30724 | Buxton |
| Remarks: P'82 by Peak Rail | | | | | | |
| 5055 | 1963 | TSO | York | 89 | 30724 | Strathspey |
| Remarks: P'91 | | | | | | |
| 5057 | 1963 | TSO | York | 89 | 30724 | Strathspey |
| Remarks: P'91 | | | | | | |
| 5060 | 1963 | TSO | York | 89 | 30724 | Strathspey |
| Remarks: P'91 | | | | | | |
| 5067 | 1963 | TSO | York | 89 | 30724 | Steamtown |
| Remarks: P'91 by W Smith | | | | | | |
| 5125 | 1967 | TSO | Derby | 88 | 30751 | Mid-Hants |
| Remarks: Mk.2. P'90 ex Mayer Newman | | | | | | |
| 5229 | 1966 | SO | Derby | 87 | 30752 | Pitsford |
| Remarks: Mk.2. P'89 | | | | | | |
| 5233 – only leased from BR | | | | | | |
| 5235 | 1966 | SO | Derby | 87 | 30752 | Peak Rail |
| Remarks: Mk.2. P'91 | | | | | | |

| Numbers | Year | Type | Built | Diag | Lot | Location |
|---------|------|------|-------|------|-----|----------|
| 5236 | 1966 | SO | Derby | 87 | 30752 | Mid-Hants |
| Remarks: Mk.2. P'91 | | | | | | |
| 5237 | 1966 | SO | Derby | 87 | 30752 | Mid-Hants |
| Remarks: Mk.2. P'91 | | | | | | |
| 5238 | 1966 | SO | Derby | 87 | 30752 | E Lancs |
| Remarks: Mk.2. P'89 | | | | | | |
| 5239 | 1966 | SO | Derby | 87 | 30752 | Mid-Hants |
| Remarks: Mk.2. P'91 | | | | | | |
| 5241 | 1966 | SO | Derby | 87 | 30752 | Manchester L Rd |
| Remarks: Mk.2. P'91 by Mus of S&I | | | | | | |
| 5242 | 1966 | SO | Derby | 87 | 30752 | Tyseley |
| Remarks: Mk.2. P'88, first intact Mk.2 pres'd | | | | | | |
| 5243 | 1966 | SO | Derby | 87 | 30752 | Mid-Hants |
| Remarks: Mk.2. P'91 | | | | | | |
| 5249 | 1966 | SO | Derby | 87 | 30752 | Mid-Hants |
| Remarks: Mk.2. P'91 | | | | | | |
| 5299 | 1968 | TSO | Derby | 86 | 30776 | Steamtown |
| Remarks: Mk.2a. P'91 | | | | | | |
| 5324 | 1968 | TSO | Derby | 86 | 30776 | Quainton |
| Remarks: Mk.2a. P'88, grounded as office | | | | | | |
| 5344 | 1968 | TSO | Derby | 86 | 30776 | W Somerset |
| Remarks: Mk.2a. P'89 | | | | | | |
| 5361 | 1968 | TSO | Derby | 86 | 30787 | Bodmin |
| Remarks: Mk.2a. P'90 | | | | | | |
| 5438 | 1969 | TSO | Derby | 105 | 30791 | Stewarts Lane |
| Remarks: Mk.2b. P'91 by VSOE | | | | | | |
| 5476 | 1969 | TSO | Derby | 105 | 30791 | Crewe? |
| Remarks: Mk.2b. P'91 by Ridings Railtours | | | | | | |
| 5517 | 1969 | TSO | Derby | 106 | 30795 | Stewarts Lane |
| Remarks: Mk.2c. P'91 by VSOE | | | | | | |

| Numbers | Year | Type | Built | Diag | Lot | Location |
|---------|------|------|-------|------|-----|----------|
| 5533 | 1970 | TSO | Derby | 106 | 30795 | Crewe? |

*Remarks:* Mk.2c. P'91 by Ridings Railtours

| | | | | | | |
|---------|------|------|-------|------|-----|----------|
| 5536 | 1970 | TSO | Derby | 106 | 30795 | Mid-Norfolk |

*Remarks:* Mk.2c. P'91 by F&DRS

| | | | | | | |
|---------|------|------|-------|------|-----|----------|
| 5541 | 1970 | TSO | Derby | 106 | 30795 | Stewarts Lane |

*Remarks:* Mk.2c. P'91 by VSOE

| | | | | | | |
|---------|------|------|-------|------|-----|----------|
| 5574 | 1970 | TSO | Derby | 106 | 30795 | Crewe? |

*Remarks:* Mk.2c. P'91 by Ridings Railtours

| | | | | | | |
|---------|------|------|-------|------|-----|----------|
| 5585 | 1970 | TSO | Derby | 106 | 30795 | Crewe? |

*Remarks:* Mk.2c. P'91 by Ridings Railtours

| | | | | | | |
|---------|------|------|-------|------|-----|----------|
| 5595 | 1970 | TSO | Derby | 106 | 30795 | Crewe? |

*Remarks:* Mk.2c. P'91 by Ridings Railtours

| | | | | | | |
|---------|------|------|-------|------|-----|----------|
| 9208<br>DB977134 | 1955 | BSO | Doncaster | 183 | 30170 | Long Marston |

*Remarks:* P'89 by Chichester & Midhurst RPS, resold to Avon Valley member '91

| | | | | | | |
|---------|------|------|-------|------|-----|----------|
| 9218<br>L&HR 73 | 1955 | BSO | Doncaster | 183 | 30170 | Lakeside |

*Remarks:* P'71

| | | | | | | |
|---------|------|------|-------|------|-----|----------|
| 9220 | 1955 | BSO | Doncaster | 183 | 30170 | Severn Valley |

*Remarks:* P'73

| | | | | | | |
|---------|------|------|-------|------|-----|----------|
| 9225<br>DB977135 | 1956<br>1983 | BSO | Doncaster | 183 | 30170 | Pitsford |

*Remarks:* P'91

| | | | | | | |
|---------|------|------|-------|------|-----|----------|
| 9227 | 1956 | BSO | Doncaster | 183 | 30170 | Bo'ness |

*Remarks:* P'88 by SRPS, at Perth till '90

| | | | | | | |
|---------|------|------|-------|------|-----|----------|
| 9229<br>9015 | 1956<br>1980 | BSO<br>BSOT | Doncaster | 183 | 30170 | Swanage |

*Remarks:* P'89

| | | | | | | |
|---------|------|------|-------|------|-----|----------|
| 9235<br>NYMR 7 | 1956 | BSO | Doncaster | 183 | 30170 | N Yorks Moors |

*Remarks:* P'70

| Numbers | Year | Type | Built | Diag | Lot | Location |
|---------|------|------|-------|------|-----|----------|
| 9241 99450 plated | 1956 | BSO | Doncaster | 183 | 30170 | E Somerset |

Remarks: P pre'77. Converted to static Mess coach in '80 & sited on siding near shed

| Numbers | Year | Type | Built | Diag | Lot | Location |
|---------|------|------|-------|------|-----|----------|
| 9254 KESR 75 'Petros' | 1956 1982 | BSO BTOD | Doncaster Stewarts Lane | 183 | 30170 | K&ESR |

Remarks: P'81, converted by BR Apprentices for use by disabled passengers & commissioned by the Queen Mother in 1982

| Numbers | Year | Type | Built | Diag | Lot | Location |
|---------|------|------|-------|------|-----|----------|
| 9256 | 1956 | BSO | Doncaster | 183 | 30170 | - |

Remarks: P' ? on Dart Valley, but badly vandalised in '74 & only underframe now remains.

| Numbers | Year | Type | Built | Diag | Lot | Location |
|---------|------|------|-------|------|-----|----------|
| 9267 NYMR 15 | 1956 | BSO | Doncaster | 183 | 30170 | N Yorks Moors |

Remarks: P'73

| Numbers | Year | Type | Built | Diag | Lot | Location |
|---------|------|------|-------|------|-----|----------|
| 9269 DB975269 041332 KESR 73 | 1956 1973 1977 | BSO | Doncaster | 183 | 30170 | K&ESR |

Remarks: P'81

| Numbers | Year | Type | Built | Diag | Lot | Location |
|---------|------|------|-------|------|-----|----------|
| 9273 | 1956 | BSO | Doncaster | 183 | 30170 | Worth Valley |

Remarks: P'86

| Numbers | Year | Type | Built | Diag | Lot | Location |
|---------|------|------|-------|------|-----|----------|
| 9274 | 1956 | BSO | Doncaster | 183 | 30170 | N Yorks Moors |

Remarks: P'82

| Numbers | Year | Type | Built | Diag | Lot | Location |
|---------|------|------|-------|------|-----|----------|
| 9275 9001 | 1956 1979 1981 | BSO BSOT | Doncaster | 183 | 30170 | Torbay |

Remarks: P'87

| Numbers | Year | Type | Built | Diag | Lot | Location |
|---------|------|------|-------|------|-----|----------|
| 9276 9000 | 1956 1980 1981 | BSO BSOT | Doncaster | 183 | 30170 | Matlock |

Remarks: P'87, stored till '89

| Numbers | Year | Type | Built | Diag | Lot | Location |
|---------|------|------|-------|------|-----|----------|
| 9278 | 1956 | BSO | Doncaster | 183 | 30244 | W Somerset |

Remarks: P'77?

| Numbers | Year | Type | Built | Diag | Lot | Location |
|---------|------|------|-------|------|-----|----------|
| 9281 | 1956 | BSO | Doncaster | 183 | 30244 | Midland |

Remarks: P'81 (reported to have been converted with a kitchen)

| Numbers | Year | Type | Built | Diag | Lot | Location |
|---------|------|------|-------|------|-----|----------|
| 9300 DB977176 | 1956 1984 | BSO | Doncaster | 183 | 30244 | Midland |

Remarks: P'90

| Numbers | Year | Type | Built | Diag | Lot | Location |
|---------|------|------|-------|------|-----|----------|
| 9315 | 1956 | BSO | Doncaster | 183 | 30244 | Lochty |
| Remarks: P'70 | | | | | | |
| 9316 | 1956 | BSO | Doncaster | 183 | 30244 | Great Central |
| | 1982 | BSOD | Derby | | | |
| Remarks: P'83 by MLST; converted by BR Apprentices for use by disabled passengers | | | | | | |
| 9356 | 1959 | BSO | Gloucester | 183 | 30443 | E Lancs |
| Remarks: P'83 | | | | | | |
| 9362 | 1959 | BSO | Gloucester | 183 | 30443 | Strathspey |
| SR 106 | | | | | | |
| Remarks: P pre'74 | | | | | | |
| 9369 | 1963 | BSO | Wolverton | 184 | 30698 | Dean Forest |
| 9010 | 1980 | BSOT | | | | |
| Remarks: P'87 | | | | | | |
| 9370 | 1963 | BSO | Wolverton | 184 | 30698 | Embsay |
| 9011 | 1980 | BSOT | | | | |
| YDR 6 | | | | | | |
| Remarks: P'88 | | | | | | |
| 9377 | 1963 | BSO | Wolverton | 184 | 30698 | Mid-Hants |
| 9003 | 1980 | BSOT | | | | |
| Remarks: P'88 | | | | | | |
| 9380 | 1963 | BSO | Wolverton | 184 | 30698 | Llangollen |
| 9014 | 1980 | BSOT | | | | |
| Remarks: P'87, painted chocolate & cream while in store at Chester Goods shed till '89 | | | | | | |
| 9383 | 1966 | BSO | Derby | 185 | 30757 | Pitsford |
| 9102 | 1986 | BSOT | | | | |
| Remarks: Mk.2. P'91 | | | | | | |
| 9385 | 1966 | BSO | Derby | 185 | 30757 | Mid Norfolk |
| Remarks: Mk.2. P'91 by F&DRS | | | | | | |
| 9389 | 1966 | BSO | Derby | 185 | 30757 | Great Central |
| 9103 | 1986 | BSOT | | | | |
| Remarks: Mk.2. P'90 by RVP, at Rushcliffe on GCR's northern extension | | | | | | |
| 9392 | 1966 | BSO | Derby | 185 | 30757 | S Devon |
| Remarks: Mk.2. P'91 by 4920 Soc | | | | | | |

| Numbers | Year | Type | Built | Diag | Lot | Location |
|---------|------|------|-------|------|-----|----------|
| 9393 | 1966 | BSO | Derby | 185 | 30757 | Mid Norfolk |

Remarks: Mk.2. P'91 by F&DRS

| 9394 | 1966 | BSO | Derby | 185 | 30757 | Peak Rail |

Remarks: Mk.2. P'91

| 9400 99370 plated | 1966 | BSO | Derby | 185 | 30757 | (Aberdeen) |

Remarks: Mk.2. P'90 by Grampian Railtours

| 9401 | 1966 | BSO | Derby | 185 | 30757 | Mid-Hants |
| 9104 | 1986 | BSOT | | | | |

Remarks: Mk.2. P'90

| 9410 | 1966 | BSO | Derby | 185 | 30757 | Gloucs-Warks |

Remarks: Mk.2. P'91 by A Lear

| 13043 NYMR 9 | 1954 | FK | Swindon | 116 | 30019 | N Yorks Moors |

Remarks: P'72, on N Yorks Moors till '77 then on Derwent Valley before returning to N Yorks Moors in '79. Mounted on Gresley bogies and on an isolated section of track at Goathland by 1984/5, probably as a Camper

| 13088 | 1954 | FK | Swindon | 116 | 30089 | ?, Wiltshire |

Remarks: P'77, on Mid-Hants till '91

| 13089 | 1954 | FK | Swindon | 116 | 30089 | Gloucs-Warks |

Remarks: P'88?

| 13092 | 1954 | FK | Swindon | 116 | 30089 | Pitsford |

Remarks: P'8? by Northants Stm Ry

| 13102 NYMR 10 | 1954 | FK | Swindon | 116 | 30089 | ? Lancs |

Remarks: P'72, on N Yorks Moors till sold by owner in '85 & body grounded in 'Preston area'

| 13125 | 1954 | FK | Swindon | 116 | 30089 | Market Bosworth |

Remarks: P mid'70s

| 13228 99825 plated | 1959 | FK | Eastleigh | 116 | 30381 | Bo'ness |

Remarks: P'90 by SRPS ex-leased

| 13229 99826 plated | 1959 | FK | Eastleigh | 116 | 30381 | Bo'ness |

Remarks: P'90 by SRPS ex-leased, at Perth till '91

| Numbers | Year | Type | Built | Diag | Lot | Location |
|---------|------|------|-------|------|-----|----------|
| 13231 | 1959 | FK | Eastleigh | 116 | 30381 | Bitton |
| DB977132 | 1983 | | | | | |

*Remarks: P'87*

13233/6/7 – only leased from BR

| | | | | | | |
|---------|------|------|-------|------|-----|----------|
| 13252 | 1962 | FK | Swindon | 120 | 30550 | * NRM |

*Remarks: Prototype Mk.2. P'82 at York, to Swindon '90 for 'NRM On Tour' display, returned to York 4/91*

13303 – only leased from BR

| | | | | | | |
|---------|------|------|-------|------|-----|----------|
| 13313 | 1962 | FK | Swindon | 116 | 30667 | Great Central |

*Remarks: P'90 by RVP*

| | | | | | | |
|---------|------|------|-------|------|-----|----------|
| 13317 | 1962 | FK | Swindon | 116 | 30667 | Steamtown |
| 99303 plated | | | | | | |

*Remarks: P'84 by TFP, sold to D Smith '86 but at Midland till '91*

| | | | | | | |
|---------|------|------|-------|------|-----|----------|
| 13320 | 1962 | FK | Swindon | 116 | 30667 | Steamtown |
| 99316 plated | | | | | | |

*Remarks: P'90, in D Smith's maroon rake*

| | | | | | | |
|---------|------|------|-------|------|-----|----------|
| 13321 | 1962 | FK | Swindon | 116 | 30667 | Steamtown |

*Remarks: P'90*

| | | | | | | |
|---------|------|------|-------|------|-----|----------|
| 13323 | 1962 | FK | Swindon | 116 | 30667 | Steamtown |
| 99302 plated | | | | | | |

*Remarks: P'83 by TFP, sold to D Smith '86 but at Midland till '91*

13326 – only leased from BR

| | | | | | | |
|---------|------|------|-------|------|-----|----------|
| 13333 | 1962 | FK | Swindon | 116 | 30667 | E Lancs |

*Remarks: P'87*

| | | | | | | |
|---------|------|------|-------|------|-----|----------|
| 13340 | 1962 | FK | Swindon | 116 | 30667 | Llangollen |

*Remarks: P'87, in store till '89 (Chester?)*

13341/4 – only leased from BR

| | | | | | | |
|---------|------|------|-------|------|-----|----------|
| 13349 | 1962 | FK | Swindon | 116 | 30667 | Telford |
| 14901 | 1967 | LFK | Eastleigh | 79 | | |

*Remarks: P'81 & on Severn Valley till '83*

| | | | | | | |
|---------|------|------|-------|------|-----|----------|
| 13407 | 1964 | FK | Derby | 121 | 30738 | Dean Forest |

*Remarks: XP64 stock. P'81*

| Numbers | Year | Type | Built | Diag | Lot | Location |
|---------|------|------|-------|------|-----|----------|
| 13438 | 1968 | FK | Derby | 123 | 30774 | Gloucs-Warks |

Remarks: Mk.2a. P'90 by A S Lear

| Numbers | Year | Type | Built | Diag | Lot | Location |
|---------|------|------|-------|------|-----|----------|
| 13442 | 1968 | FK | Derby | 123 | 30774 | Gloucs-Warks |

Remarks: Mk.2a. P'90 by A S Lear

| Numbers | Year | Type | Built | Diag | Lot | Location |
|---------|------|------|-------|------|-----|----------|
| 13453 | 1968 | FK | Derby | 123 | 30774 | Steamtown |

Remarks: Mk.2a. To be P'89 by Ridings Railtours, but sale not completed; found at Steamtown '91

| Numbers | Year | Type | Built | Diag | Lot | Location |
|---------|------|------|-------|------|-----|----------|
| 13454 | 1968 | FK | Derby | 123 | 30774 | Gloucs-Warks |
| 19454 | 1985 | SK | | | | |

Remarks: Mk.2a. P'90 by A S Lear

| Numbers | Year | Type | Built | Diag | Lot | Location |
|---------|------|------|-------|------|-----|----------|
| 13464 | 1968 | FK | Derby | 124 | 30785 | Gloucs-Warks |
| 19464 | 1985 | SK | | | | |

Remarks: Mk.2a. P'90 by A S Lear

| Numbers | Year | Type | Built | Diag | Lot | Location |
|---------|------|------|-------|------|-----|----------|
| 13480 | 1969 | FK | Derby | 125 | 30789 | Steamtown |
| DB977487 | 1987 | | | | | |

Remarks: Mk.2b. P'89 by R Edmondson

| Numbers | Year | Type | Built | Diag | Lot | Location |
|---------|------|------|-------|------|-----|----------|
| 13540 | 1970 | FK | Derby | 125 | 30797 | Bluebell |
| 19540 | 1985 | SK | | | | |

Remarks: Mk.2c. P'90 for dormitory accommodation

| Numbers | Year | Type | Built | Diag | Lot | Location |
|---------|------|------|-------|------|-----|----------|
| 13558 | 1970 | FK | Derby | 125 | 30797 | Heysham |
| 7558 | 1985 | CK | | | | |

Remarks: Mk.2c. P'89 by R Edmondson, being rebuilt at Lancastrian Works

| Numbers | Year | Type | Built | Diag | Lot | Location |
|---------|------|------|-------|------|-----|----------|
| 14007 / 17007 | 1960 | BFK | Swindon | 161 | 30382 | Southall |

Remarks: P'90 by MNLPS ex-lease

| Numbers | Year | Type | Built | Diag | Lot | Location |
|---------|------|------|-------|------|-----|----------|
| 14010 / 17010 | 1960 | BFK | Swindon | 161 | 30382 | Lochty |

Remarks: P'83

| Numbers | Year | Type | Built | Diag | Lot | Location |
|---------|------|------|-------|------|-----|----------|
| 14013 / 17013 | 1961 | BFK | Swindon | 161 | 30668 | (Bounds Green) |
| 99130 plated | | | | | | |

Remarks: P'87 by Pullman-Rail

| Numbers | Year | Type | Built | Diag | Lot | Location |
|---------|------|------|-------|------|-----|----------|
| 14018 / 17018 | 1961 | BFK | Swindon | 161 | 30668 | Tyseley |
| 99108 plated | | | | | | |

Remarks: Leased from '86 till P'88?

| Numbers | Year | Type | Built | Diag | Lot | Location |
|---------|------|------|-------|------|-----|----------|
| 14019 / 17019 | 1961 | BFK | Swindon | 161 | 30668 | Worth Valley |
| 99792 plated | | | | | | |

Remarks: P' ? as 34092 Support coach

| Numbers | Year | Type | Built | Diag | Lot | Location |
|---|---|---|---|---|---|---|
| 14021 / 17021<br>99421 plated | 1961 | BFK | Swindon | 161 | 30668 | Dairycoates |

*Remarks:* P'90 by HLPG

| 14024 / 17024 | 1963 | BFK | Swindon | 161 | 30718 | Dairycoates |

*Remarks:* P'90 by HLPG

| 14025 / 17025 | 1963 | BFK | Swindon | 161 | 30718 | Carlisle (BR) |

*Remarks:* P'90, sole item owned by Ridings Railtours

| 14026 / 17026 | 1963 | BFK | Swindon | 161 | 30718 | Great Central |

*Remarks:* P'89 by RVP member

| 14041 / 17041<br>99141 plated | 1966 | BFK | Derby | 162 | 30756 | (Didcot) |

*Remarks:* Mk.2. 3442's Support coach '89. P'89 as 71000 Support coach

| 14042 / 17042 | 1966 | BFK | Derby | 162 | 30756 | Crewe ? |

*Remarks:* Mk.2. P'91 by Manchester Pullman Co & named 'Attendance Car'

| 14055 / 17055 | 1966 | BFK | Derby | 162 | 30756 | Great Central |

*Remarks:* Mk.2. P'90 by RVP, at Rushcliffe on northern extension

14901 – see 13349

| 15055 | 1952 | CK | Eastleigh | 126 | 30022 | Indiana, USA |

*Remarks:* P'70 by Boyne City RR, Michigan, & shipped from Southampton '71. Later moved to museum at Chattanooga, Tennessee, till bought by Reggie Howell for C&J RR, first at Hopkinsville, Kentucky, but now at Jeffersonville

| 15096 | 1953 | CK | Metro-Cammell | 126 | 30005 | Great Central |

*Remarks:* P pre'74, wrongly reported written off '85

| 15207 | 1953 | CK | Metro-Cammell | 126 | 30005 | N Staffordshire |

*Remarks:* P'76

| 15208 | 1953 | CK | Metro-Cammell | 126 | 30005 | N Staffordshire |

*Remarks:* P'76

| 15296<br>DB975288 | 1952<br>1973 | CK | Cravens | 126 | 30016 | - |

*Remarks:* P'74, on Nene Valley till post'77 then on Great Central. Scrapped by '87.

| 15319 | 1953 | CK | Derby | 126 | 30033 | Quainton |

*Remarks:* P'77

| Numbers | Year | Type | Built | Diag | Lot | Location |
|---------|------|------|-------|------|-----|----------|
| 15401<br>SR 101 | 1954 | CK | Derby | 126 | 30075 | Strathspey |
| Remarks: P pre'74 | | | | | | |
| 15447 | 1953 | CK | Metro-Cammell | 126 | 30062 | Bitton |
| Remarks: P mid 70's | | | | | | |
| 15514 | 1954 | CK | Metro-Cammell | 126 | 30062 | - |
| Remarks: P pre'77, on Nene Valley till ' ? then on Great Central. Scrapped by '87. | | | | | | |
| 15553 | 1955 | CK | Metro-Cammell | 126 | 30134 | - |
| Remarks: P'74 on Severn Valley, broken up in 82. | | | | | | |
| 15565 | 1955 | CK | Metro-Cammell | 128 | 30135 | Didcot |
| Remarks: P pre'74 by GWS | | | | | | |
| 15577 | 1955 | CK | Metro-Cammell | 128 | 30135 | Didcot |
| Remarks: P pre'74 by GWS | | | | | | |
| 15611 | 1955 | CK | B R C W | 128 | 30139 | Great Central |
| Remarks: P pre'74 | | | | | | |
| 15626 / 7626 | 1956 | CK | Wolverton | 126 | 30158 | Llangollen |
| Remarks: P'87 | | | | | | |
| 15632 / 7632 | 1956 | CK | Wolverton | 126 | 30158 | W Somerset |
| Remarks: P'89 | | | | | | |
| 15644 / 7644<br>99422 plated | 1956 | CK | Wolverton | 126 | 30158 | Dairycoates |
| Remarks: P'90 by HLPG | | | | | | |
| 15663 / 7663 | 1956 | CK | Wolverton | 126 | 30158 | Matlock |
| Remarks: P'89 | | | | | | |
| 15667 / 7667 | 1956 | CK | Wolverton | 126 | 30158 | Llangollen |
| Remarks: P'87 | | | | | | |
| 15673 / 7673 | 1956 | CK | Wolverton | 126 | 30158 | Andover |
| Remarks: P'88 by SST, for Swanage | | | | | | |
| 15674 / 7674 | 1956 | CK | Wolverton | 126 | 30158 | Llangollen |
| Remarks: P'87 | | | | | | |

| Numbers | Year | Type | Built | Diag | Lot | Location |
|---|---|---|---|---|---|---|
| 15709<br>NYMR 21 | 1956 | CK | Metro-Cammell | 126 | 30179 | N Yorks Moors |
| Remarks: P'77; being used as a Camper by '85 | | | | | | |
| 15745 / 7745 | 1956 | CK | Metro-Cammell | 126 | 30179 | N Yorks Moors |
| Remarks: P'84 | | | | | | |
| 15798 | 1955 | CK | Metro-Cammell | 128 | 30180 | Mid-Hants |
| Remarks: P'76 | | | | | | |
| 15834<br>99814 plated | 1956 | CK | Metro-Cammell | 126 | 30221 | Bo'ness |
| Remarks: P'84 by SRPS, at Falkirk till '88 then at Perth till '90 | | | | | | |
| 15849 | 1956 | CK | Metro-Cammell | 126 | 30221 | Wallingford |
| Remarks: P'81, on Dean Forest till '90 | | | | | | |
| 15879<br>99205 plated | 1957 | CK | Metro-Cammell | 128 | 30222 | Bulmers |
| Remarks: P mid'70s by 6000 Loco Assoc | | | | | | |
| 15916 / 7916 | 1956 | CK | Wolverton | 126 | 30317 | E Lancs |
| Remarks: P'87? | | | | | | |
| 15925 / 7925 | 1956 | CK | Wolverton | 126 | 30317 | Llangollen |
| Remarks: P'86 | | | | | | |
| 15927 / 7927<br>KESR 86 | 1956 | CK | Wolverton | 126 | 30317 | K&ESR |
| Remarks: P'84, on Mid-Hants till '87 | | | | | | |
| 15928 / 7928 | 1956 | CK | Wolverton | 126 | 30317 | E Lancs |
| Remarks: P'88? | | | | | | |
| 15931 / 7931 | 1956 | CK | Wolverton | 126 | 30317 | Llangollen |
| Remarks: P'87 | | | | | | |
| 15932 / 7932<br>'Vanessa' | 1956<br>1985 | CK | Wolverton | 126 | 30317 | N of York |
| Remarks: Purchased by Bert Gemmell for part of 'The Sidings' Hotel at Shipton-by-Beningborough. Body grounded 17/3/85 as half of the Restaurant | | | | | | |
| 15939 / 7939 | 1956 | CK | Wolverton | 126 | 30317 | Colne Valley |
| Remarks: P'87 | | | | | | |

| Numbers | Year | Type | Built | Diag | Lot | Location |
|---|---|---|---|---|---|---|
| 15943 / 7943 | 1956 | CK | Wolverton | 126 | 30317 | Matlock |
| Remarks: P'89 | | | | | | |
| 15952 YDR 4 | 1956 | CK | Wolverton | 126 | 30317 | Embsay |
| Remarks: P'83 | | | | | | |
| 15960 | 1957 | CK | Wolverton | 126 | 30317 | Great Central |
| Remarks: P'83, on Mid-Hants till '88/9 | | | | | | |
| 15961 / 7961 KESR 87 | 1957 | CK | Wolverton | 126 | 30317 | K&ESR |
| Remarks: P'84, on Mid-Hants till '87 | | | | | | |
| 15981 / 7981 | 1957 | CK | Wolverton | 126 | 30317 | Colne Valley |
| Remarks: P'84, converted to Kitchen Car for the static Restaurant complex | | | | | | |
| 15984 / 7984 | 1957 | CK | Wolverton | 126 | 30317 | Colne Valley |
| Remarks: P'84 | | | | | | |
| 16012 | 1957 | CK | Wolverton | 126 | 30351 | Bodmin |
| Remarks: P'83, on Mid-Hants till '91 | | | | | | |
| 16019 | 1957 | CK | Wolverton | 126 | 30351 | Pitsford |
| Remarks: P'83, on Mid-Hants till '91 | | | | | | |
| 16025 | 1957 | CK | Wolverton | 126 | 30351 | Great Central |
| Remarks: Originally fitted with Wegmann bogies. P'82 by 92212 Loco Soc, restored by MSC team in a factory at Nuneaton till '84 | | | | | | |
| 16065 / 7065 | 1959 | CK | Metro-Cammell | 126 | 30471 | Bodmin |
| Remarks: P'86 | | | | | | |
| 16068 / 7068 | 1959 | CK | Metro-Cammell | 126 | 30471 | Bodmin |
| Remarks: P'86 | | | | | | |
| 16070 / 7070 | 1959 | CK | Metro-Cammell | 126 | 30471 | Great Central |
| Remarks: P'87 | | | | | | |
| 16071 / 7071 | 1959 | CK | Metro-Cammell | 126 | 30471 | Llangollen |
| Remarks: P'85 | | | | | | |
| 16083 | 1959 | CK | Metro-Cammell | 126 | 30471 | Mid-Hants |
| Remarks: P'83 | | | | | | |

| Numbers | Year | Type | Built | Diag | Lot | Location |
|---------|------|------|-------|------|-----|----------|
| 16155 / 7155 | 1961 | CK | Derby | 126 | 30665 | Darley Dale |
| Remarks: P'89 by Peak Rail, stored on BR till '90 | | | | | | |
| 16169 / 7169 | 1961 | CK | Derby | 126 | 30665 | Severn Valley |
| Remarks: P'89 | | | | | | |
| 16187 / 7187 99714 plated | 1961 | CK | Derby | 126 | 30665 | (Longsight) |
| Remarks: P'86 by Train Tours | | | | | | |
| 16191 / 7191 99719 plated | 1961 | CK | Derby | 126 | 30665 | (Longsight) |
| Remarks: P'87 by Train Tours | | | | | | |
| 16201 / 7201 | 1961 | CK | Derby | 128 | 30666 | Bo'ness |
| Remarks: P'87 by SRPS, at Falkirk till '88, Perth till '91 | | | | | | |
| 16202 | 1961 | CK | Derby | 128 | 30666 | Severn Valley |
| Remarks: P'77 | | | | | | |
| 16204 / 7204 | 1961 | CK | Derby | 128 | 30666 | Plym Valley |
| Remarks: P'87 | | | | | | |
| 16210 / 7210 | 1961 | CK | Derby | 128 | 30666 | Bluebell |
| Remarks: P'86 | | | | | | |
| 16221 / 7221 | 1961 | CK | Derby | 128 | 30666 | Steamtown |
| Remarks: P'86 by Blackpool Loco Soc | | | | | | |
| 16233 / 7233 | 1963 | CK | Derby | 126 | 30729 | N Yorks Moors |
| Remarks: P'90 | | | | | | |
| 16263 / 7263 | 1963 | CK | Derby | 126 | 30730 | Bluebell |
| Remarks: P'91 | | | | | | |
| 16267 / 7267 | 1963 | CK | Derby | 126 | 30730 | Severn Valley |
| Remarks: The last Mk.1 CK built. P'83 | | | | | | |
| 21027 | 1954 | BCK | Metro-Cammell | 171 | 30132 | Chappel |
| Remarks: P'78 | | | | | | |
| 21031 | 1954 | BCK | Metro-Cammell | 171 | 30132 | Market Bosworth |
| Remarks: P mid '70s | | | | | | |

| Numbers | Year | Type | Built | Diag | Lot | Location |
|---|---|---|---|---|---|---|
| 21034<br>99781 plated | 1954 | BCK | Metro-Cammell | 171 | 30132 | W Somerset |

*Remarks:* Leased by MNLPS 1985-8. P'89

| 21059 | 1955 | BCK | Metro-Cammell | 171 | 30132 | Midland |

*Remarks:* P'81

| 21077 | 1955 | BCK | Metro-Cammell | 172 | 30133 | - |

*Remarks:* P'76 on Mid-Hants, sold to Marple & Gillott for scrap in ?

| 21092 | 1956 | BCK | Metro-Cammell | 171 | 30185 | Gloucs-Warks |

*Remarks:* P'76, on Mid-Hants till '89

| 21096<br>99080 plated | 1956 | BCK | Metro-Cammell | 171 | 30185 | Steamtown |

*Remarks:* P'81 by A4 Loco Soc as the support coach

| 21100 | 1956 | BCK | Metro-Cammell | 171 | 30185 | N Yorks Moors |

*Remarks:* P'77, on Derwent Valley till '79

| 21103 | 1956 | BCK | Metro-Cammell | 171 | 30185 | N Norfolk |

*Remarks:* P'76?, under restoration at Norwich Victoria till '78

| 21129 | 1956 | BCK | Metro-Cammell | 172 | 30186 | Dean Forest |

*Remarks:* P'81

| 21173 | 1958 | BCK | C Roberts | 172 | 30424 | Swansea Vale |

*Remarks:* P'81, grounded by '88

| 21174<br>'Phoenix' | 1958<br>1986 | BCK | C Roberts | 172 | 30424 | W Somerset |

*Remarks:* P'82?

| 21177 | 1958 | BCK | C Roberts | 172 | 30424 | ?, USA |

*Remarks:* Went to USA '69 with 'Flying Scotsman' (fate unknown, but see 'Unidentified vehicles' at end)

| 21184 | 1958 | BCK | C Roberts | 172 | 30424 | Great Central |

*Remarks:* P'88

| 21187 | 1958 | BCK | C Roberts | 172 | 30424 | Gloucs-Warks |

*Remarks:* P'82 by GW Stm Locos Grp, on Gloucs-Warks till '89

| 21205<br>DB977094 | 1958<br>1982 | BCK | Metro-Cammell | 171 | 30425 | Swanage |

*Remarks:* P'85, at Rye House till '87

| Numbers | Year | Type | Built | Diag | Lot | Location |
|---|---|---|---|---|---|---|
| 21208 | 1958 | BCK | Metro-Cammell | 171 | 30425 | Mid-Hants |
| Remarks: P'83 | | | | | | |
| 21214 99420 plated | 1958 | BCK | Metro-Cammell | 171 | 30425 | Dairycoates |
| Remarks: P'82? by Humberside LPG as a Support coach | | | | | | |
| 21232 99040 plated | 1960 | BCK | Gloucester | 171 | 30574 | Midland |
| Remarks: P'82 by 80080 Loco Holdings, at Matlock till '83 | | | | | | |
| 21236 95408 plated 99120 plated | 1961 1981 1984 | BCK | Swindon | 171 | 30669 | Severn Valley |
| Remarks: P'81 by NRM at York & loaned to SLOA; sold to Pullman-Rail '84 & used in maroon rake except when leased to Bluebell '90-1; sold to consortium (RPR) '91 | | | | | | |
| 21238 99167 plated | 1961 1989 | BCK Spec | Swindon | 171 | 30669 | (Cathays) |
| Remarks: P'89 by Travelling College (conv to dormitory & Trainmaster's quarters with Brake) | | | | | | |
| 21240 | 1961 | BCK | Swindon | 171 | 30669 | N Yorks Moors |
| Remarks: P'91 | | | | | | |
| 21245 99356 plated | 1962 | BCK | Swindon | 171 | 30669 | (Bounds Green) |
| Remarks: P'83 by SLOA, to Pullman-Rail in '84 | | | | | | |
| 21247 'Gemma' | 1962 1989 | BCK | Swindon | 171 | 30669 | Isfield |
| 21249 99355 plated | 1962 | BCK | Swindon | 171 | 30669 | (Bounds Green) |
| Remarks: P'81 by SLOA, to Pullman-Rail in '84 | | | | | | |
| 21252 | 1963 | BCK | Derby | 171 | 30731 | Mid-Hants |
| Remarks: P'82 damaged | | | | | | |
| 21254 | 1963 | BCK | Derby | 171 | 30731 | Severn Valley |
| Remarks: P'81 by EMF | | | | | | |
| 21256 99304 plated | 1963 | BCK | Derby | 171 | 30731 | Steamtown |
| Remarks: P'83 by TFP, sold to D Smith in '86 but at Midland till '90; used in owner's maroon rake | | | | | | |

| Numbers | Year | Type | Built | Diag | Lot | Location |
|---|---|---|---|---|---|---|
| 21261<br>YDR 3 | 1963 | BCK | Derby | 171 | 30731 | Embsay |

*Remarks:* P'83

| Numbers | Year | Type | Built | Diag | Lot | Location |
|---|---|---|---|---|---|---|
| 21272<br>99129 plated | 1964 | BCK | Derby | 172 | 30732 | (Bounds Green) |

*Remarks:* P'84 by Pullman-Rail

| | | | | | | |
|---|---|---|---|---|---|---|
| 24006 | 1951 | SK | Derby | 146 | 30002 | W Somerset |

*Remarks:* P'83

| | | | | | | |
|---|---|---|---|---|---|---|
| 24127 | 1951<br>198? | SK<br>SKD | Derby | 146 | 30002 | Swanage |

*Remarks:* P'85 by SST, converted for use by the disabled at siding in Herts

| | | | | | | |
|---|---|---|---|---|---|---|
| 24199 | 1952 | SK | Doncaster | 146 | 30015 | - |

*Remarks:* P'70 by Boyne City RR, Michigan, USA, but believed scrapped when this scheme folded.

| | | | | | | |
|---|---|---|---|---|---|---|
| 24248<br>L&HR 40 | 1952 | SK | York | 146 | 30026 | - |

*Remarks:* P'70 at Lakeside; reported withdrawn '83 & scrapped '85.

| | | | | | | |
|---|---|---|---|---|---|---|
| 24307 | 1951 | SK | Eastleigh | 146 | 30020 | W Somerset |

*Remarks:* P mid 70's

| | | | | | | |
|---|---|---|---|---|---|---|
| 24377<br>L&HR 41 | 1954 | SK | B R C W | 146 | 30007 | - |

*Remarks:* P'70 at Lakeside; reported withdrawn '83 & scrapped '85.

| | | | | | | |
|---|---|---|---|---|---|---|
| 24381<br>L&HR 42 | 1954 | SK | B R C W | 146 | 30007 | Lakeside |

*Remarks:* P'70; withdrawn '85 & since used as store.

| | | | | | | |
|---|---|---|---|---|---|---|
| 24396 | 1954 | SK | B R C W | 146 | 30007 | Weldon Bridge |

*Remarks:* P'74, on Severn Valley till '82, body then grounded at 'Anglers Arms' as 'The Pullman Dining Car'!

| | | | | | | |
|---|---|---|---|---|---|---|
| 24421 | 1953 | SK | Derby | 146 | 30030 | W Somerset |

*Remarks:* P'85

| | | | | | | |
|---|---|---|---|---|---|---|
| 24434<br>'Gillian' | 1953<br>1985 | SK | Derby | 146 | 30030 | N of York |

*Remarks:* Purchased by Bert Gemmell to form part of 'The Sidings' Hotel at Shipton-by-Beningborough. Body was grounded 17/3/85 as part of the Bedroom section

| Numbers | Year | Type | Built | Diag | Lot | Location |
|---------|------|------|-------|------|-----|----------|
| 24449<br>L&HR 43 | 1954 | SK | Swindon | 146 | 30088 | - |

*Remarks:* P'70 at Lakeside; reported withdrawn '83 & scrapped '86.

| 24458 | 1954 | SK | Swindon | 146 | 30088 | Mid-Hants |

*Remarks:* P'83

| 24551 | 1955 | SK | York | 146 | 30070 | - |

*Remarks:* P'70 by Boyne City RR, Michigan, USA, but believed scrapped when this scheme folded.

| 24576<br>DB977189 | 1953<br>1983 | SK | B R C W | 146 | 30057 | Pitsford |

*Remarks:* P'90

| 24656 | 1953 | SK | B R C W | 146 | 30057 | Great Central |

*Remarks:* P mid '70s, on Nene Valley till post'77

| 24676<br>'Dorothy' | 1953<br>1985 | SK | Cravens | 146 | 30058 | N of York |

*Remarks:* Purchased by Bert Gemmell to form part of 'The Sidings' Hotel at Shipton-by-Beningborough. Body was grounded 17/3/85 as part of the Bedroom section

| 24726 | 1953 | SK | Wolverton | 146 | 30073 | - |

*Remarks:* P'72 on Severn Valley, broken up '83.

| 24731<br>L&HR 44 | 1953 | SK | Wolverton | 146 | 30073 | - |

*Remarks:* P'70 at Lakeside, W'83 & broken up '85.

| 24778 | 1954 | SK | Swindon | 146 | 30078 | W Somerset |

*Remarks:* P'83

| 24799<br>L&HR 45 | 1954 | SK | B R C W | 146 | 30137 | - |

*Remarks:* P'70 at Lakeside, broken up '85.

| 24804 | 1954 | SK | B R C W | 146 | 30137 | N Yorks Moors |

*Remarks:* P'77, on Derwent Valley till '79

| 24808<br>NYMR 20 | 1954 | SK | B R C W | 146 | 30137 | N Yorks Moors |

*Remarks:* P'77

| 24825 | 1955 | SK | Derby | 146 | 30153 | Gwili |

*Remarks:* P'87

| Numbers | Year | Type | Built | Diag | Lot | Location |
|---------|------|------|-------|------|-----|----------|
| 24839 | 1955 | SK | Derby | 146 | 30153 | Severn Valley |

*Remarks:* P'87 for Bridgnorth accommodation siding

| Numbers | Year | Type | Built | Diag | Lot | Location |
|---------|------|------|-------|------|-----|----------|
| 24843 | 1955 | SK | Derby | 146 | 30153 | Gwili |

*Remarks:* P'87

| Numbers | Year | Type | Built | Diag | Lot | Location |
|---------|------|------|-------|------|-----|----------|
| 24845 | 1955 | SK | Derby | 146 | 30153 | Severn Valley |

*Remarks:* P'87 for Bridgnorth accommodation siding

| Numbers | Year | Type | Built | Diag | Lot | Location |
|---------|------|------|-------|------|-----|----------|
| 24886 | 1955 | SK | Derby | 146 | 30153 | - |

*Remarks:* P'82 at Butterley, fire gutted '89 after welding; body broken up '90, but underframe used to carry body of Pullman Car 'Midland' (qv) during '91

| Numbers | Year | Type | Built | Diag | Lot | Location |
|---------|------|------|-------|------|-----|----------|
| 24888 | 1955 | SK | Derby | 146 | 30153 | Dartford |

*Remarks:* P'88? by N Downs Stm Rly

| Numbers | Year | Type | Built | Diag | Lot | Location |
|---------|------|------|-------|------|-----|----------|
| 24918 | 1955 | SK | Derby | 146 | 30153 | Wallingford |

*Remarks:* P'81, on Dean Forest till '90

| Numbers | Year | Type | Built | Diag | Lot | Location |
|---------|------|------|-------|------|-----|----------|
| 24949 | 1956 | SK | Derby | 146 | 30154 | Gloucs-Warks |

*Remarks:* P'83, on Dart Valley till '88?

| Numbers | Year | Type | Built | Diag | Lot | Location |
|---------|------|------|-------|------|-----|----------|
| 24959 | 1956 | SK | Derby | 146 | 30154 | Chappel |

*Remarks:* P'83?

| Numbers | Year | Type | Built | Diag | Lot | Location |
|---------|------|------|-------|------|-----|----------|
| 24977 'Lydia' | 1956 1985 | SK | Derby | 146 | 30208 | N of York |

*Remarks:* Purchased by Bert Gemmell to form part of 'The Sidings' Hotel at Shipton-by-Beningborough. Body was grounded 17/3/85 as end part of the Bedroom section, rebuilt to include a four-poster bed!

| Numbers | Year | Type | Built | Diag | Lot | Location |
|---------|------|------|-------|------|-----|----------|
| 24984 | 1956 | SK | Derby | 146 | 30208 | N Yorks Moors |

*Remarks:* P'83

| Numbers | Year | Type | Built | Diag | Lot | Location |
|---------|------|------|-------|------|-----|----------|
| 24985 | 1956 | SK | Derby | 146 | 30208 | W Somerset |

*Remarks:* P'83, on Dart Valley till '90

| Numbers | Year | Type | Built | Diag | Lot | Location |
|---------|------|------|-------|------|-----|----------|
| 24993 | 1956 | SK | Derby | 146 | 30208 | Quainton |

*Remarks:* P'77

| Numbers | Year | Type | Built | Diag | Lot | Location |
|---------|------|------|-------|------|-----|----------|
| 24997 | 1956 | SK | Derby | 146 | 30208 | Nene Valley |

*Remarks:* P'83

| Numbers | Year | Type | Built | Diag | Lot | Location |
|---------|------|------|-------|------|-----|----------|
| 25020 | 1956 | SK | Derby | 146 | 30208 | Gloucs-Warks |

*Remarks:* P'83

| Numbers | Year | Type | Built | Diag | Lot | Location |
|---|---|---|---|---|---|---|
| 25032 | 1956 | SK | Derby | 146 | 30208 | Mid-Hants |
| Remarks: P'84 by Fowler 3F Soc | | | | | | |
| 25040 | 1956 | SK | Derby | 146 | 30208 | Bitton |
| Remarks: P'81 | | | | | | |
| 25142 NYMR 18 | 1956 | SK | Wolverton | 147 | 30155 | N Yorks Moors |
| Remarks: P'76 | | | | | | |
| 25189 | 1957 | SK | Metro-Cammell | 147 | 30230 | Great Central |
| Remarks: Converted to the 'Autobuffet' '62. P'85 by RVP member | | | | | | |
| 25225 | 1957 | SK | Metro-Cammell | 147 | 30230 | Foxfield |
| Remarks: P mid 70's | | | | | | |
| 25231 | 1957 | SK | Metro-Cammell | 147 | 30230 | Foxfield |
| Remarks: P mid 70's | | | | | | |
| 25251 / 18251 | 1957 | SK | Metro-Cammell | 146 | 30231 | Gloucs-Warks |
| Remarks: P'88 | | | | | | |
| 25252 / 18252 | 1957 | SK | Metro-Cammell | 146 | 30231 | Moy |
| Remarks: P'87? on Strathspey, sold '90 to become a restaurant at Invermoy House Hotel | | | | | | |
| 25258 / 18258 | 1957 | SK | Metro-Cammell | 146 | 30231 | Llangollen |
| Remarks: P'86 | | | | | | |
| 25265 / 18265 | 1957 | SK | Metro-Cammell | 146 | 30231 | Buxton |
| Remarks: P'88 | | | | | | |
| 25299 | 1957 | SK | Wolverton | 146 | 30349• | Bitton |
| Remarks: P'81 • Lot 30349 is unique in having single-bolster bogies | | | | | | |
| 25307 'Claire' | 1957 1991 | SK Sal | Wolverton | 146 | 30349 | Torbay |
| Remarks: P'83, converted to Open Saloon with Bar for the 'Devonian Pullman' set | | | | | | |
| 25308 / 18308 | 1957 | SK | Wolverton | 146 | 30349 | W Somerset |
| Remarks: P'83, on Dart Valley till '90 | | | | | | |
| 25312 | 1957 | SK | Wolverton | 146 | 30349 | Great Central |
| Remarks: P'83 | | | | | | |

| Numbers | Year | Type | Built | Diag | Lot | Location |
|---------|------|------|-------|------|-----|----------|
| 25323 | 1957 | SK | Wolverton | 146 | 30349 | W Somerset |

*Remarks:* P'83, on Dart Valley till '90

| Numbers | Year | Type | Built | Diag | Lot | Location |
|---------|------|------|-------|------|-----|----------|
| 25337 L&HR 46 | 1957 | SK | Wolverton | 146 | 30349 | Lakeside |

*Remarks:* P'82

| Numbers | Year | Type | Built | Diag | Lot | Location |
|---------|------|------|-------|------|-----|----------|
| 25341 | 1957 | SK | Wolverton | 146 | 30349 | Gloucs-Warks |

*Remarks:* P'83, on Dart Valley till '88?

| Numbers | Year | Type | Built | Diag | Lot | Location |
|---------|------|------|-------|------|-----|----------|
| 25346 | 1957 | SK | Wolverton | 146 | 30349 | Severn Valley |

*Remarks:* P'82

| Numbers | Year | Type | Built | Diag | Lot | Location |
|---------|------|------|-------|------|-----|----------|
| 25347 | 1957 | SK | Wolverton | 146 | 30349 | Pitsford |

*Remarks:* P'82, on Mid-Hants till '91

| Numbers | Year | Type | Built | Diag | Lot | Location |
|---------|------|------|-------|------|-----|----------|
| 25355 | 1957 | SK | Wolverton | 146 | 30349 | Dart Valley ? |

*Remarks:* P'83

| Numbers | Year | Type | Built | Diag | Lot | Location |
|---------|------|------|-------|------|-----|----------|
| 25362 / 18362 | 1957 | SK | Wolverton | 146 | 30349 | Meadowhall |

*Remarks:* P'89 by S Yorks RPS

| Numbers | Year | Type | Built | Diag | Lot | Location |
|---------|------|------|-------|------|-----|----------|
| 25364 L&HR 47 | 1957 | SK | Wolverton | 146 | 30349 | Lakeside |

*Remarks:* P'83

| Numbers | Year | Type | Built | Diag | Lot | Location |
|---------|------|------|-------|------|-----|----------|
| 25366 / 18366 | 1957 | SK | Wolverton | 146 | 30349 | Great Central |

*Remarks:* P'87

| Numbers | Year | Type | Built | Diag | Lot | Location |
|---------|------|------|-------|------|-----|----------|
| 25385 / 18385 | 1957 | SK | Wolverton | 146 | 30349 | E Lancs |

*Remarks:* P'86

| Numbers | Year | Type | Built | Diag | Lot | Location |
|---------|------|------|-------|------|-----|----------|
| 25410 / 18410 | 1957 | SK | Wolverton | 146 | 30350 | Llangollen |

*Remarks:* P'87

| Numbers | Year | Type | Built | Diag | Lot | Location |
|---------|------|------|-------|------|-----|----------|
| 25417 / 18417 | 1957 | SK | Wolverton | 146 | 30350 | Llangollen |

*Remarks:* P'87

| Numbers | Year | Type | Built | Diag | Lot | Location |
|---------|------|------|-------|------|-----|----------|
| 25421 / 18421 | 1957 | SK | Wolverton | 146 | 30350 | Llangollen |

*Remarks:* P'87

| Numbers | Year | Type | Built | Diag | Lot | Location |
|---------|------|------|-------|------|-----|----------|
| 25424 / 18424 | 1957 | SK | Wolverton | 146 | 30350 | Swanage |

*Remarks:* P'87

| Numbers | Year | Type | Built | Diag | Lot | Location |
|---------|------|------|-------|------|-----|----------|
| 25444 / 18444 | 1957 | SK | Wolverton | 146 | 30350 | Blaenavon |
| Remarks: P'85 | | | | | | |
| 25446 KESR 63 | 1957 | SK | Wolverton | 146 | 30350 | K&ESR |
| Remarks: P'77 | | | | | | |
| 25451 | 1957 | SK | Wolverton | 146 | 30350 | Gloucs-Warks |
| Remarks: P'82, on Mid-Hants till '88? | | | | | | |
| 25454 | 1957 | SK | Wolverton | 146 | 30350 | W Somerset |
| Remarks: P'83, on Dart Valley till '90 | | | | | | |
| 25460 | 1958 | SK | York | 146 | 30374 | Swansea Vale |
| Remarks: P'83 | | | | | | |
| 25472 | 1958 | SK | York | 146 | 30374 | Embsay |
| Remarks: P'83 | | | | | | |
| 25488 / 18488 | 1958 | SK | York | 146 | 30374 | N Yorks Moors |
| Remarks: P'84 | | | | | | |
| 25498 | 1958 | SK | York | 146 | 30374 | Severn Valley |
| Remarks: P'83 | | | | | | |
| 25500 | 1958 | SK | York | 146 | 30374 | Quainton |
| Remarks: P'83, on Dart Valley till '91 | | | | | | |
| 25501 | 1958 | SK | York | 146 | 30374 | Gloucs-Warks |
| Remarks: P'83, on Dart Valley till '88? | | | | | | |
| 25508 | 1964 | SK | Derby | 152 | 30737 | N Yorks Moors |
| Remarks: XP64 stock. P'81 by Diesel Traction Grp | | | | | | |
| 25509 | 1964 | SK | Derby | 152 | 30737 | Dean Forest |
| Remarks: XP64 stock. P'81 | | | | | | |
| 25560 / 18560 | 1958 | SK | Wolverton | 146 | 30426 | Bodmin |
| Remarks: P'86 | | | | | | |
| 25562 / 18562 | 1958 | SK | Wolverton | 146 | 30426 | Meadowhall |
| Remarks: P'89 by S Yorks RPS | | | | | | |

| Numbers | Year | Type | Built | Diag | Lot | Location |
|---------|------|------|-------|------|-----|----------|
| 25572 / 18572 99314 plated | 1958 | SK | Wolverton | 146 | 30426 | Bodmin |
| *Remarks:* P'88 | | | | | | |
| 25591 / 18591 | 1958 | SK | Wolverton | 146 | 30426 | Plym Valley |
| *Remarks:* P'87 | | | | | | |
| 25594 / 18594 | 1958 | SK | Wolverton | 146 | 30426 | Severn Valley |
| *Remarks:* P'87 for Bridgnorth accommodation siding | | | | | | |
| 25607 / 18607 DB977513 | 1958 | SK | Wolverton | 146 | 30426 | Foxfield |
| *Remarks:* P'89 | | | | | | |
| 25618 / 18618 | 1958 | SK | Wolverton | 146 | 30426 | Gloucs-Warks |
| *Remarks:* P'89, conv'd for use as Santa's grotto! | | | | | | |
| 25631 / 18631 | 1958 | SK | Wolverton | 146 | 30426 | Gloucs-Warks |
| *Remarks:* P'89 | | | | | | |
| 25639 | 1958 | SK | Wolverton | 146 | 30426 | Nene Valley |
| *Remarks:* P'83? | | | | | | |
| 25650 / 18650 | 1958 | SK | Wolverton | 146 | 30426 | Bodmin |
| *Remarks:* P'88 | | | | | | |
| 25686 / 18686 | 1958 | SK | Wolverton | 146 | 30426 | Severn Valley |
| *Remarks:* P'87 for Bridgnorth accommodation siding | | | | | | |
| 25693 | 1958 | SK | Wolverton | 146 | 30426 | Dart Valley ? |
| *Remarks:* P'83 | | | | | | |
| 25697 | 1958 | SK | Wolverton | 146 | 30426 | Colne Valley |
| *Remarks:* P'81 | | | | | | |
| 25700 | 1958 | SK | Wolverton | 146 | 30426 | N Yorks Moors |
| *Remarks:* P'81 | | | | | | |
| 25728 / 18728 | 1961 | SK | Derby | 146 | 30685 | Bluebell |
| *Remarks:* P'91 | | | | | | |
| 25729 / 18729 | 1961 | SK | Derby | 146 | 30685 | Steamtown |
| *Remarks:* P'91, in D Smith's maroon rake | | | | | | |

| Numbers | Year | Type | Built | Diag | Lot | Location |
|---------|------|------|-------|------|-----|----------|
| 25743 / 18743 | 1961 | SK | Derby | 146 | 30685 | Gloucs-Warks |
| Remarks: P'91 | | | | | | |
| 25752 / 18752 | 1961 | SK | Derby | 146 | 30685 | Bluebell |
| Remarks: P'91 | | | | | | |
| 25756 / 18756<br>99722 plated | 1961 | SK | Derby | 146 | 30685 | (Longsight) |
| Remarks: P'90 by TrainTours | | | | | | |
| 25767 / 18767<br>99710 plated | 1961 | SK | Derby | 146 | 30685 | (Longsight) |
| Remarks: P'86 by TrainTours | | | | | | |
| 25769 / 18769 | 1961 | SK | Derby | 146 | 30685 | Bluebell |
| Remarks: P'91 | | | | | | |
| 25771 / 18771 | 1961 | SK | Derby | 146 | 30685 | Severn Valley |
| Remarks: P'91 by consortium (RPR) | | | | | | |
| 25776 / 18776<br>99166 plated | 1961<br>1989 | SK<br>Spec | Derby | 146 | 30685 | (Cathays) |
| Remarks: P'89 by Travelling College (conv to staff dormitory) | | | | | | |
| 25778 / 18778<br>99168 plated | 1961<br>1989 | SK<br>Spec | Derby | 146 | 30685· | (Cathays) |
| Remarks: P'89 by Travelling College (conv to saloon) | | | | | | |
| 25795 / 18795<br>99162 plated | 1961<br>1989 | SK<br>Spec | Derby | 146 | 30685 | (Cathays) |
| Remarks: P'89 by Travelling College (conv to dormitory) | | | | | | |
| 25806 / 18806 | 1961 | SK | Derby | 146 | 30685 | Longsight ? |
| Remarks: P'90 by TrainTours | | | | | | |
| 25807 / 18807<br>DB977420 | 1961<br>1986 | SK | Derby | 146 | 30685 | Llangollen |
| Remarks: P'90 | | | | | | |
| 25808 / 18808<br>99716 plated | 1961 | SK | Derby | 146 | 30685 | (Longsight) |
| Remarks: P'87 by TrainTours | | | | | | |
| 25828 / 18828 | 1961 | SK | Derby | 146 | 30685 | E Lancs |
| Remarks: P'87 | | | | | | |

| Numbers | Year | Type | Built | Diag | Lot | Location |
|---------|------|------|-------|------|-----|----------|
| 25832 / 18832 | 1961 | SK | Derby | 146 | 30685 | Tyseley |
| *Remarks:* P'88 by Tolemans | | | | | | |
| 25837 / 18837 99717 plated | 1961 | SK | Derby | 146 | 30685 | (Longsight) |
| *Remarks:* P'87 by TrainTours | | | | | | |
| 25843 / 18843 | 1961 | SK | Derby | 146 | 30685 | Tyseley |
| *Remarks:* P'88 by Tolemans | | | | | | |
| 25845 / 18845 | 1961 | SK | Derby | 146 | 30685 | Tyseley |
| *Remarks:* P'88 by Tolemans | | | | | | |
| 25853 / 18853 99164 plated | 1962 1989 | SK Spec | Derby | 146 | 30685 | (Cathays) |
| *Remarks:* P'89 by Travelling College (conv to dormitory) | | | | | | |
| 25856 / 18856 99160 plated | 1962 1989 | SK Spec | Derby | 146 | 30685 | (Cathays) |
| *Remarks:* P'89 by Travelling College (conv to dormitory) | | | | | | |
| 25857 / 18857 99711 plated | 1962 | SK | Derby | 146 | 30685 | Tyseley |
| *Remarks:* P'86, with TrainTours till '89 | | | | | | |
| 25861 / 18861 | 1962 | SK | Derby | 146 | 30685 | Quainton |
| *Remarks:* P'89 by Dart Valley?, but if so promptly resold same year | | | | | | |
| 25862 / 18862 99718 plated | 1962 | SK | Derby | 146 | 30685 | (Longsight) |
| *Remarks:* P'87 by TrainTours | | | | | | |
| 25869 / 18869 | 1962 | SK | Derby | 146 | 30685 | Blunsdon |
| *Remarks:* P'91 | | | | | | |
| 25871 / 18871 99161 plated | 1962 1989 | SK Spec | Derby | 146 | 30685 | (Cathays) |
| *Remarks:* P'89 by Travelling College (conv to dormitory) | | | | | | |
| 25891 / 18891 DB977518 | 1962 | SK | Derby | 146 | 30685 | Foxfield |
| *Remarks:* P'89 | | | | | | |
| 25893 / 18893 99712 plated | 1962 | SK | Derby | 146 | 30685 | (Longsight) |
| *Remarks:* P'86 by TrainTours | | | | | | |

| Numbers | Year | Type | Built | Diag | Lot | Location |
|---|---|---|---|---|---|---|
| 25917 / 18917 | 1962 | SK | Derby | 147 | 30686 | E Somerset |

*Remarks:* P'88

| 25955 / 18955<br>99315 plated | 1962 | SK | Derby | 147 | 30686 | Steamtown |

*Remarks:* P'91, in D Smith's maroon rake

| 25972<br>99629 | 1962<br>1979 | SK<br>Exhib | Derby<br>Stewarts Lane | 147 | 30686<br>30950 | Long Marston |

*Remarks:* P'90 by Avon Valley member

| 25994 / 18994<br>99163 plated | 1962<br>1989 | SK<br>Spec | Derby | 146 | 30719 | (Cathays) |

*Remarks:* P'89 by Travelling College (conv to dormitory)

| 26013 / 19013<br>99713 plated | 1962 | SK | Derby | 146 | 30719 | (Longsight) |

*Remarks:* P'86 by TrainTours

| 26025 | 1962 | SK | Derby | 146 | 30719 | Matlock |

*Remarks:* P'83 by TFP, resold to Peak Rail '86 but remained at Midland till '89

| 26043 | 1962 | SK | Derby | 146 | 30719 | Darley Dale |

*Remarks:* P'83 by TFP, at Midland till '87, Buxton till '90

| 26049 | 1962 | SK | Derby | 146 | 30719 | Matlock |

*Remarks:* P'83 by TFP, resold to Peak Rail '86 but remained at Midland till '89

| 26157 | 1962 | SK | York | 146 | 30726 | Matlock |

*Remarks:* P'83 by TFP, resold to Peak Rail '86 but remained at Midland till '89

| 26169 / 19169<br>10000<br>99882 plated | 1962<br>1985 | SK<br>SLF | York<br>Resco | 146 | 30726 | (Steamtown) |

*Remarks:* P'84 by FSE, re-sold to Resco, rebuilt as luxury Sleeper & leased to GS&WR as 'State Car' in 'Royal Scotsman' till '89, then 'Imperial State Car' in 'Queen of Scots' from '90

| 26193 | 1962 | SK | York | 146 | 30726 | Nene Valley |

*Remarks:* P'83

| 26208 / 19208<br>99884 plated | 1962<br>1985 | SK<br>SLF | York<br>Resco | 146 | 30726 | (Steamtown) |

*Remarks:* P'85 by Resco, rebuilt as Sleeper & leased to GS&WR as 'Sleeper 2' in 'Royal Scotsman' till '89, then 'State Car 84' in 'Queen of Scots' from '90

| Numbers | Year | Type | Built | Diag | Lot | Location |
|---------|------|------|-------|------|-----|----------|
| 34083 | 1952 | BSK | Derby | 181 | 30003 | Swindon |

*Remarks:* To be Exhib Van 99614 '71, but not conv. P'87 by Active Force Ltd (Swindon Rly Eng Ltd)

| Numbers | Year | Type | Built | Diag | Lot | Location |
|---------|------|------|-------|------|-----|----------|
| 34111 Army 5318 | 1951 | BSK | Wolverton | 181 | 30025 | Bitton |

*Remarks:* P'89 ex Marchwood (for spares, also to be stationary Buffet & display coach)

| Numbers | Year | Type | Built | Diag | Lot | Location |
|---------|------|------|-------|------|-----|----------|
| 34181 L&HR 70 | 1951 | BSK | Wolverton | 181 | 30025 | - |

*Remarks:* P'70 on Lakeside & Haverthwaite Ry, but cut up during '91.

| Numbers | Year | Type | Built | Diag | Lot | Location |
|---------|------|------|-------|------|-----|----------|
| 34369 DB975475 | 1954 1976 | BSK | Wolverton | 181 | 30074 3891 | ICI Wilton |

*Remarks:* P'91 by NELPG as 60532 Support coach

| Numbers | Year | Type | Built | Diag | Lot | Location |
|---------|------|------|-------|------|-----|----------|
| 34393 | 1954 | BSK | Wolverton | 181 | 30074 | Great Central |

*Remarks:* P pre'74

| Numbers | Year | Type | Built | Diag | Lot | Location |
|---------|------|------|-------|------|-----|----------|
| 34460 | 1953 | BSK | Gloucester | 181 | 30060 | Caerphilly |

*Remarks:* P pre'77 at Dinting

The basic Mk 1 design now forms the largest type of coaching stock design in private hands and is the 'bread and butter' vehicle of so many private railways. This picture was taken in 1990 at Wansford station on the Nene Valley Railway and depicts two Mk 1s just outshopped by the NVR's C&W Department — SK No 26193 and BSK No 35043. *Murray Brown*

| Numbers | Year | Type | Built | Diag | Lot | Location |
|---|---|---|---|---|---|---|
| 34525<br>99966 plated | 1955 | BSK | Wolverton | 181 | 30095 | (Craigentinny) |

*Remarks:* P'87 by HLPG, sold to GS&WR '89 for new 'Royal Scotsman'

| 34531<br>DB977410 | 1955<br>1986 | BSK | Wolverton | 181 | 30095 | Long Marston |

*Remarks:* Used in SAS training at Moreton-on-Lugg. P'89 by Avon Valley member, moved to Long Marston '90

| 34535 | 1955 | BSK | Wolverton | 181 | 30095 | Torbay |

*Remarks:* P'87

| 34537 | 1955<br>1990 | BSK<br>BSKD | Wolverton | 181 | 30095 | Llangollen |

*Remarks:* P'87, converted for disabled

| 34538 | 1955 | BSK | Wolverton | 181 | 30095 | Llangollen |

*Remarks:* P'91

| 34539 | 1955 | BSK | Wolverton | 181 | 30095 | Brechin |

*Remarks:* P'83?

| 34540<br>DB977311 | 1955<br>1985 | BSK | Wolverton | 181 | 30095 | ? |

*Remarks:* P'89 by Llanelli & Dist Ry Soc

| 34550 | 1955 | BSK | Wolverton | 181 | 30095 | Torbay |

*Remarks:* P'83

| 34556 | 1955 | BSK | Wolverton | 181 | 30095 | Stewarts Lane |

*Remarks:* P'90 by VSOE

| 34557<br>99760 plated | 1955 | BSK | Wolverton | 181 | 30095 | N Yorks Moors |

*Remarks:* P'89 by NELPG after lease as Support coach

| 34558 | 1955<br>1986 | BSK<br>DBSK | Wolverton | 181 | 30095 | Buxton |

*Remarks:* P'83 by Peak Rail

| 34562 | 1955 | BSK | Wolverton | 181 | 30095 | Severn Valley |

*Remarks:* P'74 by 75069 Fund

| Numbers | Year | Type | Built | Diag | Lot | Location |
|---------|------|------|-------|------|-----|----------|
| 34612<br>99056 plated | 1955 | BSK | Gloucester | 181 | 30141 | Exbridge |

*Remarks*: P pre'74 by FSE as Support coach & based at Steamtown till '87, then on W Somerset till grounded '90 at a caravan park

| 34618 | 1955 | BSK | Gloucester | 182 | 30142 | Mid-Hants |

*Remarks*: P'77

| 34620<br>DB975289 | 1955<br>1973 | BSK | Gloucester | 182 | 30142 | Bodmin |

*Remarks*: P'90

| 34623 | 1955 | BSK | Gloucester | 182 | 30142 | Colne Valley |

*Remarks*: P'90

| 34624 | 1955 | BSK | Gloucester | 182 | 30142 | E Lancs |

*Remarks*: P'90

| 34625<br>99045 plated | 1955 | BSK | Gloucester | 182 | 30142 | Midland |

*Remarks*: P'90 by P Wood as 44932 Support coach

| 34626 | 1955 | BSK | Gloucester | 182 | 30142 | - |

*Remarks*: P'77 by Resco, its u'frame (& gangways) intended for GNR 127 but used under GWR 233 instead (qv).

| 34627 | 1955 | BSK | Gloucester | 182 | 30142 | Stewarts Lane |

*Remarks*: P'90 by VSOE

| 34634<br>DB975149 | 1955<br>1971 | BSK | C Roberts | 182 | 30143 | Blunsdon |

*Remarks*: P'83 (sat on sleepers in '88)

| 34641<br>DB977495 | 1955<br>1990 | BSK | C Roberts | 182 | 30143 | Chappel |

*Remarks*: P'91 by E Anglian Rly Museum

| 34665 | 1955 | BSK | Wolverton | 181 | 30156 | Dean Forest |

*Remarks*: P'87

| 34666<br>99030 plated | 1955 | BSK | Wolverton | 181 | 30156 | Steamtown |

*Remarks*: Leased by Dart Valley in '85, P'88? for use as LMS 5407 Assoc Support coach from '89

| Numbers | Year | Type | Built | Diag | Lot | Location |
|---------|------|------|-------|------|-----|----------|
| 34671<br>99512 plated | 1955 | BSK | Wolverton | 181 | 30156 | Didcot |
| *Remarks:* P'87 by GWS as Support coach | | | | | | |
| 34672 | 1955 | BSK | Wolverton | 181 | 30156 | Crewe Heritage |
| *Remarks:* P'89? | | | | | | |
| 34675<br>DB977500 | 1955 | BSK | Wolverton | 181 | 30156 | Sheffield |
| *Remarks:* P'89 by S Yorks RPS | | | | | | |
| 34678 | 1955<br>1989 | BSK<br>BSKD | Wolverton | 181 | 30156 | Gloucs-Warks |
| *Remarks:* P'87, converted for disabled | | | | | | |
| 34699 | 1955 | BSK | Wolverton | 181 | 30156 | N Yorks Moors |
| *Remarks:* P'83 by Deltic Pres Soc | | | | | | |
| 34712 | 1955 | BSK | Wolverton | 181 | 30156 | Pitsford |
| *Remarks:* P'90 | | | | | | |
| 34738 | 1955 | BSK | Wolverton | 181 | 30156 | Great Central |
| *Remarks:* P pre'74 | | | | | | |
| 34756<br>DB975084 | 1955<br>1970 | BSK | Wolverton | 182 | 30157 | Plym Valley |
| 34769<br>DB975047 | 1955 | BSK | Wolverton | 182 | 30157 | W Somerset |
| *Remarks:* P'90 | | | | | | |
| 34925 | 1957 | BSK | C Roberts | 182 | 30225 | Stewarts Lane |
| *Remarks:* P'90 by VSOE | | | | | | |
| 34929 | 1957 | BSK | C Roberts | 182 | 30225 | Gloucs-Warks |
| *Remarks:* P'82 | | | | | | |
| 34935 | 1956 | BSK | Metro-Cammell | 182 | 30229 | ? |
| *Remarks:* P'90 by County Bridge Ltd | | | | | | |
| 34941 | 1956 | BSK | Metro-Cammell | 182 | 30229 | Blunsdon |
| *Remarks:* P'90 | | | | | | |
| 34945 | 1956 | BSK | Metro-Cammell | 182 | 30229 | Plym Valley |
| *Remarks:* P'83 | | | | | | |

| Numbers | Year | Type | Built | Diag | Lot | Location |
|---------|------|------|-------|------|-----|----------|
| 34947 | 1956 | BSK | Metro-Cammell | 182 | 30229 | Mid-Hants |

*Remarks:* P'77, at Quainton till '85

| 34949 | 1956 | BSK | Metro-Cammell | 182 | 30229 | E Lancs |

*Remarks:* P'90

| 34952 | 1956 | BSK | Metro-Cammell | 182 | 30229 | Stewarts Lane |

*Remarks:* P'90 by VSOE after use as 44932 Support coach

| 34953 | 1956 | BSK | Metro-Cammell | 182 | 30229 | Market Bosworth |

*Remarks:* P'90

| 34991<br>99538 plated | 1956<br>1982 | BSK | Metro-Cammell | 182 | 30229 | (Stewarts Lane) |

*Remarks:* P'81 by Sea Containers, became 'Baggage Car 9' in VSOE train

| 35006<br>DB975660<br>6337 | 1956<br>1978<br>1990 | BSK | Metro-Cammell | 182 | 30229 | Gloucs-Warks |

*Remarks:* P'91 by 35006 Loco Ltd

| 35012 | 1957 | BSK | Metro-Cammell | 182 | 30229 | Gwili |

*Remarks:* P'90

35028 – see 35270

| 35043 | 1957 | BSK | Gloucester | 181 | 30233 | Nene Valley |

*Remarks:* P'89

| 35059 | 1957 | BSK | Gloucester | 181 | 30233 | Swanage |

*Remarks:* P'86, at Rye House till '89

| 35069 | 1957 | BSK | Gloucester | 181 | 30233 | Strathspey |

*Remarks:* P'87

| 35070 | 1957 | BSK | Gloucester | 181 | 30233 | E Lancs |

*Remarks:* P'88?

| 35072 | 1957 | BSK | Gloucester | 181 | 30233 | Torbay |

*Remarks:* P'87

| 35073 | 1957 | BSK | Gloucester | 181 | 30233 | Steamtown |

*Remarks:* P'88, in D Smith's maroon rake by '91

| Numbers | Year | Type | Built | Diag | Lot | Location |
|---------|------|------|-------|------|-----|----------|
| 35089 NYMR 22 | 1957 | BSK | Gloucester | 181 | 30233 | N Yorks Moors |

Remarks: P'77

35116 – only leased from BR

| 35123 99070 plated | 1958 | BSK | C Roberts | 181 | 30386 | Bo'ness |

Remarks: P'87 by Sovereign Pres Grp, at Steamtown till 14/7/90

| 35128 | 1958 | BSK | C Roberts | 181 | 30386 | Southport |

Remarks: P'89

| 35129 DB977426 | 1958 | BSK | C Roberts | 181 | 30386 | Sheffield |

Remarks: P'89 by S Yorks RPS

| 35130 | 1958 | BSK | C Roberts | 181 | 30386 | Bodmin |

Remarks: P'88

| 35131 99090 plated | 1958 | BSK | C Roberts | 181 | 30386 | Bulmers |

Remarks: P'87 by 6202 Loco Soc

| 35158 | 1958 | BSK | C Roberts | 181 | 30386 | Bulmers |

Remarks: P'90

| 35169 | 1958 | BSK | C Roberts | 181 | 30386 | Colne Valley |

Remarks: P'81

| 35174 Army 5319 | 1958 | BSK | C Roberts | 181 | 30386 | Bitton |

Remarks: P'89

| 35188 DB977330 | 1958 1985 | BSK | Wolverton | 181 | 30427 | Llangollen |

Remarks: P'86 after use in SAS training at MOD Moreton-on-Lugg

35189 – only leased from BR

| 35192 | 1958 | BSK | Wolverton | 181 | 30427 | Quainton |

Remarks: P'89 by Peak Rail, but resold '90 before delivery

| 35193 | 1958 | BSK | Wolverton | 181 | 30427 | Darley Dale |

Remarks: P'89, stored on BR till '90

| Numbers | Year | Type | Built | Diag | Lot | Location |
|---------|------|------|-------|------|-----|----------|
| 35200 | 1958 | BSK | Wolverton | 181 | 30427 | Darley Dale |

Remarks: P'89, stored on BR till '90

| 35204 | 1958 | BSK | Wolverton | 181 | 30427 | Dairycoates |

Remarks: To be P'89 by Ridings Railtours, but after being vandalised was rejected, then P'90 by HLPG

| 35207 | 1958 | BSK | Wolverton | 181 | 30427 | Mid-Hants |

Remarks: P'83

| 35215 | 1958 | BSK | Wolverton | 181 | 30427 | Glenfinnan |
| DB975662 | 1978 | | | | | |

Remarks: P'90 at Station Museum

| 35219 | 1958 | BSK | Wolverton | 181 | 30427 | Bulmers |
| 99850 plated | | | | | | |

Remarks: P'76 by 6000 Loco Association

| 35239 | 1958 | BSK | Wolverton | 181 | 30427 | Nene Valley |

Remarks: P mid '70s

| 35248 | 1958 | BSK | Wolverton | 181 | 30427 | Nene Valley |

Remarks: P'83

| 35255 | 1958 | BSK | Wolverton | 181 | 30427 | Bitton |

Remarks: P'81, cage conv'd for disabled in '88

| 35257 | 1958 | BSK | Wolverton | 181 | 30427 | W Somerset |

Remarks: P'81

| 35270 | 1958 | BSK | Wolverton | 181 | 30427 | Brightlingsea |
| 35028 | 1980? | | | | | |
| | 1989 | Spec | Sail & Steam | | | |

Remarks: P'80 by MNLPS, at Hereford till '88? Converted to Luxury Saloon

| 35293 | 1960 | BSK | Gloucester | 181 | 30573 | Matlock? |

Remarks: P'89? by Peak Rail

| 35305 | 1962 | BSK | Wolverton | 181 | 30699 | Steamtown |

Remarks: P'91

| 35308 | 1962 | BSK | Wolverton | 181 | 30699 | Gloucs-Warks |

Remarks: P'89

| 35314 | 1962 | BSK | Wolverton | 181 | 30699 | E Lancs |

Remarks: P'90

| Numbers | Year | Type | Built | Diag | Lot | Location |
|---------|------|------|-------|------|-----|----------|
| 35322 | 1962 | BSK | Wolverton | 181 | 30699 | Nene Valley |

Remarks: P'89 by R Edmondson, to be 70000's Support coach but stored till Oct'91

| 35326 | 1962 | BSK | Wolverton | 181 | 30699 | S Devon |

Remarks: P'89 by R Edmondson, sold to M Oakley '91 in exchange for 2 'Ironclads'

| 35330 | 1962 | BSK | Wolverton | 181 | 30699 | Lakeside |

Remarks: P'89

| 35333<br>99180 plated | 1962 | BSK | Wolverton | 181 | 30699 | (Didcot) |

Remarks: P'91 by 6024 Pres Soc

| 35334 | 1962<br>1990 | BSK<br>DTBSK | Wolverton | 181 | 30699 | Great Central |

Remarks: P'88, one comp't fire-damaged

| 35337<br>99715 plated | 1962 | BSK | Wolverton | 181 | 30699 | Tyseley |

Remarks: P'86, with Train Tours till '88

| 35340 | 1962 | BSK | Wolverton | 181 | 30699 | Llangollen |

Remarks: P'91

| 35342 | 1962 | BSK | Wolverton | 181 | 30699 | Llangollen |

Remarks: P'91

| 35343 | 1962 | BSK | Wolverton | 181 | 30699 | N Staffs |

Remarks: P'91

| 35362<br>99950 plated | 1962 | BSK | Wolverton | 181 | 30699 | NRM |

Remarks: P'85 by the 'Friends of the NRM' for use as Support coach

| 35405<br>99815 plated | 1962 | BSK | Wolverton | 182 | 30700 | Bo'ness |

Remarks: Sold to Fulmar Services, Invergordon '83. P'85 by SRPS, at Falkirk till '88, then Perth till '90

| 35407<br>99886 plated | 1963<br>1985 | BSK<br>Spec | Wolverton | 181 | 30721 | St Leonards |

Remarks: P'84 by Resco, leased to GS&WR as 'Royal Scotsman' Staff/Gen van '85-9, 'Service Car 1' in 'Queen of Scots' '90. Britannia's Support coach '91, then to storage

| 35414 | 1963 | BSK | Wolverton | 181 | 30721 | Corton |

Remarks: P'83, grounded at Pleasurewood Hills Pk

| Numbers | Year | Type | Built | Diag | Lot | Location |
|---------|------|------|-------|------|-----|----------|
| 35449<br>99241 plated | 1963 | BSK | Wolverton | 181 | 30728 | Severn Valley |

*Remarks:* P'90 by Bert Hitchen as 34027 Support coach

| 35451<br>99313 plated | 1963 | BSK | Wolverton | 181 | 30721 | Worth Valley |

*Remarks:* P'89 by Bahamas Loco Soc, at Steamtown till '90

| 35459<br>99723 plated | 1963 | BSK | Wolverton | 181 | 30721 | (Longsight) |

*Remarks:* P'90 by TrainTours

| 35461<br>99720 plated | 1963 | BSK | Wolverton | 181 | 30721 | (Longsight) |

*Remarks.* P'87 by TrainTours

| 35463<br>99312 plated | 1963 | BSK | Wolverton | 181 | 30721 | Steamtown |

*Remarks:* P'89 by D Smith as 48151 Support coach, at Midland till '90

| 35464 | 1963 | BSK | Wolverton | 181 | 30721 | N Yorks Moors |

*Remarks:* P'91 as 34072 Support coach

| 35467<br>99242 plated | 1963 | BSK | Wolverton | 181 | 30721 | Severn Valley |

*Remarks:* P'89 by consortium (RPR) as Support coach

| 35468 | 1963 | BSK | Wolverton | 181 | 30721 | * NRM |

*Remarks:* P'90 as Support coach

| 35469 | 1963<br>1990 | BSK<br>Spec | Wolverton<br>RFS | 181 | 30721 | (Bounds Green) |

*Remarks:* Used as 3440's Support coach '89. P'90 by SLOA & converted as ETHEL replacement

| 35473 | 1963 | BSK | Wolverton | 181 | 30721 | N Staffs |

*Remarks:* P'91

| 35476<br>99041 plated | 1963 | BSK | Wolverton | 181 | 30721 | Midland |

*Remarks:* P'90 by B Ewart as 46203/80080 Support coach

| 35486<br>99405 plated | 1963 | BSK | Wolverton | 181 | 30721 | Thornton Jct Yd |

*Remarks:* P'90 by J Cameron as 60009 Support coach

| Numbers | Year | Type | Built | Diag | Lot | Location |
|---------|------|------|-------|------|-----|----------|
| 35494 | 1963 | BSK | Wolverton | 181 | 30721 | Blaenavon |

*Remarks:* P'82?

| 43003 KWVR 32 | 1954 | CL | Doncaster | 313 | 30094 | Worth Valley |

| 43010 | 1954 | CL | Doncaster | 313 | 30094 | N Tyneside |

*Remarks:* P'74, on Bluebell till '86

| 43012 | 1954 | CL | Doncaster | 313 | 30094 | Pitsford |

*Remarks:* P'78, on Mid-Hants till '89

| 43024 SR 102 | 1954 | CL | Doncaster | 313 | 30094 | Strathspey |

| 43034 | 1954 | CL | Doncaster | 313 | 30094 | N Norfolk |

*Remarks:* P'75 by M&GNJRS

| 43041 | 1954 | CL | Doncaster | 313 | 30094 | N Norfolk |

*Remarks:* P'75 by M&GNJRS

| 43043 | 1954 | CL | Doncaster | 313 | 30094 | Great Central |

*Remarks:* P'78 by RVP member, stored at Hertford till '79, then at Nene Valley till '82

| 43046 | 1954 | CL | Doncaster | 313 | 30094 | * NRM |

*Remarks:* P'78, loaned to N Yorks Moors till '83

| 43128 KWVR 20 | 1954 | BS | York | 371 | 30045 | Worth Valley |

*Remarks:* P mid '70s

| 43140 | 1954 1983? | BS DTS | York Blunsdon | 371 | 30045 | Blunsdon |

*Remarks:* P mid '70s, on Nene Valley till '79, then on West Somerset till '81. Expected to move to E Kent soon

| 43145 KWVR 30 | 1954 | BS | York | 371 | 30045 | Worth Valley |

*Remarks:* P mid '70s

| 43147 | 1954 | BS | York | 371 | 30045 | Pitsford |

*Remarks:* P'72, stored near Cambridge till '73, then at Chappel till '89

| 43157 | 1954 | BS | York | 371 | 30045 | Chappel |

*Remarks:* P'78

| Numbers | Year | Type | Built | Diag | Lot | Location |
|---------|------|------|-------|------|-----|----------|
| 43161 | 1954 | BS | York | 371 | 30045 | Mid-Hants |

*Remarks:* P'78, for sale in '84/5

| Numbers | Year | Type | Built | Diag | Lot | Location |
|---------|------|------|-------|------|-----|----------|
| 43172 (ex-53172) | 1954 | BS | Doncaster | 371 | 30093 | N Tyneside |

*Remarks:* P'73, on Bluebell till '86

| Numbers | Year | Type | Built | Diag | Lot | Location |
|---------|------|------|-------|------|-----|----------|
| 43181 (ex-53181) KWVR 12 | 1954 | BS | Doncaster | 371 | 30093 | - |

*Remarks:* P' ? on Worth Valley, scrapped at Chesterfield in '75.

| Numbers | Year | Type | Built | Diag | Lot | Location |
|---------|------|------|-------|------|-----|----------|
| 43182 (ex-53182) | 1954 | BS | Doncaster | 371 | 30093 | Llangollen |

*Remarks:* P'78

| Numbers | Year | Type | Built | Diag | Lot | Location |
|---------|------|------|-------|------|-----|----------|
| 43186 (ex-53186) | 1954 | BS | Doncaster | 371 | 30093 | Midland |

*Remarks:* P'71 but stored in Derby till '75

| Numbers | Year | Type | Built | Diag | Lot | Location |
|---------|------|------|-------|------|-----|----------|
| 43190 (ex-53190) | 1954 | BS | Doncaster | 371 | 30093 | Quainton |

*Remarks:* P'77, at Mid-Hants till '85

| Numbers | Year | Type | Built | Diag | Lot | Location |
|---------|------|------|-------|------|-----|----------|
| 43231 (ex-53231) Army 5301 | 1954 | BS | Doncaster | 371 | 30093 | - |

*Remarks:* W' ? & sold to Army for Longmoor Military Railway. P'70 but at Longmoor till '71, stored at Eastleigh till '73, Cranmore till '80. Broken up by Worth Valley '82.

| Numbers | Year | Type | Built | Diag | Lot | Location |
|---------|------|------|-------|------|-----|----------|
| 43264 (ex-53049?) | 1955 | BS | Swindon | 372 | 30047 | E Somerset |

*Remarks:* P'82 ex RNAD Trecwn

| Numbers | Year | Type | Built | Diag | Lot | Location |
|---------|------|------|-------|------|-----|----------|
| 43266 (ex-53051?) | 1955 | BS | Swindon | 372 | 30047 | Gwili |

*Remarks:* P'82 ex RNAD Trecwn

| Numbers | Year | Type | Built | Diag | Lot | Location |
|---------|------|------|-------|------|-----|----------|
| 43275 (ex-53086?) Army 3034 | 1955 | BS | York | 371 | 30087 | N Staffs |

*Remarks:* W'65, sold to Army '70. P'82 from MODAD Radway Green

| Numbers | Year | Type | Built | Diag | Lot | Location |
|---------|------|------|-------|------|-----|----------|
| 43289 (ex-53100?) Army 5310 | 1955 | BS | York | 371 | 30087 | E Somerset |

*Remarks:* W'65, sold to Longmoor Military Ry. P'70, at Longmoor till '71 then Eastleigh till '73

| Numbers | Year | Type | Built | Diag | Lot | Location |
|---------|------|------|-------|------|-----|----------|
| 43300 (ex-53111?) Army ? | 1955 | BS | York | 371 | 30087 | N Staffs |

*Remarks:* W'65, sold to Army '70. P'82 from MODAD Radway Green

| Numbers | Year | Type | Built | Diag | Lot | Location |
|---------|------|------|-------|------|-----|----------|
| 43345 (ex-53156?) KWVR 10 | 1955 | BS | York | 371 | 30087 | Worth Valley |

*Remarks:* P pre'74

| Numbers | Year | Type | Built | Diag | Lot | Location |
|---------|------|------|-------|------|-----|----------|
| 43349 (ex-53160?) SR 104 | 1955 | BS | York | 371 | 30087 | Strathspey |

Remarks: P pre'74

| 43357 (ex-53168?) | 1955 | BS | York | 371 | 30087 | N Norfolk |

Remarks: P'77

| 43359 (ex-53170?) | 1955 | BS | York | 371 | 30087 | N Norfolk |

Remarks: P'78 by M&GNJRS, at Cambridge till ' ?

| 46069 Army 3301 | 1954 | S | Derby | 326 | 30051 | - |

Remarks: Large end-windows fitted by the Army. P'78 on Mid-Hants, to be an office, but broken up '83.

| 46093 KWVR 9 | 1954 | S | Derby | 326 | 30051 | - |

Remarks: P' ?, on Worth Valley till '73 then at Radstock till '76; scrapped in Glasgow.

| 46097 | 1954 | S | Derby | 326 | 30051 | Midland |

Remarks: P'71, stored in Derby till '75 (near derelict in '87)

| 46116 | 1954 | S | Wolverton | 326 | 30038 | Gloucs-Warks |

Remarks: P'77, on Mid-Hants till '83

| 46130 | 1954 | S | Wolverton | 326 | 30038 | Llangollen |

Remarks: P'77

| 46132 | 1954 | S | Wolverton | 326 | 30038 | Gwili |

Remarks: P'82 from RNAD Fishguard

| 46137 | 1954 | S | Wolverton | 326 | 30038 | Swansea Vale |

Remarks: P'?

| 46139 | 1954 | S | Wolverton | 326 | 30038 | Great Central |

Remarks: P'72 by RVP, at Manningtree till '73 then Chappel till '81; sold to GCR '83.

| 46140 | 1954 | S | Wolverton | 326 | 30038 | - |

Remarks: P'?? by FSE at Steamtown? In 1980 it came to Butterley from Ellastone Staffs & remained till sold for filming *London's Burning* at Nene Valley Jan'90; rolled onto its side, it was scrapped on site.

| 46141 | 1954 | S | Wolverton | 326 | 30038 | Padiham |

Remarks: P'76, on Nene Valley till '79, W Somerset till '85, then Wallingford till a short stay on Nene Valley for Jan'90 filming of *London's Burning*

| Numbers | Year | Type | Built | Diag | Lot | Location |
|---------|------|------|-------|------|-----|----------|
| 46142 NYMR 11 | 1954 | S | Wolverton | 326 | 30038 | Brechin |

Remarks: P pre'74, on N Yorks Moors till '80

| 46145 KWVR 15 | 1954 | S | Wolverton | 326 | 30038 | Worth Valley |

Remarks: P pre'74

| 46147 | 1954 | S | Wolverton | 326 | 30038 | N Norfolk |

Remarks: P'78 by M&GNJRS, under restoration at Cambridge till ' ?

| 46157 KWVR 16 | 1954 | S | Wolverton | 326 | 30038 | Worth Valley |

Remarks: P pre'74

| 46213 | 1954 | S | Derby | 326 | 30098 | - |

Remarks: P'?? by FSE at Steamtown? In 1980 it came to Butterley from Ellastone Staffs, but was broken up for spares '83.

| 46218 SR 107 | 1954 | S | Derby | 326 | 30098 | Moy |

Remarks: P mid '70s, on Strathspey till sold '90 to be restaurant at Invermoy House Hotel

| 46228 KWVR 8 | 1954 | S | Derby | 326 | 30098 | - |

Remarks: P' ? on Worth Valley, body broken up for spares ' ?; its underframe was used as a crane-runner, but was cut up during '84.

| 46235 | 1954 | S | Derby | 326 | 30098 | - |

Remarks: P' ?, on N Yorks Moors till '77, then at Embsay. Advertised in Railway World July'84, apparently without success, & cut-up 1984/5.

| 48001 | 1955 | SLO | Doncaster | 330 | 30092 | Great Central |

Remarks: P'78 by RVP & stored at Hertford till '79, moving to Nene Valley till '82. Sold to GCR in '83.

| 48004 | 1955 | SLO | Doncaster | 330 | 30092 | Midland |

Remarks: P post'77

| 48006 | 1955 | SLO | Doncaster | 330 | 30092 | - |

Remarks: P'78 on Dart Valley, but scrapped by '90.

| 48007 KWVR 7 | 1955 | SLO | Doncaster | 330 | 30092 | - |

Remarks: P' ?, on Worth Valley till '73 then at Radstock till '76; scrapped in Glasgow.

| Numbers | Year | Type | Built | Diag | Lot | Location |
|---------|------|------|-------|------|-----|----------|
| 48008 | 1955 | SLO | Doncaster | 330 | 30092 | - |

*Remarks:* P'78 on Dart Valley, but scrapped by '90.

| Numbers | Year | Type | Built | Diag | Lot | Location |
|---------|------|------|-------|------|-----|----------|
| 48009 | 1955 | SLO | Doncaster | 330 | 30092 | - |

*Remarks:* P'78 on Dart Valley, but scrapped '91.

| Numbers | Year | Type | Built | Diag | Lot | Location |
|---------|------|------|-------|------|-----|----------|
| 48010<br>KWVR 18 | 1955 | SLO | Doncaster | 330 | 30092 | - |

*Remarks:* P' ? on Worth Valley, scrapped at Kettering in '75.

| Numbers | Year | Type | Built | Diag | Lot | Location |
|---------|------|------|-------|------|-----|----------|
| 48011<br>KWVR 17 | 1955 | SLO | Doncaster | 330 | 30092 | Worth Valley |

*Remarks:* P pre'74

| Numbers | Year | Type | Built | Diag | Lot | Location |
|---------|------|------|-------|------|-----|----------|
| 48015 | 1955 | SLO | Doncaster | 330 | 30092 | N Tyneside |

*Remarks:* P'75, on Bluebell till '86

| Numbers | Year | Type | Built | Diag | Lot | Location |
|---------|------|------|-------|------|-----|----------|
| 48018<br>KWVR 19 | 1955 | SLO | Doncaster | 330 | 30092 | Worth Valley |

*Remarks:* P mid '70s

It is pleasing that so many of the BR suburban coaches have survived, despite being a nightmare for maintenance reasons (they are more often than not referred to as 'Rot Boxes'!). Clearly this one does not come into that category — 1954-built Third No 46218, seen at its former home of the Strathspey Railway. It has now been sold to a catering concern. *Hugh Madgin*

| Numbers | Year | Type | Built | Diag | Lot | Location |
|---------|------|------|-------|------|-----|----------|
| 48026 | 1955 | SLO | Doncaster | 330 | 30092 | - |

*Remarks:* P'75 by M&GNJRS, used on N Norfolk till W'82; dismantled '88, u'frame used to store GER bodies.

The following 7 vehicles are the only surviving APT vehicles:

| Numbers | Year | Type | Built | Diag | Lot | Location |
|---------|------|------|-------|------|-----|----------|
| 48103 Set 370.006 | 1978 | DTS | Derby | LE201 | 30923 | * Crewe Heritage Centre |

*Remarks:* P'88

| Numbers | Year | Type | Built | Diag | Lot | Location |
|---------|------|------|-------|------|-----|----------|
| 48106 Set 370.006 | 1978 | DTS | Derby | LE201 | 30923 | * Crewe HC |

*Remarks:* P'88

| Numbers | Year | Type | Built | Diag | Lot | Location |
|---------|------|------|-------|------|-----|----------|
| 48404 | 1978 | TRSB | Derby | LK201 | 30925 | * Crewe HC |

*Remarks:* P'88

| Numbers | Year | Type | Built | Diag | Lot | Location |
|---------|------|------|-------|------|-----|----------|
| 48602 | 1978 | TBF | Derby | LJ101 | 30927 | * Crewe HC |

*Remarks:* P'88

| Numbers | Year | Type | Built | Diag | Lot | Location |
|---------|------|------|-------|------|-----|----------|
| 48603 | 1978 | TBF | Derby | LJ101 | 30927 | * Crewe HC |

*Remarks:* P'88

| Numbers | Year | Type | Built | Diag | Lot | Location |
|---------|------|------|-------|------|-----|----------|
| 49002 | 1978 | M | Crewe | LC501 | 30928 | * Crewe HC |

*Remarks:* P'88

| Numbers | Year | Type | Built | Diag | Lot | Location |
|---------|------|------|-------|------|-----|----------|
| 49006 | 1978 | M | Crewe | LC501 | 30928 | * Crewe HC |

*Remarks:* P'88

| Numbers | Year | Type | Built | Diag | Lot | Location |
|---------|------|------|-------|------|-----|----------|
| 50341 NYMR D10 | 1957 | DMBS | Gloucester | 536 | 30278 | - |

*Remarks:* Class 100. P'73, on N Yorks Moors till '85, then at Swanage till '86 & W Somerset till scrapped '91 at Snailwell

| Numbers | Year | Type | Built | Diag | Lot | Location |
|---------|------|------|-------|------|-----|----------|
| 50397 (DB975137) | 1957 | DMBS | Park Royal | 635 | 30286 | Market Bosworth |

*Remarks:* Class 103. P' ?, used as Observation Car

| Numbers | Year | Type | Built | Diag | Lot | Location |
|---------|------|------|-------|------|-----|----------|
| 50413 | 1958 | DMBS | Park Royal | 635 | 30286 | W Somerset |

*Remarks:* Class 103. P'76?, sold to D+EG '82

| Numbers | Year | Type | Built | Diag | Lot | Location |
|---------|------|------|-------|------|-----|----------|
| 50414 | 1958 | DMBS | Park Royal | 635 | 30286 | W Somerset |

*Remarks:* Class 103. P'76?

| Numbers | Year | Type | Built | Diag | Lot | Location |
|---------|------|------|-------|------|-----|----------|
| 50416 DB975005 | 1957 1967 | DMBS | Wickham | 606 | 30288 | Chasewater |

*Remarks:* P'81

| Numbers | Year | Type | Built | Diag | Lot | Location |
|---------|------|------|-------|------|-----|----------|
| 51017 | 1959 | DMSL | Swindon | 551 | 30413 | Brechin |

Remarks: Class 126. P'83?

| Numbers | Year | Type | Built | Diag | Lot | Location |
|---------|------|------|-------|------|-----|----------|
| 51043 | 1959 | DMBSL | Swindon | 608 | 30414 | Brechin |

Remarks: Class 126. P'83

| Numbers | Year | Type | Built | Diag | Lot | Location |
|---------|------|------|-------|------|-----|----------|
| 51118 NYMR D11 | 1957 | DMBS | Gloucester | 536 | 30444 | W Somerset |

Remarks: Class 100. P'73, on N Yorks Moors till '85, then at Swanage till '86

| Numbers | Year | Type | Built | Diag | Lot | Location |
|---------|------|------|-------|------|-----|----------|
| 51203 | 1959 | DMBS | Metro-Cammell | 523 | 30467 | Darlington |

Remarks: Class 101. P'91

| Numbers | Year | Type | Built | Diag | Lot | Location |
|---------|------|------|-------|------|-----|----------|
| 51485 | 1959 | DMBS | Cravens | 548 | 30503 | W Somerset |

Remarks: Class 105. P'82

| Numbers | Year | Type | Built | Diag | Lot | Location |
|---------|------|------|-------|------|-----|----------|
| 51591 | 1959 | DMBS | Derby | 588 | 30521 | Midland |
| 55966 | 1985 | DMPMV | | | | |

Remarks: Class 127. P'84 by NRM but returned to BR '85 for conversion to parcels van. P'90 for the second time

| Numbers | Year | Type | Built | Diag | Lot | Location |
|---------|------|------|-------|------|-----|----------|
| 51592 | 1959 | DMBS | Derby | 588 | 30521 | S Devon |

Remarks: Class 127. P'84, resold '90

| Numbers | Year | Type | Built | Diag | Lot | Location |
|---------|------|------|-------|------|-----|----------|
| 51604 | 1959 | DMBS | Derby | 588 | 30521 | S Devon |

Remarks: Class 127. P'84, resold '90

| Numbers | Year | Type | Built | Diag | Lot | Location |
|---------|------|------|-------|------|-----|----------|
| 51610 | 1959 | DMBS | Derby | 588 | 30521 | Blunsdon |
| 55967 | 1985 | DMPMV | | | | |

Remarks: Class 127. P'90

| Numbers | Year | Type | Built | Diag | Lot | Location |
|---------|------|------|-------|------|-----|----------|
| 51616 | 1959 | DMBS | Derby | 588 | 30521 | Great Central |

Remarks: Class 127. P'84 by Red Triangle Soc

| Numbers | Year | Type | Built | Diag | Lot | Location |
|---------|------|------|-------|------|-----|----------|
| 51618 | 1959 | DMBS | Derby | 588 | 30521 | Llangollen |

Remarks: Class 127. P'85

| Numbers | Year | Type | Built | Diag | Lot | Location |
|---------|------|------|-------|------|-----|----------|
| 51622 | 1959 | DMBS | Derby | 588 | 30521 | Great Central |

Remarks: Class 127. P'84 by Red Triangle Soc

| Numbers | Year | Type | Built | Diag | Lot | Location |
|---------|------|------|-------|------|-----|----------|
| 51625 | 1959 | DMBS | Derby | 588 | 30521 | Midland |
| 55976 | 1985 | DMPMV | | | | |

Remarks: Class 127. P'90

| Numbers | Year | Type | Built | Diag | Lot | Location |
|---------|------|------|-------|------|-----|----------|
| 51627 | 1959 | DMBS | Derby | 588 | 30521 | Crewe HC |
| 55986 | 1985 | DMPMV | | | | |

*Remarks:* Class 127. P'91

| Numbers | Year | Type | Built | Diag | Lot | Location |
|---------|------|------|-------|------|-----|----------|
| 51813 | 1961 | DMBC | B R C W | 564 | 30592 | E Lancs |

*Remarks:* Class 110. P'90

| 51842 | 1961 | DMCL | B R C W | 563 | 30593 | E Lancs |

*Remarks:* Class 110. P'90

| 51941 | 1957 | DMBS | Derby | 634 | 30601 | Severn Valley |

*Remarks:* Class 108. P'91

| 52064 | 1957 | DMCL | Derby | 638 | 30660 | Severn Valley |

*Remarks:* Class 108. P'91

| 52071 | 1961 | DMBC | B R C W | 564 | 30691 | Lakeside |

*Remarks:* Class 110. P'90

| 52077 | 1961 | DMCL | B R C W | 563 | 30692 | Lakeside |

*Remarks:* Class 110. P'90

| 54207 | 1958 | DTCL | Derby | 640 | 30409 | Scunthorpe |

*Remarks:* Class 108. P'91 by Appleby-Frodingham RPS (Br Steel)

| 55966 | 1959 | DMBS | Derby | 588 | 30521 | Midland |
|---|---|---|---|---|---|---|
| | 1985 | DMPMV | | | | |

*Remarks:* Class 127. P'90

| 55967 | 1959 | DMBS | Derby | 588 | 30521 | Blunsdon |
|---|---|---|---|---|---|---|
| | 1985 | DMPMV | | | | |

*Remarks:* Class 127. P'90

| 55976 | 1959 | DMBS | Derby | 588 | 30521 | Midland |
|---|---|---|---|---|---|---|
| | 1985 | DMPMV | | | | |

*Remarks:* Class 127. P'90

| 56097 | 1957 | DTCL | Gloucester | 537 | 30279 | W Somerset |
| NYMR D12 | | | | | | |

*Remarks:* Class 100. P'74, on N Yorks Moors till '85, then at Swanage till '86

| 56099 | 1957 | DTCL | Gloucester | 537 | 30279 | - |
| NYMR D13 | | | | | | |

*Remarks:* Class 100. P'74, on N Yorks Moors till '85, then at Swanage till '86 & W Somerset till scrapped '91 at Snailwell

| Numbers | Year | Type | Built | Diag | Lot | Location |
|---------|------|------|-------|------|-----|----------|
| 56121 | 1959 | DTCL | Cravens | 526 | 30281 | W Somerset |

*Remarks:* Class 105. P'82

| 56160 | 1957 | DTCL | Park Royal | 645 | 30287 | Market Bosworth |
| DB975228 | 1972 | | | | | |

*Remarks:* Class 103. P'78, operated as Observation Car equipped with a bar

| 56168 | 1958 | DTCL | Park Royal | 645 | 30287 | W Somerset |

*Remarks:* Class 103. P'76?

| 56169 | 1958 | DTCL | Park Royal | 645 | 30287 | W Somerset |

*Remarks:* Class 103. P'76?, sold to D+EG '82

| 56171 | 1957 | DTCL | Wickham | 607 | 30289 | Chasewater |
| DB975006 | 1967 | | | | | |

*Remarks:* P'81

| 56301 | 1957 | DTCL | Gloucester | 537 | 30445 | Chasewater |

*Remarks:* Class 100

The humble diesel multiple unit has had a relatively hard time convincing enthusiasts of its necessity to be preserved, but there is now a growing number in safe hands. The West Somerset Railway is one of the few private railways which has encouraged diesel traction and this Cravens twin unit, comprising DTCL No 56121 and DMBS No 51485, is pictured at Minehead on 17 March 1991. *Mike Jones*

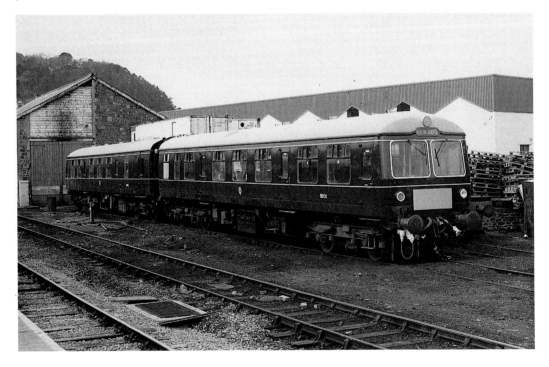

| Numbers | Year | Type | Built | Diag | Lot | Location |
|---------|------|------|-------|------|-----|----------|
| 56317 | 1957 | DTCL | Gloucester | 537 | 30445 | Gwili |

Remarks: Class 100. P'77

| 56456 | 1958 | DTCL | Cravens | 533 | 30470 | Llangollen |
| 54456 | 1983 | | | | | |

Remarks: Class 105. P'84

| 59003 | 1957 | TS | Derby | 555 | 30212 | Dart Valley |

Remarks: Class 116. P'84

| 59004 | 1957 | TS | Derby | 555 | 30212 | Dart Valley |

Remarks: Class 116. P'84

| 59098 | 1960 | TFLRB | Swindon | 560 | 30537 | N Yorks Moors |

Remarks: Class 126. P'73, used as a Camping coach. Grounded at Goathland '79 so that bogies could be used under BR Pullman parlour cars 'Opal' & 'Garnet' (qv)

| 59099 | 1960 | TFLRB | Swindon | 560 | 30537 | N Yorks Moors |

Remarks: Class 126. P'73, used as a Camping coach. Grounded at Goathland '79 so that bogies could be used under BR Pullman parlour cars 'Garnet' & 'Opal' (as above)

| 59245 | 1958 | TBSL | Derby | 546 | 30412 | Scunthorpe |

Remarks: Class 108. P'91 by A-FRPS (British Steel's staff)

| 59276 | 1959 | TSLRB | Swindon | 561 | 30336 | Great Central |

Remarks: Class 120. P'84

| 59404 | 1959 | TCK | Swindon | 571 | 30416 | Brechin |

Remarks: Class 126. P'83?

| 59444 | 1958 | TC | Derby | 555 | 30448 | Chasewater |

Remarks: Class 116. P'90

| 59575 | 1960 | TSLRB | Metro-Cammell | 625 | 30615 | Manchester |
| KWVR 24 | | | | | | |

Remarks: Class 101. P'73, used on Worth Valley till '84

| 59701 | 1961 | TSL | B R C W | 648 | 30594 | Severn Valley |

Remarks: Class 110. P'91

| 59719 | 1959 | TCL | Derby | 599 | 30597 | ? |

Remarks: Class 115. P'91 by Dart Wyvern Assoc, Burton-on-Trent

| 60000 | 1956 | DMBSO | Eastleigh | 650 | 30329 | St Leonards |
| Unit 1001 | | | | | | |

Remarks: P'89 by Hastings Diesel Grp

| Numbers | Year | Type | Built | Diag | Lot | Location |
|---------|------|------|-------|------|-----|----------|
| 60001 Unit 1001 | 1956 | DMBSO | Eastleigh | 650 | 30329 | St Leonards |
| Remarks: P'89 by HDG | | | | | | |
| 60016 Unit 1012 'Mountfield' | 1957 1990 | DMBSO | Eastleigh | 651 | 30395 | Swanage |
| Remarks: P'90 by HDG | | | | | | |
| 60018 Unit 1013 | 1957 | DMBSO | Eastleigh | 651 | 30395 | Swanage |
| Remarks: P'89 by HDG, stored till '90 | | | | | | |
| 60019 Unit 1013 | 1957 | DMBSO | Eastleigh | 651 | 30395 | St Leonards |
| Remarks: P'89 by HDG | | | | | | |
| 60500 | 1956 | TTSO | Eastleigh | 670 | 30331 | St Leonards |
| Remarks: P'89 by HDG | | | | | | |
| 60501 | 1956 | TTSO | Eastleigh | 670 | 30331 | St Leonards |
| Remarks: P'89 by HDG | | | | | | |
| 60502 | 1956 | TTSO | Eastleigh | 670 | 30331 | St Leonards |
| Remarks: P'89 by HDG | | | | | | |
| 60527 | 1957 | TTSO | Eastleigh | 671 | 30397 | Swanage |
| Remarks: P'89 by HDG, stored till '90 | | | | | | |
| 60528 | 1957 | TTSO | Eastleigh | 671 | 30397 | St Leonards |
| Remarks: P'89 by HDG | | | | | | |
| 60529 | 1957 | TTSO | Eastleigh | 671 | 30397 | St Leonards |
| Remarks: P'89 by HDG | | | | | | |
| 60700 | 1956 | TFK | Eastleigh | 660 | 30330 | St Leonards |
| Remarks: P'89 by HDG | | | | | | |
| 60708 | 1957 | TFK | Eastleigh | 661 | 30396 | St Leonards |
| Remarks: P'90 by HDG | | | | | | |
| 60709 | 1957 | TFK | Eastleigh | 661 | 30396 | St Leonards |
| Remarks: P'89 by HDG | | | | | | |

| Numbers | Year | Type | Built | Diag | Lot | Location |
|---------|------|------|-------|------|-----|----------|
| 60750 DB975386 Lab 4 'Hastings' | 1958 | TRB | Eastleigh | 678 | 30393 | St Leonards |

Remarks: W'64, used by RTC Derby for tilting tests. P'90 by HDG

| Numbers | Year | Type | Built | Diag | Lot | Location |
|---------|------|------|-------|------|-----|----------|
| 61824 (DB977720) | 1960 | MBSO | Pressed Steel | 416 | 30630 | Yoker (BR) |

Remarks: Class 303. P'91 (see 75808 for remarks)

| Numbers | Year | Type | Built | Diag | Lot | Location |
|---------|------|------|-------|------|-----|----------|
| 65451 | 1959 | DMBSO | Wolverton | 407 | 30477 | E Lancs |

Remarks: Class 504. P'91 by Barclay Pres Grp

| Numbers | Year | Type | Built | Diag | Lot | Location |
|---------|------|------|-------|------|-----|----------|
| 65461 | 1959 | DMBSO | Wolverton | 407 | 30477 | E Lancs |

Remarks: Class 504. P'91 by Class 504 Grp

| Numbers | Year | Type | Built | Diag | Lot | Location |
|---------|------|------|-------|------|-----|----------|
| 75758 (DB977721 | 1960 | DTSO | Pressed Steel | 439 | 30629 | Yoker (BR) |

Remarks: Set 303.048. P'91 (see 75808 for remarks)

| Numbers | Year | Type | Built | Diag | Lot | Location |
|---------|------|------|-------|------|-----|----------|
| 75808 75814 (DB977719) | 1960 1991 | BDTSO | Pressed Steel | 439 | 30631 | Yoker (BR) |

Remarks: Set 303.048. P'91, given to Glasgow Museum of Transport & renumbered to resemble scrapped member of this unit. (Intended to be static exhibit at Kelvin Hall from c'93)

| Numbers | Year | Type | Built | Diag | Lot | Location |
|---------|------|------|-------|------|-----|----------|
| 77172 | 1959 | DTSO | Wolverton | 443 | 30478 | E Lancs |

Remarks: Class 504. P'91 by Barclay Pres Grp

| Numbers | Year | Type | Built | Diag | Lot | Location |
|---------|------|------|-------|------|-----|----------|
| 77182 | 1959 | DTSO | Wolverton | 443 | 30478 | E Lancs |

Remarks: Class 504. P'91 by Class 504 Grp

| Numbers | Year | Type | Built | Diag | Lot | Location |
|---------|------|------|-------|------|-----|----------|
| 79441 SR 105 'Glenfiddich' | 1956 | TFLRB | Swindon | 560 | 30197 | Strathspey |

Remarks: Class 126. P' ? by Wm Grant & Sons

| Numbers | Year | Type | Built | Diag | Lot | Location |
|---------|------|------|-------|------|-----|----------|
| 79443 | 1956 | TFLRB | Swindon | 560 | 30197 | N Yorks Moors |

Remarks: Class 126. P'73, used as static buffet at Goathland

| Numbers | Year | Type | Built | Diag | Lot | Location |
|---------|------|------|-------|------|-----|----------|
| 79960 | 1958 | R'bus | W-und-M | 611 | 30482 | N Norfolk |

Remarks: P'67

| Numbers | Year | Type | Built | Diag | Lot | Location |
|---------|------|------|-------|------|-----|----------|
| 79962 KWVR 62 | 1958 | R'bus | W-und-M | 611 | 30482 | Worth Valley |

Remarks: P'67

| Numbers | Year | Type | Built | Diag | Lot | Location |
|---------|------|------|-------|------|-----|----------|
| 79963 | 1958 | R'bus | W-und-M | 611 | 30482 | N Norfolk |

Remarks: P'67

| Numbers | Year | Type | Built | Diag | Lot | Location |
|---------|------|------|-------|------|-----|----------|
| 79964 KWVR 64 | 1958 | R'bus | W-und-M | 611 | 30482 | Worth Valley |

Remarks: Original Buessing engine replaced by AEC type in 1960's. P'67

| Numbers | Year | Type | Built | Diag | Lot | Location |
|---------|------|------|-------|------|-----|----------|
| 79976 | 1958 | R'bus | AC Cars | 614 | 30479 | Bodmin |

Remarks: P'73 by Somerset Railway Museum & at Bleadon & Uphill till loaned to the formative Bodmin & Wenford in '85

| Numbers | Year | Type | Built | Diag | Lot | Location |
|---------|------|------|-------|------|-----|----------|
| 79978 'Premier' | 1958 | R'bus | AC Cars | 614 | 30479 | Colne Valley |

Remarks: P'68, on N Yorks Moors till '79 then on Kent & E Sussex till '84

The end of the BR Bury line third rail contact system in October 1991 saw the demise of the captive Class 504 units, but thanks to the interest and generosity of a group and an individual, we will still be able to enjoy the indescribable basic pleasure of trundling along in these spartan but interesting coaches. The two preserved sets are based, appropriately, on the East Lancashire Railway and are seen at Ramsbottom on 5 October 1991, just after hand-over from BR, with power being provided by Class 25 No 25901, sandwiched in the middle. Vehicles are: DMBSO No 65451 + DTSO No 77172 and DMBSO No 65461 + DTSO No 77182. *Peter Marsh*

| Numbers | Year | Type | Built | Diag | Lot | Location |
|---------|------|------|-------|------|-----|----------|
| 79979 | 1958 | R'bus | AC Cars | 614 | 30479 | Strathspey |

Remarks: Body P c'76/7

| 79998 DB975003 Lab 16 'Gemini' | 1957 1966 | DMBS | Derby | 406 | 30368 | E Lancs |

Remarks: P'86 by W Yorks Transport Mus, at Bradford Hammerton St till '89

| 79999 DB975004 Lab 16 'Gemini' | 1957 1966 | DTCL | Derby | 442 | 30369 | E Lancs |

Remarks: P'86 by W Yorks Transport Mus, at Bradford Hammerton St till '89

80021 – see 1883

| 80030 | 1962 | RK | C Roberts | 702 | 30585 | Brechin |

Remarks: Sold Fulmar Svcs, Invergordon '83. P'85

| 80307 | 1959 | POS | Wolverton | 721 | 30487 | Kidderminster |

Remarks: P'91, donated to SVR by GPO

| 80501 | 1952 | BG | Derby | 711 | 30009 | Chinnor |

Remarks: P'90

| 80509 | 1952 | BG | Derby | 711 | 30009 | Llangollen |

Remarks: P'89

| 80518 | 1952 | BG | Derby | 711 | 30009 | Llangollen |

Remarks: P'87

| 80566 | 1954 | BG | Derby | 711 | 30039 | Old Oak Common |

Remarks: P'82 by Diesel Traction Grp, reportedly for NYMR, at Swindon till '90

| 80590 | 1955 | BG | Wolverton | 711 | 30040 | Midland |

Remarks: P'91

| 80591 | 1955 | BG | Wolverton | 711 | 30040 | Worth Valley |

Remarks: P'87

| 80686 | 1955 | BG | Metro-Cammell | 711 | 30136 | Midland |

Remarks: P'82

| 80702 | 1955 | BG | Metro-Cammell | 711 | 30136 | Bodmin |

Remarks: P'87

| Numbers | Year | Type | Built | Diag | Lot | Location |
|---------|------|------|-------|------|-----|----------|
| 80736 | 1956 | BG | B R C W | 711 | 30140 | W Somerset |
| Remarks: P'90 | | | | | | |
| 80741 | 1956 | BG | B R C W | 711 | 30140 | Llangollen |
| Remarks: P'87, fitted with temporary kitchen '90 | | | | | | |
| 80742 | 1956 | BG | B R C W | 711 | 30140 | W Somerset |
| Remarks: P'90 by GW Rolling Stock Grp | | | | | | |
| 80753 | 1956 | BG | B R C W | 711 | 30140 | Mid-Hants |
| Remarks: P'86 | | | | | | |
| 80776 | 1956 | BG | B R C W | 711 | 30140 | Severn Valley |
| | 1989 | BSOD | S V R | | | |
| Remarks: P'87, converted for handicapped | | | | | | |
| 80785 | 1956 | BG | B R C W | 711 | 30140 | Colne Valley |
| Remarks: P'86?, now the Exhibition coach | | | | | | |
| 80792 | 1956 | BG | B R C W | 711 | 30140 | Colne Valley |
| Remarks: P'86? | | | | | | |
| 80796 | 1956 | BG | B R C W | 711 | 30140 | N Yorks Moors |
| Remarks: P'87 | | | | | | |
| 80797 | 1956 | BG | B R C W | 711 | 30140 | Tintern |
| Remarks: P'85, Café in station picnic area | | | | | | |
| 80827 | 1955 | BG | Cravens | 711 | 30144 | Steamtown |
| Remarks: P'88 | | | | | | |
| 80905 | 1957 | BG | Pressed Steel | 711 | 30162 | Sheffield |
| Remarks: P'88 by S Yorks RPS | | | | | | |
| 80972 | 1956 | BG | York | 711 | 30173 | W Somerset |
| 'Lorna Doone' | 1991 | BSOD | W S R | | | |
| Remarks: P'90, converted for disabled | | | | | | |
| 80993 | 1956 | BG | York | 711 | 30173 | E Lancs |
| Remarks: P'81 | | | | | | |
| 81013 / 84013 | 1956 | BG | York | 711 | 30173 | Arley |
| Remarks: P'88 on Severn Valley | | | | | | |

| Numbers | Year | Type | Built | Diag | Lot | Location |
|---|---|---|---|---|---|---|
| 81020 / 84020 | 1956 | BG | Cravens | 711 | 30224 | Midland |
| Remarks: P'91 | | | | | | |
| 81022 / 84022 | 1956 | BG | Cravens | 711 | 30224 | Bodmin |
| Remarks: P'87? | | | | | | |
| 81025 / 84025 99783 plated | 1956 | BG | Cravens | 711 | 30224 | (Southall) |
| Remarks: P'88 by MNLPS, at Bulmers till '89 | | | | | | |
| 81031 / 84031 | 1956 | BG | Cravens | 711 | 30224 | Pitsford |
| Remarks: P'88? | | | | | | |
| 81033 / 84033 | 1956 1990 | BG KBG | Cravens | 711 | 30224 | N Norfolk |
| Remarks: P'87, conv'd to Kitchen van '90 complete with a generator | | | | | | |
| 81039 / 84039 | 1956 | BG | Cravens | 711 | 30224 | Gloucs-Warks |
| Remarks: P'? | | | | | | |
| 81062 | 1957 | BG | Metro-Cammell | 711 | 30228 | Rainhill |
| Remarks: P'83? by Rainhill Library Museum | | | | | | |
| 81101 / 84101 | 1958 | BG | Metro-Cammell | 711 | 30228 | Mid-Hants |
| Remarks: P'86, Generator van from '87 | | | | | | |
| 81107 / 84107 | 1958 | BG | Metro-Cammell | 711 | 30228 | Llangollen |
| Remarks: P'89 | | | | | | |
| 81131 | 1958 | BG | Metro-Cammell | 711 | 30228 | - |
| Remarks: Sold to Fulmar Services, Invergordon '83. P'84 by SRPS but fire damaged at Falkirk; broken up '88. | | | | | | |
| 81144 / 84144 | 1958 | BG | Metro-Cammell | 711 | 30228 | Midland |
| Remarks: P'89 | | | | | | |
| 81156 / 84156 | 1958 | BG | Metro-Cammell | 711 | 30228 | E Somerset |
| Remarks: P'87 | | | | | | |
| 81295 | 1957 | BG | Pressed Steel | 711 | 30323 | Chappel |
| Remarks: P'82? for use as Buffet | | | | | | |
| 81343 / 84343 | 1957 | BG | Pressed Steel | 711 | 30400 | Great Central |
| Remarks: P'87 by Task Undertakings Ltd | | | | | | |

| Numbers | Year | Type | Built | Diag | Lot | Location |
|---------|------|------|-------|------|-----|----------|
| 81507 / 84507 | 1957 | BG | Pressed Steel | 711 | 30484 | Colne Valley |
| Remarks: P'88 | | | | | | |
| 81554 / 84554 | 1958 | BG | Pressed Steel | 711 | 30484 | Matlock |
| Remarks: P'90 by N Notts Loco Grp | | | | | | |
| 86149 / 93149 | 1958 | GUV | Pressed Steel | 811 | 30417 | Crewe Heritage |
| Remarks: P'91 | | | | | | |
| 86178 / 93178 | 1958 | GUV | Pressed Steel | 811 | 30417 | Tyseley |
| Remarks: P'87 | | | | | | |
| 86183 / 93183 | 1958 | GUV | Pressed Steel | 811 | 30417 | Buxton |
| Remarks: P'88 | | | | | | |
| 86226 / 93226 | 1958 | GUV | Pressed Steel | 811 | 30417 | Tunbridge Wells |
| Remarks: P'91 by TWERPS | | | | | | |
| 86253 / 93253 | 1958 | GUV | Pressed Steel | 811 | 30417 | Crewe Heritage |
| Remarks: P'91 by Mr Ratcliffe | | | | | | |
| 86283 / 93283 93418 | 1958 1987 | GUV | Pressed Steel | 811 | 30417 | E Lancs |
| Remarks: P'87 | | | | | | |
| 86350 / 93350 94066 | 1958 1985 | GUV | Pressed Steel | 811 | 30417 | Sheffield |
| Remarks: P'88 by S Yorks RPS | | | | | | |
| 86380 / 93380 | 1958 | GUV | Pressed Steel | 811 | 30417 | Midland |
| Remarks: P'87? | | | | | | |
| 86383 / 93383 | 1958 | GUV | Pressed Steel | 811 | 30417 | Sheffield |
| Remarks: P'88 by S Yorks RPS | | | | | | |
| 86460 / 93460 | 1958 | GUV | Pressed Steel | 811 | 30417 | Mid-Hants |
| Remarks: P'88 | | | | | | |
| 86470 / 93470 | 1958 | GUV | Pressed Steel | 811 | 30417 | Sheffield |
| Remarks: P'88 by S Yorks RPS | | | | | | |
| 86533 / 93533 | 1960 | GUV | St.Rollox | 811 | 30402 | Crewe Heritage |
| Remarks: P'91? | | | | | | |

| Numbers | Year | Type | Built | Diag | Lot | Location |
|---------|------|------|-------|------|-----|----------|
| 86545 / 93545 | 1959 | GUV | St.Rollox | 811 | 30403 | N Yorks Moors |
| *Remarks:* P'89 | | | | | | |
| 86565 / 93565 | 1959 | GUV | St.Rollox | 811 | 30403 | Sheffield |
| *Remarks:* P'88 by S Yorks RPS | | | | | | |
| 86566 / 93566 | 1959 | GUV | St.Rollox | 811 | 30403 | Blunsdon |
| *Remarks:* P'90 | | | | | | |
| 86568 / 93568 | 1959 | GUV | St.Rollox | 811 | 30403 | Bodmin |
| *Remarks:* P'87 | | | | | | |
| 86639 / 93639 | 1959 | GUV | St.Rollox | 811 | 30403 | N Yorks Moors |
| *Remarks:* P'89 | | | | | | |
| 86674 / 93674 | 1959 | GUV | Pressed Steel | 811 | 30565 | Mid-Hants |
| *Remarks:* P'88? | | | | | | |
| 86690 / 93690 | 1959 | GUV | Pressed Steel | 811 | 30565 | Mid-Hants |
| *Remarks:* P'88 | | | | | | |
| 86802 / 93802 94073 | 1959 1985 | GUV | Pressed Steel | 811 | 30565 | Sheffield |
| *Remarks:* P'88 by S Yorks RPS | | | | | | |
| 86813 / 93813 | 1959 | GUV | Pressed Steel | 811 | 30565 | N Yorks Moors |
| *Remarks:* P'89 | | | | | | |
| 86814 / 93814 | 1959 | GUV | Pressed Steel | 811 | 30565 | Mid-Hants |
| *Remarks:* P'88? | | | | | | |
| 86868 / 93868 | 1960 | GUV | Pressed Steel | 811 | 30616 | Bristol Ind Mus |
| *Remarks:* P'87 | | | | | | |
| 86869 / 93869 | 1960 | GUV | Pressed Steel | 811 | 30616 | E Lancs |
| *Remarks:* P'87 | | | | | | |
| 86918 / 93918 | 1960 | GUV | Pressed Steel | 811 | 30616 | E Lancs |
| *Remarks:* P'87 | | | | | | |
| 86972 / 93972 | 1960 | GUV | Pressed Steel | 811 | 30616 | Sheffield |
| *Remarks:* P'88 by S Yorks RPS | | | | | | |

| Numbers | Year | Type | Built | Diag | Lot | Location |
|---------|------|------|-------|------|-----|----------|
| 87247 | 1954 | FVY | Faverdale | 800 | 30125 | Darlington |
| DB975642 | 1977 | | | | | |

*Remarks:* P'89 at Rly Centre

| 87537 | 1959 | FVY | Faverdale | 800 | 30344 | Nene Valley |

*Remarks:* P'86?

| 87888 | 1960 | FVY | Faverdale | 800 | 30384 | Burnham-on-Crouch |

*Remarks:* Body P'91 at Mangapps Farm, ex Snailwell

| 87905 | 1960 | FVY | Faverdale | 800 | 30384 | * NRM |

| 87937 | 1960 | FVY | Faverdale | 800 | 30384 | Tanfield |
| DB975306 | 1973 | | | | | |

*Remarks:* P'77 by Stephenson & Hawthorns Loco Trust, u'frame used under body of NER CLY 70 (qv)

| 87948 | 1960 | FVY | Faverdale | 800 | 30384 | Worth Valley |
| DB975957 | 1980 | | | | | |

*Remarks:* P'87

| 92004 | 1957 | PMVY | Swindon | 805 | 30345 | Gwili |

*Remarks:* P'77

| 92035 | 1957 | PMVY | Swindon | 805 | 30345 | S Devon |

| 92040 | 1957 | PMVY | Swindon | 805 | 30345 | Caerphilly |

| 92060 | 1957 | PMVY | Swindon | 805 | 30345 | Tanfield ? |
| DB975347 | 1973 | | | | | |
| 070888 | 1980 | | | | | |

*Remarks:* P'81 by Stephenson & Hawthorns Loco Trust

| 92067 | 1958 | PMVY | Swindon | 805 | 30383 | S Devon |
| DB975307 | 1973 | | | | | |

*Remarks:* P'81

| 92069 | 1958 | PMVY | Swindon | 805 | 30383 | Dean Forest |
| DB975383 | 1974 | | | | | |

*Remarks:* P'84

| 92076 | 1958 | PMVY | Swindon | 805 | 30383 | Tyseley |

| 92080 | 1958 | PMVY | Swindon | 805 | 30383 | Severn Valley |

*Remarks:* P'78 by 4150 Loco Fund

| 92090 | 1958 | PMVY | Swindon | 805 | 30383 | Severn Valley |

*Remarks:* P'73 by Erlestoke Manor Fund, at Ashchurch till '76

| Numbers | Year | Type | Built | Diag | Lot | Location |
|---|---|---|---|---|---|---|
| 92091 | 1958 | PMVY | Swindon | 805 | 30383 | Torbay |

*Remarks: P'87*

| 92097 | 1958 | PMVY | Swindon | 805 | 30383 | N Norfolk |

*Remarks: P'75*

| 92110 DB975381 | 1958 1974 | PMVY | Swindon | 805 | 30383 | - |

*Remarks: P'83 by Cotswold Diesel Pres Grp & at Gloucs-Warks till broken up '84.*

| 94109 041838 | 1959 1985 | CCTY | Earlestown | 816 | 30549 | Burnham-on-Crouch |

*Remarks: P'89 at Mangapps Farm*

| 94125 | 1959 | CCTY | Earlestown | 816 | 30549 | Great Central |

*Remarks: P'84 by RVP*

| 94181 | 1959 | CCTY | Earlestown | 816 | 30549 | Stewarts Lane |

*Remarks: P'86 by VSOE*

| 94259 | 1959 | CCTY | Earlestown | 816 | 30549 | Brechin |

*Remarks: P'82*

| 94264 DB977357 | 1960 | CCTY | Earlestown | 816 | 30549 | E Lancs |

*Remarks: P'90*

| 94286 041869 | 1960 | CCTY | Earlestown | 816 | 30549 | Great Central |

*Remarks: P'90 by N Tilsey*

| 94338 (DB977303) | 1960 | CCTY | Earlestown | 816 | 30562 | Embsay |

*Remarks: P'88*

| 94388 041644 | 1960 1982 | CCTY | Earlestown | 816 | 30562 | Haverhill |

*Remarks: P'88? by 'Trains of Thought'*

| 94434 | 1960 | CCTY | Earlestown | 816 | 30562 | Colne Valley |

*Remarks: P'83?*

| 94464 | 1960 | CCTY | Earlestown | 816 | 30563 | N Norfolk |

*Remarks: P'82?*

| Numbers | Year | Type | Built | Diag | Lot | Location |
|---------|------|------|-------|------|-----|----------|
| 94501<br>DB977097 | 1960<br>1982 | CCTY | Earlestown | 816 | 30563 | Swindon |

Remarks: P'88 by Active Force Ltd (latterly Swindon Railway Engineering Ltd)

| Numbers | Year | Type | Built | Diag | Lot | Location |
|---------|------|------|-------|------|-----|----------|
| 94502<br>DB977072 | 1960 | CCTY | Earlestown | 816 | 30563 | W Somerset |

Remarks: P'91

| 94518<br>DB977073 | 1960<br>1981 | CCTY | Earlestown | 816 | 30563 | Dean Forest |

Remarks: P'88?

| 94534 | 1960 | CCTY | Earlestown | 816 | 30563 | E Lancs |

Remarks: P'91 by Barclay Loco Grp

| 94536<br>041760 ? | 1960 | CCTY | Earlestown | 816 | 30563 | Colne Valley |

Remarks: W'83 (traces of a number ending ..1760 under paint)

| 94578 | 1960 | CCTY | Earlestown | 816 | 30563 | Quainton |

Remarks: P'85

| 94597 | 1960 | CCTY | Earlestown | 816 | 30564 | Dairycoates |

Remarks: P'84?, on Severn Valley till '89 as Store for BR Pullmans; now held by HLPG due to payment dispute

| 94605<br>024610 | 1960<br>1985 | CCTY | Earlestown | 816 | 30564 | Great Central |

Remarks: P'90 by Deltic PS

| 94606 | 1960 | CCTY | Earlestown | 816 | 30564 | Great Central |

Remarks: P'83 by RVP

| 94677 | 1960 | CCTY | Earlestown | 816 | 30564 | Llangollen |

Remarks: P'89

| 94691<br>DB977358 | 1960<br>1986 | CCTY | Earlestown | 816 | 30564 | Llangollen |

Remarks: P'89

| 94707 | 1961 | CCTY | Earlestown | 816 | 30614 | Great Central |

Remarks: P'83 by RVP

| 94709<br>041870 | 1961 | CCTY | Earlestown | 816 | 30614 | Great Central |

Remarks: P'90 by 9F Grp ?

| Numbers | Year | Type | Built | Diag | Lot | Location |
|---------|------|------|-------|------|-----|----------|
| 94713 DB977076 | 1961 1981 | CCTY | Earlestown | 816 | 30614 | W Somerset |

*Remarks:* P'91

| 94737 | 1961 | CCTY | Earlestown | 816 | 30614 | Colne Valley |

*Remarks:* P'83

| 94796 | 1961 | CCTY | Earlestown | 816 | 30614 | Nene Valley |

*Remarks:* P'86

| 94817 | 1961 | CCTY | Earlestown | 816 | 30614 | Sheffield |

*Remarks:* P'88 by S Yorks RPS

| 94869 | 1961 | CCTY | Earlestown | 816 | 30614 | Mid-Norfolk |

*Remarks:* P'90 by F&DRS

| 94889 | 1961 | CCTY | Earlestown | 816 | 30614 | Colne Valley |

*Remarks:* P'84

| 94917 | 1961 | CCTY | Earlestown | 816 | 30651 | W Somerset |

*Remarks:* P'81

| 96202 082962 | 1962 1967 | GUV | Doncaster | 817 | 30674 | Great Central |

*Remarks:* Prototype, built on LNER underframe from CL 32480 (later 88030, built 1930 at Dukinfield to Diag.50). P'89 by RVP

| 96300 DB975056 | 1957 1971 | HBY | Earlestown | 751 | 30146 | Llangollen |

*Remarks:* Converted to Train Heating Van '71. P'88, Generator Van '90

| 96336 DE321099 | 1957 1966 | HBY | Earlestown | 751 | 30146 | Rutland |

*Remarks:* Converted to Train Heating Van '66. P'81, on Great Central till c'86

| 96347 DE321101 | 1957 1966 | HBY | Earlestown | 751 | 30146 | Colne Valley |

*Remarks:* Converted to Train Heating Van '66. P'86

| 96369 | 1957 | HBY | Earlestown | 751 | 30146 | * NRM |

| 96403 | 1957 | HBY | Earlestown | 751 | 30146 | Quainton |

*Remarks:* P'72

| DB975874 | 1979 | R'bus | BL Workington | | | * NRM |

*Remarks:* 4-wheel prototype railbus 'LEV1'. P'87

| Numbers | Year | Type | Built | Diag | Lot | Location |
|---------|------|------|-------|------|-----|----------|
| DB977091 | 1982 | TSO | BL Workington | | | Shepherdswell |

*Remarks:* Experimental, using Leyland coach body on u'frame from Mk.1 BCK 21234. P'86, on Nene Valley till '91 then loaned to E Kent Ry for 5 years

*Others:*
Unidentified RU (built BRCW 1959) at Manchester Liverpool Rd on loan from builders

*Unidentified vehicles:*
Coach at 'Victoria Station' restaurant, Universal Studios, Los Angeles (may be 21177)
Possible SK at Loch Awe as snack bar
BG P'90 by S Yorks RPS
Horse box underframe intended to carry body of GWR TZ 254 at Cranmore

*Also:*
VSOE has 2 Ferry vans at Stewarts Lane — 21,70239,7000-7 in storage, & its wrongly identified twin in service

# THE PULLMAN CAR COMPANY

The first 'Number' shown is the Schedule Number from the 1960 list; 'Car' is the Car Type letter taken from the 1932 list; 'User' is the first Company to employ the Car after construction.

| Numbers | Year | Type | Built | Car | User | Location |
|---|---|---|---|---|---|---|
| - Midland | 1874 | S | Detroit/Derby | - | MR | Midland |
| MR 21 | 1888 | | | | | |

*Remarks:* Clerestory. Toured abroad 1874-7, lent to GNR briefly during 1879, sold to MR 1888. Body grounded at Skipton in ' ?. P'74, but stored at Normanton Barracks till moved to Butterley in '81

| Numbers | Year | Type | Built | Car | User | Location |
|---|---|---|---|---|---|---|
| - | 1874 | TB | Detroit/Derby | - | MR | Midland |
| MR 1-4? | | | | | | |

*Remarks:* Clerestory. Built for & owned by the MR. Body grounded at Bradford in ' ?. P'75, moved to Butterley & grounded as a bothy

| Numbers | Year | Type | Built | Car | User | Location |
|---|---|---|---|---|---|---|
| - | 1874 | CP | Detroit/Derby | - | MR | Midland |
| | 1875 | FP | | | | |
| MR 5-8? | | | | | | |

*Remarks:* Clerestory. Built for & owned by the MR. Body grounded at Bradford in ' ?. P'75, moved to Butterley & grounded as a bothy

| Numbers | Year | Type | Built | Car | User | Location |
|---|---|---|---|---|---|---|
| 3 Balmoral | 1882 | S | Detroit/Derby | - | GNR | Brighton |

*Remarks:* Clerestory 6-wheel, rebuilt with bogies c1895. W'07, stored till '18 then body grounded as dwelling at Seaford, Sussex, with that of 'Dunrobin' below. P'87, being restored using parts from 'Dunrobin'

| Numbers | Year | Type | Built | Car | User | Location |
|---|---|---|---|---|---|---|
| 4 Culross | 1882 | S | Detroit/Derby | - | GNR | - |
| Dunrobin | 1885 | | | | | |

*Remarks:* Clerestory 6-wheel. Historical details as per 'Balmoral' above. Only frame & few panels existed '90.

| Numbers | Year | Type | Built | Car | User | Location |
|---|---|---|---|---|---|---|
| 32 Emerald | 1910 | FK | B R C W | G | SECR | Betws-y-Coed |
| 101 | 1955 | | | | | |
| 022xxx | 1959 | Camp | P Pk or Lancing | | | |

*Remarks:* Remodelled 1924; damaged by fire '55, only used for training till '59. Became a Camping Coach on BR(M) & in use till P' ? by Conwy Valley Railway Museum.

| Numbers | Year | Type | Built | Car | User | Location |
|---|---|---|---|---|---|---|
| 43 Sapphire | 1910 | FP | B R C W | G | SECR | Seaburn |
| | 1924 | FK | | | | |
| NAAFI 37 | 1942 | | | | | |
| P.51 | 1960 | Camp | P Pk or Lancing | | | |

*Remarks:* Rebuilt 1937, used by the NAAFI 1942-8, W'60 & converted to 'Holiday Coach' for BR(S). P'??, at Ashford till '84 then Isfield. Restored by Allen Industries at Woolwich, & in '88 became part of restaurant at Ocean Park (nr Sunderland)

| 47 Alicante | 1912 | FK | Cravens | G | SECR | Marazion |
|---|---|---|---|---|---|---|
| | 1935 | CP | Preston Park | | | |
| | c1950 | FP | Preston Park | | | |
| 9874 | 1963 | Camp | P Pk or Lancing | | | |

*Remarks:* Latterly a Camping Coach for BR(W) Staff Assoc. Reported sold June'84, together with the other 5, to E & K Hitchens, Long Rock, Penzance (despite its steelwork being severely corroded)

| 50 Mimosa | 1914 | FK | B R C W | G | SECR | Marazion |
|---|---|---|---|---|---|---|
| | 1935 | CP | Preston Park | | | |
| | c1950 | FP | Preston Park | | | |
| 9869 | 1963 | Camp | P Pk or Lancing | | | |

*Remarks:* Latterly a Camping Coach for BR(W) Staff Assoc. (See remarks under No 47)

One of the best-known and historical 'preserved' coaches sits on the platform at Butterley on the Midland Railway Centre's line. One of the three earliest Pullman vehicles surviving, 'Midland', which later became MR No 21, is a tangible, just, reminder of a bygone age of luxury travel. It began its 'new lease of life' in preservationists' hands after its far-flung career (including service overseas) exactly 100 years after it was built, and reached Butterley in 1981. The MRC still has hopes of renovating the body and placing it on a suitable underframe. *Murray Brown*

| Numbers | Year | Type | Built | Car | User | Location |
|---------|------|------|-------|-----|------|----------|
| 59 Topaz | 1914 | FP | B R C W | G | SECR | * NRM |

*Remarks:* W'60 for preservation & at Clapham till 1973. Restored to original condition at Steamtown in '84

| Numbers | Year | Type | Built | Car | User | Location |
|---------|------|------|-------|-----|------|----------|
| 92 Malaga | 1921 | FK | Longhedge | H | SECR | Shepperton |

*Remarks:* 12-wheel. W'61, P'63 by Ian Allan & used as their Board Room & Executive Dining room

| Numbers | Year | Type | Built | Car | User | Location |
|---------|------|------|-------|-----|------|----------|
| 97 Calais | 1921 | FP | B R C W | H | SECR | Marazion |
| Car No 97 | 1947 | TP | Preston Park | | | |
| 9870 | 1963 | Camp | P Pk or Lancing | | | |

*Remarks:* 12-wheel. Latterly a Camping Coach for BR(W) Staff Assoc. (See remarks under No 47)

| Numbers | Year | Type | Built | Car | User | Location |
|---------|------|------|-------|-----|------|----------|
| 99 Padua | 1920 | FP | B R C W | H | SECR | Seaburn |
| Car No 99 | 1946 | SG | Preston Park | | | |
| P.59 | 1960 | Camp | P Pk or Lancing | | | |
| DW150431 | | | | | | |

*Remarks:* 12-wheel. W'60 for conversion to 'Holiday Coach' for BR(S), later in departmental use. P'?? by W H McAlpine & at Market Overton till '??. Sold to Resco '??, but remained at Steamtown till resold '88 to become part of a restaurant at Ocean Park (nr Sunderland)

| Numbers | Year | Type | Built | Car | User | Location |
|---------|------|------|-------|-----|------|----------|
| 102 Rosalind | 1921 | FK | B R C W | H | SECR | Seaburn |
| NAAFI 18 | 1942 | | | | | |
| P.47 | 1960 | Camp | P Pk or Lancing | | | |
| DW150430 | | | | | | |

*Remarks:* 12-wheel. Used by the NAAFI from 1942-8, W'60 for conversion to 'Holiday Coach' for BR(S) & later in departmental use. P' ? by W H McAlpine & at Market Overton till '??. Sold '88 & left Steamtown to become part of a restaurant at Ocean Park (nr Sunderland) with 43 & 99 above, plus BR 4328 (qv)

| Numbers | Year | Type | Built | Car | User | Location |
|---------|------|------|-------|-----|------|----------|
| 113 Car No 13 | 1921 | TK | Clayton | J | LBSCR | Torbay |
| | 1947 | Obs | Preston Park | | SR | |
| 280 | 1957 | | | | | |
| 'Devon Belle' | | | | | | |

*Remarks:* Second-hand underframe from a 1918 LNWR Ambulance coach. Remodelled 1937 with Bar counter; rebuilt as Observation Car in '47 & sold to BR(M) '57. P'68

| Numbers | Year | Type | Built | Car | User | Location |
|---------|------|------|-------|-----|------|----------|
| 114 Car No 14 | 1921 | TK | Clayton | J | LBSCR | California, USA |
| | 1947 | Obs | Preston Park | | SR | |
| 281 | 1957 | | | | | |

*Remarks:* Second-hand underframe from a 1918 LNWR Ambulance coach. Remodelled 1937 with Bar counter; rebuilt as Observation Car in '47 & sold to BR(M) '57. P'68, going to USA on the 'Flying Scotsman' tour in '69; sold '73? for use as a Restaurant at 150 Chestnut Street, San Francisco

| Numbers | Year | Type | Built | Car | User | Location |
|---------|------|------|-------|-----|------|----------|
| 119 Cambria | 1920 | FK | Clayton | - | GER | K&ESR |
| | 1924 | FB | Longhedge | | | |
| DE960820 | 1938 | | | | | |
| KESR 71 | | | | | | |

*Remarks:* 12-wheel. Kitchen removed 1924, rebuilt 1934 & Wc'38 for conversion to a Mess/tool van. P'80 from Beighton

| Numbers | Year | Type | Built | Car | User | Location |
|---|---|---|---|---|---|---|
| 135 Elmira | 1921 | FK | Clayton | J | SECR | Ravenglass |
| | 1933 | CK | Preston Park | | | |
| Car No 135 | 1948 | TK | Preston Park | | | |
| 022261 | 1960 | Camp | P Pk or Lancing | | | |

*Remarks:* Second-hand underframe from a 1914 LNWR Ambulance coach. P'68

| 136 Formosa | 1921 | FK | Clayton | J | SECR | Isfield |
|---|---|---|---|---|---|---|
| | 1934 | CK | Preston Park | | | |
| Maid of Kent | 1948 | FK | Preston Park | | | |
| CC.161 | 1960 | Camp | P Pk or Lancing | | | |

*Remarks:* Second-hand underframe from a 1914 LNWR Ambulance coach. Latterly a Camping Coach for BR(E) at Kings Lynn. P'83 by GCR Coach Group, moved to storage near Banbury till '86

| 137 Maid of Kent | 1921 | FK | Clayton | J | SECR | Ravenglass |
|---|---|---|---|---|---|---|
| | 1934 | CK | Preston Park | | | |
| Car No 137 | 1948 | TK | Preston Park | | | |
| 022262 | 1960 | Camp | P Pk or Lancing | | | |

*Remarks:* Second-hand underframe from a 1914 LNWR Ambulance coach. P'68

| 153 Aurora | 1923 | FG | B R C W | F | SR | Marazion |
|---|---|---|---|---|---|---|
| Car No 503 | 1950 | TG | Preston Park | | | |
| Aurora | 1952 | FG | Preston Park | | | |
| 9873 | 1963 | Camp | P Pk or Lancing | | | |

*Remarks:* Latterly a Camping Coach for BR(W) Staff Assoc. (See remarks under No 47)

| 154 Flora | 1923 | FG | B R C W | F | SR | Marazion |
|---|---|---|---|---|---|---|
| Car No 154 | 1946 | TG | Preston Park | | | |
| Flora | 1948 | FG | Preston Park | | | |
| 9871 | 1963 | Camp | P Pk or Lancing | | | |

*Remarks:* Latterly a Camping Coach for BR(W) Staff Assoc. (See remarks under No 47)

| 155 Juno | 1923 | FG | B R C W | F | SR | Marazion |
|---|---|---|---|---|---|---|
| Car No 502 | 1950 | TG | Preston Park | | | |
| Juno | 1952 | FG | Preston Park | | | |
| 9872 | 1963 | Camp | P Pk or Lancing | | | |

*Remarks:* Latterly a Camping Coach for BR(W) Staff Assoc. (See remarks under No 47)

| 156 Montana | 1923 | FG | B R C W | F | SR | Barnwell Jn. |
|---|---|---|---|---|---|---|
| CC.165 | 1960 | Camp | P Pk or Lancing | | | |

*Remarks:* Latterly a Camping coach for BR(E). P'67 as dwelling at Kindrum Kennels (Cambs)

| 157 Car No 54 | 1923 | TK | Clayton | K | LNER | Bluebell |
|---|---|---|---|---|---|---|
| | 1937 | TB | Preston Park | | | |
| LNER 490 | 1942 | | | | | |
| 'Fiona' | | | | | | |

*Remarks:* Loaned to LNER 1942-6. P'63, on Dart Valley till '70, then at Tyseley till sold to Sea Containers & moved to Steamtown in '80. Resold (partly dismantled) to Bluebell in '84 & moved in '86. ('Fiona' in 70's or 80's?)

| Numbers | Year | Type | Built | Car | User | Location |
|---------|------|------|-------|-----|------|----------|
| 175 Fingall | 1924 | FK | B R C W | K | SR | Bluebell |

*Remarks:* P'63, at Beaulieu till '72 then at Haven Street on IoW till '79.

| Numbers | Year | Type | Built | Car | User | Location |
|---------|------|------|-------|-----|------|----------|
| 184 Theodora | 1926 | FK | Metro C&W | K | SR | K&ESR |
|  | 1932 | CK | Preston Park |  |  |  |
|  | 1946 | FK | P Pk or Metro? |  |  |  |
| 184 | 1958 | KBar | Preston Park |  |  |  |
| 7874 | 1960 |  |  |  |  |  |
| KESR 51 |  |  |  |  |  |  |

*Remarks:* Painted SR Green when rebuilt 1958, sold to BR(S) 1960. W'63, P'64

| Numbers | Year | Type | Built | Car | User | Location |
|---------|------|------|-------|-----|------|----------|
| 185 Barbara | 1926 | FK | Metro C&W | K | SR | K&ESR |
|  | 1932 | CK | Preston Park |  |  |  |
| 185 | 1946 | KBar | Preston Park |  |  |  |
| 7877 | 1960 |  |  |  |  |  |
| KESR 52 |  |  |  |  |  |  |

*Remarks:* Branded 'Refreshment Car' in 1946; painted SR Green when rebuilt 1958, sold to BR(S) 1960. W'63, P'64

| Numbers | Year | Type | Built | Car | User | Location |
|---------|------|------|-------|-----|------|----------|
| 193 Car No 35 | 1926 | TP | B R C W | K | SR | - |
|  | 1946 | SP | Preston Park |  |  |  |
| Wye | 1964 |  |  |  |  |  |

*Remarks:* P'63 at Beaulieu; deliberately destroyed by burning in 1971/2?

| Numbers | Year | Type | Built | Car | User | Location |
|---------|------|------|-------|-----|------|----------|
| 194 Car No 36 | 1926 | TP | B R C W | K | SR | Colne Valley |
|  | 1946 | SP | Preston Park |  |  |  |
| 'Morella' | 1968 |  |  |  |  |  |
| 99204 plated |  |  |  |  |  |  |
| 'Hermione' | 1989 |  |  |  |  |  |

*Remarks:* P'67 by Bulmers & used as Cinema Car in the 'Cider Train'. Sold to VSOE '86, at Swindon till '87 & Stewarts Lane till '88. Refurbished & renamed by '89

| Numbers | Year | Type | Built | Car | User | Location |
|---------|------|------|-------|-----|------|----------|
| 208 Leona | 1927 | FP | Midland C&W | K | LNER | Elsenham |
| Car No 208 | 1947 | TG | Preston Park |  |  |  |
| Leona | 1988 |  |  |  |  |  |

*Remarks:* W'67. P' ? as bar at 'The Pullman' Inn, Cressing, Essex. Original name restored when moved to new restaurant complex near Cambridge c'87/8

| Numbers | Year | Type | Built | Car | User | Location |
|---------|------|------|-------|-----|------|----------|
| 210 Marcelle | 1927 | FK | Metro C&W | K | LNER | Kensington |
| Car No 105 | 1946 | TK | P Pk or Metro? |  |  |  |
| Hebe | 1964 | FK | Preston Park |  |  |  |

*Remarks:* Latterly part of the standby set for the 'Blue Pullman'. P' ? in an arcade at 26 Kensington High St but one end believed dismantled, leaving only ¾ body intact, & some uncertainty over whether running gear exists

| Numbers | Year | Type | Built | Car | User | Location |
|---------|------|------|-------|-----|------|----------|
| 213 Minerva | 1927 | FK | Midland C&W | K | LNER | (Stewarts Lane) |
|  | 1951 | FG | Preston Park | U |  |  |
| 99535 plated | 1981 |  | Steamtown | K |  |  |

*Remarks:* Rebuilt 1951 for the 'Golden Arrow' set & made to resemble the new Cars. P' ?, at Lytham till sold to Sea Containers 1980 & restored by them to near its original appearance

| Numbers | Year | Type | Built | Car | User | Location |
|---------|------|------|-------|-----|------|----------|
| 219 Car No 64 | 1928 | SK | Midland C&W | K | SR | Bluebell |
|  | 1937 | TP | Preston Park |  |  |  |
| 'Christine' | 1968 |  |  |  |  |  |
| 99201 plated |  |  |  |  |  |  |

*Remarks:* P'67 by Bulmers & used as Restaurant Car in the 'Cider Train'. Sold to VSOE '86, at Swindon till '87 then moved to Stewarts Lane & promptly resold

| Numbers | Year | Type | Built | Car | User | Location |
|---------|------|------|-------|-----|------|----------|
| 228 Car No 75 | 1928 | TP | Metro C&W | K | LNER | Hilderstone |
| LNER 481 | 1942 |  |  |  |  |  |

*Remarks:* Loaned to LNER 1942-8. P' ? at the 'Spot Gate' Inn (Staffs)

Sea Containers Ltd owns the Venice Simplon Orient Express Pullman vehicles which offer the ultimate in long-distance luxury travel with a London to Venice service, Wagon Lits vehicles being used for the French side of the Channel. The British-based Pullmans, which are frequently used for charter work, are maintained at Stewarts Lane depot. It is here that 'Minerva' is pictured undergoing bogie attention on 14 November 1987. *David Brown*

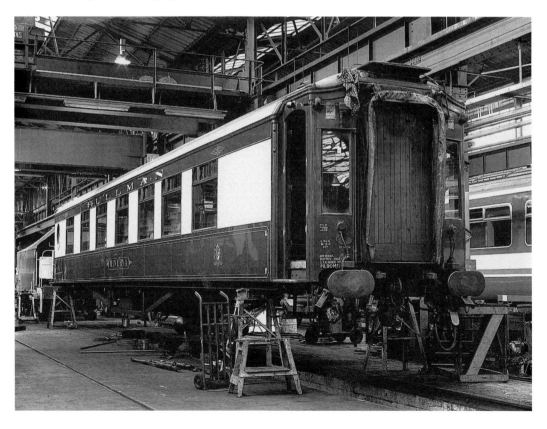

| Numbers | Year | Type | Built | Car | User | Location |
|---------|------|------|-------|-----|------|----------|
| 229 Car No 76 | 1928 | TP | Metro C&W | K | LNER | Stewarts Lane |
| LNER 482 | 1942 | | | | | |
| 'Eve' | 1968 | | | | | |
| 99202 plated | | | | | | |

*Remarks:* Loaned to LNER 1942-8. P'67 by Bulmers & used as Bar Car in the 'Cider Train'. Sold to VSOE '86, at Swindon till '87

| 232 Car No 79 | 1928 | TB | Metro C&W | K | LNER | N Yorks Moors |
|---------|------|------|-------|-----|------|----------|
| LNER 487 | 1942 | | | | | |

*Remarks:* Loaned to LNER 1942-8. W'65 then? Donated to NYMR '73, but restored on siding at Rotherham until '90

| 238 Phyllis | 1928 | FK | Metro C&W | K | LNER | ? |
|---------|------|------|-------|-----|------|----------|

*Remarks:* P'68 by Esmond Lewis-Evans & at Ashford till '83

| 239 Agatha | 1928 | FP | Metro C&W | K | LNER | Stewarts Lane |
|---------|------|------|-------|-----|------|----------|
| LNER 468 | 1942 | | | | | |

*Remarks:* Loaned to LNER 1942-8. P'63, at Beaulieu till '72, then Haven Street IoW till purchased '77 by FSE on behalf of an unknown buyer (Sea Containers!). Restoration virtually halted '82 while gutted (due to body damage), at Steamtown till '86, Swindon till '87

| 242 Ursula | 1928 | FP | Metro C&W | K | LNER | Hilderstone |
|---------|------|------|-------|-----|------|----------|

*Remarks:* P' ? at 'Spot Gate' Inn (Staffs)

| 243 Lucille | 1928 | FP | Metro C&W | K | LNER | (Stewarts Lane) |
|---------|------|------|-------|-----|------|----------|
| 99541 plated | 1985 | T | Hill/St Lane | | | |

*Remarks:* P'68 by Esmond Lewis-Evans, at Ashford stored 1983-5 till sold to VSOE

| 245 (Ibis) | 1925 | FK | B R C W | K | CIWL | (Stewarts Lane) |
|---------|------|------|-------|-----|------|----------|
| CIWL 52 | 1925 | | | | | |
| Ibis | 1928 | | Midland C&W | | | |
| 99534 plated | 1981 | | Steamtown | | | |

*Remarks:* Used in Italy 1925-8. P'68, on Dart Valley till '70 then at Tyseley till sold to Sea Containers in '80

| 246 (Lydia) | 1925 | FK | B R C W | K | CIWL | Wisconsin, USA |
|---------|------|------|-------|-----|------|----------|
| CIWL 55 | 1925 | | | | | |
| Lydia | 1928 | | Midland C&W | | | |

*Remarks:* Used in Italy 1925-8. P'68 & exported, delivery to the NRM at Green Bay via the 'Flying Scotsman' tour in '69

| 247 (Leona) | 1925 | FP | B R C W | K | CIWL | Wisconsin, USA |
|---------|------|------|-------|-----|------|----------|
| CIWL 53 | 1925 | | | | | |
| Princess | 1928 | FK | Midland C&W | | | |
| Elizabeth | | | | | | |
| Isle of Thanet | 1950 | FG | Preston Park | | | |

*Remarks:* Used in Italy 1925-8. P'68, as per No 246 (data prior to 1928 deduced but not confirmed!)

| Numbers | Year | Type | Built | Car | User | Location |
|---------|------|------|-------|-----|------|----------|
| 254 Zena | 1928 | FP | Metro C&W | K | GWR | (Stewarts Lane) |
| 99536 plated | 1981 | | Steamtown | | | |

*Remarks:* P'67?, on Worth Valley till sold to Sea Containers in '80. Fitted with false underframe trussing during restoration

| 255 Ione | 1928 | FK | Metro C&W | K | GWR | (Stewarts Lane) |
|---------|------|------|-------|-----|------|----------|
| 99539 plated | 1982 | | Steamtown | | | |

*Remarks:* P'68, said to be on Dart Valley but bought by Tyseley in '70 from private owner at Peterborough; resold to Sea Containers in '80

| 261 Car No 83 | 1931 | TP | B R C W | K | LNER | Stewarts Lane |
|---------|------|------|-------|-----|------|----------|
| LNER 483 | 1942 | | | | | |
| 'Prinia' | 1968 | | | | | |
| 99203 plated | | | | | | |

*Remarks:* Loaned to LNER 1942-8. P'67 by Bulmers & used as Museum Car in the 'Cider Train'. Sold to VSOE '86, at Swindon till '87

| 262 Car No 84 | 1931 | TP | B R C W | K | LNER | Worth Valley |
|---------|------|------|-------|-----|------|----------|
| LNER 484 | 1942 | | | | | |
| 'Lorna' | 1966 | | | | | |
| 'Mary' | 1977 | | | | | |

*Remarks:* Loaned to LNER 1942-8. P'66 & named after owner's wife; later, after sale to K&WVR, renamed after the widow of Bishop Eric Treacy

| 264 Ruth | 1932 | CK | Metro C&W | A | SR | Bulmers |
|---------|------|------|-------|-----|------|----------|

*Remarks:* P'73, later sold to 6000 Loco Assoc

| 278 Bertha | 1932 | CK | Metro C&W | A | SR | Bluebell |
|---------|------|------|-------|-----|------|----------|

*Remarks:* W'67? P'73, at Ashford till '76, on Nene Valley till '80, then Mid-Hants till '82

| 279 Hazel | 1932 | FK | Metro C&W | B | SR | Moulton |
|---------|------|------|-------|-----|------|----------|

*Remarks:* P'72 at 'Black Bull' Inn (Yorks)

| 280 Audrey | 1932 | FK | Metro C&W | B | SR | (Stewarts Lane) |
|---------|------|------|-------|-----|------|----------|
| 99537 plated | 1981 | | Steamtown | | | |

*Remarks:* P'72 by David Lowther, at Ashford till '?? then stored till sold to Sea Containers in '80. Rebuild at Steamtown involved conversion for loco-haulage & fitting false underframe trussing

| 281 Gwen | 1932 | FK | Metro C&W | B | SR | Stewarts Lane |
|---------|------|------|-------|-----|------|----------|

*Remarks:* P'72 by Whitbread, at 'Horseless Carriage' Inn, Chingford, Essex, till '81, then Colne Valley till sold to VSOE '88

| 282 Doris | 1932 | FK | Metro C&W | B | SR | Finsbury Park |
|---------|------|------|-------|-----|------|----------|

*Remarks:* P'72 in a siding beside the station.

| 283 Mona | 1932 | FK | Metro C&W | B | SR | Winsford |
|---------|------|------|-------|-----|------|----------|

*Remarks:* P'72 at 'Brighton Belle' Inn (Cheshire)

| Numbers | Year | Type | Built | | Car | User | Location |
|---------|------|------|-------|---|-----|------|----------|
| 284 Vera | 1932 | FK | Metro C&W | | B | SR | (Stewarts Lane) |
| | 1989 | RFS | Kilnhurst | | | | |
| 99543 plated | 1990 | | | | | | |

*Remarks:* P'72 at Westleton, Suffolk. Sold to VSOE summer '85 but not removable till adjacent field harvested! Moved to Kilnhurst Oct'89 to be converted for loco haulage, utilising BR Mk.1 headstocks & couplings. Original bogies sold for use under 'Bertha' (qv), being replaced with BR(S) B5 bogies, then fitted out during '90 at Stewarts Lane

| Numbers | Year | Type | Built | | Car | User | Location |
|---------|------|------|-------|---|-----|------|----------|
| 285 Car No 85 | 1932 | TP | Metro C&W | | C | SR | Mickleover |

*Remarks:* P'72 at 'Nags Head' Inn (Derbys)

| 286 Car No 86 | 1932 | TP | Metro C&W | | C | SR | Stewarts Lane |

*Remarks:* P'72 by Allied Breweries but kept in store till sold to Sea Containers '79; at Steamtown till '86 then Swindon till '87, but still unrestored

| 287 Car No 87 | 1932 | TP | Metro C&W | | C | SR | N Norfolk |

*Remarks:* P'72 by Allied Breweries but kept in store till loaned to N Norfolk in March '75

| 288 Car No 88 | 1932 | DMTP | Metro C&W | | D | SR | Stewarts Lane |
| Set 2051/3051 | | | | | | | |

*Remarks:* P'72 by Trumans, but kept in storage till donated to Chappel '80; loan to Swanage from '82 till sold to VSOE '90

| 289 Car No 89 | 1932 | DMTP | Metro C&W | | D | SR | Rowarth |
| Set 2051/3051 | | | | | | | |

*Remarks:* P'72 at 'Little Mill' Inn. Auctioned '76 & reported bought by Billy Smarts for Windsor Safari Park, but removal found too costly

| 290 Car No 90 | 1932 | DMTP | Metro C&W | | D | SR | Steamtown |
| Set 2052/3052 | | | | | | | |

*Remarks:* P'72 by British Transport Hotels, stored at Wolverton till '79, on Nene Valley till '90, briefly at Padiham then Steamtown '91. 60% of interior gutted by fire 18/6/91 during restoration

| 291 Car No 91 | 1932 | DMTP | Metro C&W | | D | SR | N Norfolk |
| Set 2052/3052 | | | | | | | |

*Remarks:* P'72 by Allied Breweries but kept in store till loaned to N Norfolk in March '75

| 292 Car No 92 | 1932 | DMTP | Metro C&W | | D | SR | Preston Park |
| Set 2053/3053 | | | | | | | |

*Remarks:* P'72 by Allied Breweries but kept in store till sold in '77, changing hands twice that year

| 293 Car No 93 | 1932 | DMTP | Metro C&W | | D | SR | Preston Park |
| Set 2053/3053 | | | | | | | |

*Remarks:* P'72 & with 292 since.

| Numbers | Year | Type | Built | Car | User | Location |
|---------|------|------|-------|-----|------|----------|
| 301 Perseus<br>99530 plated | 1951<br>1981 | FP | B R C W<br>Steamtown | U | BR(S) | (Stewarts Lane) |

*Remarks:* P' ? by Scottish & Newcastle Breweries, stored till '77, then briefly on N Yorks Moors before sold to FSE & moved to Steamtown. Sold to Sea Containers in '80 & rebuilt to resemble the older Cars

| | | | | | | |
|---------|------|------|-------|-----|------|----------|
| 302 Phoenix<br>99531 plated | 1952<br>1981 | FP | Preston Park<br>Steamtown | K | BR(S) | (Stewarts Lane) |

*Remarks:* Built to resemble Type U Cars, using the underframe of 'Rainbow' (176, Metro, 1927) saved after its body was destroyed by fire at Micheldever in '36. P'73 for a restaurant near Lyon (France); repatriated after sale to Sea Containers in '80

| | | | | | | |
|---------|------|------|-------|-----|------|----------|
| 304 Aries | 1952 | FK | Preston Park | U | BR(S) | Rochdale |

*Remarks:* P'69 at 'Yew Tree' Inn

| | | | | | | |
|---------|------|------|-------|-----|------|----------|
| 305 Aquila<br>99200 plated | 1951 | FK | B R C W | U | BR(S) | Colne Valley |

*Remarks:* P'68 by Bulmers, at Hereford till sold to VSOE '86, Swindon till '87, then Stewarts Lane. Resold '88, but not moved till '89

| | | | | | | |
|---------|------|------|-------|-----|------|----------|
| 306 Orion | 1951<br>1978 | FK | B R C W<br>Wolverton | U | BR(S) | Seaton |

*Remarks:* P'72, at Ashford till sold to Peco in '77. Restored at Wolverton before moving to Beer in '78.

| | | | | | | |
|---------|------|------|-------|-----|------|----------|
| 307 Carina | 1951 | FK | B R C W | U | BR(S) | Stewarts Lane |

*Remarks:* P'73, at a restaurant near Lyons (France) till repatriated by Sea Containers '80. Stored at Steamtown till '86 & Swindon till '87, but still unrestored

| | | | | | | |
|---------|------|------|-------|-----|------|----------|
| 308 Cygnus<br>99532 plated | 1951<br>1981 | FP | B R C W<br>Steamtown | U | BR(S) | (Stewarts Lane) |

*Remarks:* P' ? by Scottish & Newcastle Breweries, stored till '77, then briefly on N Yorks Moors before sold to FSE & moved to Steamtown. Sold to Sea Containers in '80 & rebuilt to resemble the older Cars

| | | | | | | |
|---------|------|------|-------|-----|------|----------|
| 310 Pegasus<br>The Trianon Bar | 1951 | Bar | B R C W | U | BR(S) | Tyseley |

*Remarks:* P'76

Henceforth the traditional Pullman outline was abandoned in favour of a bodyshell similar to BR Mk.1 vehicles (Type B built to Diagram P.130, Type D built to Diagram P.132)

| | | | | | | |
|---------|------|------|-------|-----|------|----------|
| 311 Eagle<br>95403 plated | 1960 | FK | Metro-Cammell | B | BR(E) | * NRM |

*Remarks:* P'78

| Numbers | Year | Type | Built | Car | User | Location |
|---------|------|------|-------|-----|------|----------|
| 313 Finch | 1960 | FK | Metro-Cammell | B | BR(E) | (Craigentinny) |
| 'State Car No 4' | 1990 | SLF | Dairycoates | | | |
| 99964 plated | | | | | | |

*Remarks:* P'79 by M Bayliss, on W Somerset till '82 then Carlisle Currock (pattern for dual-braking SLOA Cars). Stored at Steamtown '84/5 (dispute with BR over missing fittings!) then Severn Valley. Sold to GS&WR '89 & rebuilt as Sleeper for new 'Royal Scotsman'

| 315 Heron | 1960 | FK | Metro-Cammell | B | BR(E) | Great Central |
|-----------|------|-----|---------------|---|-------|---------------|

*Remarks:* Body P'?, at Casterton till sold to 71000 Loco Trust in '87 & re-bogied at Loughborough

| 316 Magpie | 1960 | FK | Metro-Cammell | B | BR(E) | Steamtown |
|------------|------|-----|---------------|---|-------|-----------|
| DB975608 | | | | | | |

*Remarks:* Body P'81, at Casterton till '87, then reported at both Plym Valley & Muswell Hill. Found stored for conversion to static restaurant at Steamtown '90

| 317 Raven | 1960 | FK | Metro-Cammell | B | BR(E) | Dairycoates |
|-----------|------|-----|---------------|---|-------|-------------|

*Remarks:* P'79 by M Bayliss, on W Somerset till '83 then Severn Valley till sold to GS&WR '89; now held by HLPG due to dispute over restoration fees for the other five cars

| 318 Robin | 1960 | FK | Metro-Cammell | B | BR(E) | N Yorks Moors |
|-----------|------|-----|---------------|---|-------|---------------|

*Remarks:* P'80, then shod with Gresley bogies.

| 319 Snipe | 1960 | FK | Metro-Cammell | B | BR(E) | (Craigentinny) |
|-----------|------|-----|---------------|---|-------|----------------|
| 99965 plated | 1990 | Obs | Dairycoates | | | |

*Remarks:* P'79 by M Bayliss, on W Somerset till '83 then Severn Valley. Sold to GS&WR '89 & rebuilt with end verandah as Observation Car for new 'Royal Scotsman'

| 320 Stork | 1960 | FK | Metro-Cammell | B | BR(E) | Muswell Hill |
|-----------|------|-----|---------------|---|-------|--------------|
| DB975609 | | | | | | |

*Remarks:* Body P'81, at Casterton till it became part of a restaurant c'86

| 321 Swift | 1960 | FK | Metro-Cammell | B | BR(E) | Pitsford |
|-----------|------|-----|---------------|---|-------|----------|

*Remarks:* Body P' ?, at Casterton till purchased for Northants Stm Rly scheme in '85 (ex dept'l)

| 324 Amber | 1960 | FP | Metro-Cammell | D | BR(E) | (Craigentinny) |
|-----------|------|-----|---------------|---|-------|----------------|
| 'State Car No 1' | 1990 | SLF | Dairycoates | | | |
| 99961 plated | | | | | | |

*Remarks:* P'79 by M Bayliss, on W Somerset till '83 then Severn Valley. Sold to GS&WR '89 & rebuilt as Sleeper for new 'Royal Scotsman'

| 325 Amethyst | 1960 | FP | Metro-Cammell | D | BR(E) | Strathspey |
|--------------|------|-----|---------------|---|-------|------------|
| SR 108 | | | | | | |

*Remarks:* P'79, shod with B2 bogies

| 326 Emerald | 1960 | FP | Metro-Cammell | D | BR(E) | * NRM |
|-------------|------|-----|---------------|---|-------|-------|
| 95402 plated | | | | | | |

*Remarks:* P'78

| Numbers | Year | Type | Built | Car | User | Location |
|---------|------|------|-------|-----|------|----------|
| 327 Garnet | 1960 | FP | Metro-Cammell | D | BR(E) | N Yorks Moors |

*Remarks:* P'79 then shod with DMU bogies taken from BR 59098/9 (qv)

| 328 Opal | 1960 | FP | Metro-Cammell | D | BR(E) | N Yorks Moors |

*Remarks:* P'79 then shod with DMU bogies taken from BR 59098/9 (qv)

| 329 Pearl | 1960 | FP | Metro-Cammell | D | BR(E) | (Craigentinny) |
| 'State Car No 2' | 1990 | SLF | Dairycoates | | | |
| 99962 plated | | | | | | |

*Remarks:* P'79 by M Bayliss, on W Somerset till '83 then Severn Valley. Sold to GS&WR '89 & rebuilt as Sleeper for new 'Royal Scotsman'

| 331 Topaz | 1960 | FP | Metro-Cammell | D | BR(E) | (Craigentinny) |
| 'State Car No 3' | 1990 | SLF | Dairycoates | | | |
| 99963 plated | | | | | | |

*Remarks:* P'80 by M Bayliss, stored at Taunton till '83, then on Severn Valley. Sold to GS&WR '89 & rebuilt as Sleeper for new 'Royal Scotsman'

| 332 | 1960 | SK | Metro-Cammell | C | BR(E) | Pannal Station |
| 'Mae' | 1982 | | | | | |

*Remarks:* P'79?, on N Yorks Moors till '82, shod with B1 bogies. Now a static restaurant at 'Platform One' Inn (nr Harrogate, Yorks)

| 333 | 1960 | SK | Metro-Cammell | C | BR(E) | Casterton |
| 'Magna' | | | | | | |

*Remarks:* P' ?, shod with B1 bogies & used as a restaurant

| 335 | 1960 | SK | Metro-Cammell | C | BR(E) | (Bounds Green) |
| DB975584 | | | | | | |
| 99335 plated | | | | | | |

*Remarks:* P'82 by SLOA & converted to replace 354.

| 337 | 1960 | SK | Metro-Cammell | C | BR(E) | Great Central |

*Remarks:* Body P'81, on Nene Valley till ' ?, at Casterton till '87; re-bogied at Loughborough

| 340 | 1960 | SK | Metro-Cammell | C | BR(E) | Hurn |

*Remarks:* P'79 at 'Avon Causeway' Hotel (Hurn Stn)

| 346 | 1960 | SK | Metro-Cammell | C | BR(E) | Casterton |
| 'Castra' | | | | | | |

*Remarks:* P' ?, shod with B1 bogies & used as a restaurant

| 347 | 1960 | SP | Metro-Cammell | E | BR(E) | (Bounds Green) |
| 99347 plated | | | | | | |
| Car B | | | | | | |

*Remarks:* P'81 by SLOA

| Numbers | Year | Type | Built | Car | User | Location |
|---------|------|------|-------|-----|------|----------|
| 348<br>99348 plated<br>Car C | 1960 | SP | Metro-Cammell | E | BR(E) | (Bounds Green) |
| *Remarks:* P'81 by SLOA | | | | | | |
| 349<br>99349 plated<br>Car D | 1960 | SP | Metro-Cammell | E | BR(E) | (Bounds Green) |
| *Remarks:* P'81 by SLOA | | | | | | |
| 350<br>99350 plated<br>Car E | 1960 | SP | Metro-Cammell | E | BR(E) | (Bounds Green) |
| *Remarks:* P'81 by SLOA | | | | | | |
| 351<br>99351 plated<br>Car F | 1960 | SP | Metro-Cammell | E | BR(E) | (Bounds Green) |
| *Remarks:* P'81 by SLOA | | | | | | |
| 352<br>99352 plated<br>Car G | 1960 | SP | Metro-Cammell | E | BR(E) | (Bounds Green) |
| *Remarks:* P'81 by SLOA | | | | | | |
| 353<br>99353 plated<br>Car H | 1960 | SP | Metro-Cammell | E | BR(E) | (Bounds Green) |
| *Remarks:* P'81 by SLOA | | | | | | |
| 354 Hadrian Bar<br>99354 plated | 1961<br>1983 | Bar<br>Shop | Metro-Cammell<br>Carlisle | E | BR(E) | (Bounds Green) |
| *Remarks:* P'81 by SLOA | | | | | | |

# MINOR COMPANIES

| Numbers | Year | Type | Built | Diag | Lot | Location |
|---------|------|------|-------|------|-----|----------|

## CITY & SOUTH LONDON RAILWAY (Tube Stock)

| 30 | c1890 | | Ashbury | | | Covent Garden |

*Remarks:* 'Padded Cell' stock. P'38, at York till '73 then Syon Park till '79

| 135 | 1902 | | | | | W Ruislip |

*Remarks:* Monitor roof. P' ? by LURS

| 163 | 1907 | | | | | W Ruislip |

*Remarks:* Monitor roof. Body P'74 by LURS from site near Hampton Court

## GREAT NORTHERN, PICCADILLY & BROMPTON RAILWAY (Tube Stock)

| 51 | 1909 | DM | Hungarian RCM | | | Covent Garden |
| 128 | 1926 | | | | | |
| L16 | 1929 | | | | | |

*Remarks:* 'Gate Stock' EMU. Became Ballast motor car in '29. Put aside for preservation in 50's, but only rear end remains, to show 'gate' arrangement

## LONDON ELECTRIC RAILWAY (Tube Stock)

| 297 | 1927 | DM | Union Constr? | | | * Science Mus |
| 3327 | 1933 | | | | | |

*Remarks:* 'Standard Stock' EMU with Monitor roof, on Piccadilly initially, later Bakerloo & Central. P'61

| 5294 | 1925 | DTO | | | | ? |
| S26 | 1966 | | | | | |

*Remarks:* To IoW 1966. Reported P'90

| Numbers | Year | Type | Built | Diag | Lot | Location |
|---------|------|------|-------|------|-----|----------|

# LONDON TRANSPORT (LPTB, 1933 on)

EMU Tube Stock:

| Numbers | Year | Type | Built | Diag | Lot | Location |
|---------|------|------|-------|------|-----|----------|
| 3045 | 1930 | DM | Union Constr | | | IoWSR |
| S19 | 1968 | | | | | |
| 083569 | 1985 | | | | | |

*Remarks:* Body P'86?, grounded as a store

| 10177 | 1938 | DM | | | | Alderney |

*Remarks:* P'85 by N Downs, at Chatham till '87

| 11149 | 1938 | DM | Metro-Cammell | | | Covent Garden |

*Remarks:* P'78, cab end section only

| 11177 | 1938 | DM | | | | Alderney |

*Remarks:* P'85 by N Downs, at Chatham till '87

| 11182 | 1939 | DM | Metro-Cammell | | | Covent Garden |

*Remarks:* P'78, restored '79 by LT at Acton

EMU Surface Stock:

| 8063 | 1935 | TC | Metro-Cammell | N | | Ealing Common |
| 08063 | 1950 | | | Q35 | | |

*Remarks:* P'72? by LURS, at Ashford till '?? then W Ruislip

| 13028 | 1937 | DM | B R C W | O | | Quainton |
| 53028 | 195x | | | CO | | |

*Remarks:* P'84

| 013063 | 1937 | TT | Gloucester | O | | Quainton |
| | | | | COP | | |

*Remarks:* P'84

| 01x1xx | 1938 | T | Gloucester | Q | | Chappel |
| 22624 | 1949 | DM | | R38 | | |

| 14233 | 1939 | DM | Gloucester | P | | Quainton |
| 54233 | 195x | | | CP | | |

*Remarks:* Rebuilt after WW2 bomb damage using part of Q38 trailer 013167. P'81

| 14256 | 1939 | DM | Gloucester | P | | N Woolwich |
| 54256 | 195x | | | CP | | |

*Remarks:* P'82 from W Ruislip

| Numbers | Year | Type | Built | Diag | Lot | Location |
|---------|------|------|-------|------|-----|----------|
| 22679 | 1949 | DM | Metro-Cammell | R49 | | Ealing Common |

Remarks: In store, intended for preservation

# METROPOLITAN RAILWAY

| Numbers | Year | Type | Built | Diag | Lot | Location |
|---------|------|------|-------|------|-----|----------|
| 3 | 1896 | MV | B R C W | | | Covent Garden |
| BDV700 | 1936 | | | | | |

Remarks: W'36 for departmental use. Restored '63, displayed at Clapham till '75, stored at W Ruislip till '79

| Numbers | Year | Type | Built | Diag | Lot | Location |
|---------|------|------|-------|------|-----|----------|
| 4 | 1904 | TTO | Metro C&W | | | N Woolwich |
| 9486 | 1933 | | | | | |

Remarks: P'85 ex Shoeburyness, to N Woolwich '86

| Numbers | Year | Type | Built | Diag | Lot | Location |
|---------|------|------|-------|------|-----|----------|
| 249 | 1932 | DMT | B R C W | MW | | Dartford |
| 2749 | 1933 | T | | | | |
| ESL118B | 1961 | | | | | |

Remarks: EMU, P'87 by N Downs Rly

| Numbers | Year | Type | Built | Diag | Lot | Location |
|---------|------|------|-------|------|-----|----------|
| 258 | 1932 | DMT | B R C W | MW | | Dartford |
| 2758 | 1933 | T | | | | |
| ESL118A | 1961 | | | | | |

Remarks: EMU, P'87 by N Downs Rly

| Numbers | Year | Type | Built | Diag | Lot | Location |
|---------|------|------|-------|------|-----|----------|
| 368 | 1899 | C | Ashbury | | | Bluebell |
| | 1906 | TF | | | | |
| 9702 | 1933 | | | | | |
| 515 | 1940 | C | | | | |

Remarks: EMU 1906-40. P'61

| Numbers | Year | Type | Built | Diag | Lot | Location |
|---------|------|------|-------|------|-----|----------|
| 387 | 1900 | BT | Cravens | | | Bluebell |
| | 1907 | DMT | | | | |
| 2761 | 1933 | | | | | |
| 512 | 1940 | DTBT | | | | |

Remarks: EMU 1907-40. P'61

| Numbers | Year | Type | Built | Diag | Lot | Location |
|---------|------|------|-------|------|-----|----------|
| 394 | 1900 | T | Ashbury | | | Bluebell |
| | 1921 | DTT | | | | |
| 6702 | 1933 | | | | | |
| 518 | 1940 | | | | | |

Remarks: EMU 1921-40. P'61

| Numbers | Year | Type | Built | Diag | Lot | Location |
|---------|------|------|-------|------|-----|----------|
| 400 | 1900 | S | Neasden | | | Covent Garden |
| | 1921 | DTT | | | | |
| 6703 | 1933 | | | | | |
| 519 | 1940 | | | | | |

Remarks: EMU 1921-40. P'62, stored at Clay Cross & Preston Park till restoration by LT at W Ruislip '76-8, but not on display till arrival Covent Garden in '79

| Numbers | Year | Type | Built | Diag | Lot | Location |
|---------|------|------|-------|------|-----|----------|
| 412 | 1900 | C | Ashbury | | | Bluebell |
| | 1906 | TF | | | | |
| 9705 | 1933 | | | | | |
| 516 | 1940 | C | | | | |

*Remarks:* EMU 1906-40. P'61

| | | | | | | |
|---------|------|------|-------|------|-----|----------|
| 427 | 1905 | DTF | Metro C&W | | | Worth Valley |
| | | BT | | | | |
| KWVR 4 | | | | | | |

*Remarks:* P' ? by VCT

| | | | | | | |
|---------|------|------|-------|------|-----|----------|
| 465 | 1920 | T | Metro C&W | | | Worth Valley |
| KWVR 2 | | | | | | |

*Remarks:* P' ? by VCT

| | | | | | | |
|---------|------|------|-------|------|-----|----------|
| 509 | 1923 | F | Metro C&W | | | Worth Valley |
| KWVR 3 | | | | | | |

*Remarks:* P' ? by VCT

*Others:*
'Jubilee' stock coach built Cravens c1887-93 at Ealing Common depot pending restoration for Covent Garden
Body of EMU trailer (LT6554?) P'85 at Gloucester

# METROPOLITAN DISTRICT RAILWAY

| | | | | | | |
|---------|------|------|-------|------|-----|----------|
| ? | c1864 | ? | ? | | | K&ESR |
| 100 | 1980 | FY | | | | |

*Remarks:* Maybe once 8-wheeled, body grounded in two parts at Dymchurch c1901-7. P' ? by Resco, restored
on new running gear '79, on K&ESR till '84, at Fawley till '88

| | | | | | | |
|---------|------|------|-------|------|-----|----------|
| ? | 1901 | BTY | Ashbury | | | Winchcombe |
| 37M | 1907 | | | | | |
| 2527 | 1925 | | | | | |

*Remarks:* Sold to Taff Vale 1907; body grounded as a dwelling c1927. End compartment P'70's at
Winchcombe Rly Museum, rest demolished — in use as second-hand bookstore.

| | | | | | | |
|---------|------|------|-------|------|-----|----------|
| 644 | 1923 | DM | Gloucester | G | | Covent Garden |
| 238 | 1928 | | | | | |
| 4148 | 1933 | | | Q23 | | |
| 4248 | 1965 | | | | | |

*Remarks:* Monitor roof EMU. P' ?, at Syon Park till '79

| | | | | | | |
|---------|------|------|-------|------|-----|----------|
| 662 | 1923 | DM | Gloucester | G | | Gloucester |
| 274 | 1929 | | | | | |
| 4184 | 1934 | | | Q23 | | |

*Remarks:* Monitor roof EMU. P' ? by its builder but later ceded to Gloucs City Council

| Numbers | Year | Type | Built | Diag | Lot | Location |
|---------|------|------|-------|------|-----|----------|

## LIVERPOOL OVERHEAD RAILWAY

| | | | | | | |
|---------|------|------|-------|------|-----|----------|
| 3 | 1892 | DMBT | Brown Marshall | | | Liverpool Mus |

*Remarks:* EMU. P'57?

| | | | | | | |
|---------|------|------|-------|------|-----|----------|
| 7 | 1895<br>1947 ? | TT | Brown Marshall | | | Southport? |

*Remarks:* EMU. Body only? P' ? from scrap merchant

## BARNUM & BAILEY ('Greatest Show On Earth')

see Alexandra (Newport & South Wales) Dock and Railway (GWR, Section 1)

## BASS BREWERIES

| | | | | | | |
|---------|------|------|-------|------|-----|----------|
| | 1889 | Sal | | | | ? |

*Remarks:* 4-wheel. P'65 by Staffordshire C C, at Shugborough Hall till '85?

## DORMAN, LONG & CO

| | | | | | | |
|---------|------|------|-------|------|-----|----------|
| | c1880 | Sal | | | | Tanfield |

*Remarks:* 4-wheel. Pc'76

## SWANSEA HARBOUR TRUST

| | | | | | | |
|---------|------|------|-------|------|-----|----------|
| | c1911 | Sal | | | | Caerphilly |

*Remarks:* 4-wheel. Built using MSLR u'frame dated 1850-60, acquired via Brecon & Merthyr in 1890's. P'69, at Caerleon, Gwent till '86

## WAR DEPARTMENT RAILWAYS

| | | | | | | |
|---------|------|------|-------|------|-----|----------|
| | 1885 | | Metro C&W | | | Beverley |

*Remarks:* Rigid 8-wheel Clerestory built for Sudan, ran on Suakin-Berber Rly & reputedly used by Lord Kitchener. Repatriated c1898, at Woolwich till c1914 then Shoeburyness. P'90 at Museum of Army Transport

# IRISH RAILWAYS

(NB: All companies operate over 5'3" gauge track, unless otherwise shown)

| Numbers | Year | Type | Built | Diag | Lot | Location |
|---------|------|------|-------|------|-----|----------|

## BELFAST & COUNTY DOWN RAILWAY

[Diagrams per 1945 Diagram Book, created to show all surviving stock]

| Numbers | Year | Type | Built | Diag | Lot | Location |
|---------|------|------|-------|------|-----|----------|
| 39 | 1903 | BTZ | Queens Quay? | 37 | | Downpatrick |

*Remarks:* Body sold Nov'53

| 152 | 1897 | CL | Ashbury | 7 | | Downpatrick |
|-----|------|-----|---------|---|---|-------------|

*Remarks:* Body sold Dec'59. P'87

| 153 | 1897 | ROY | Ashbury | 12 | | Downpatrick |
|-----|------|-----|---------|----|---|-------------|

*Remarks:* Clerestory. Sold to farmer at Hillsborough Dec'53 & grounded as henhouse. Body P'84 by D&ARC

| 154 | 1918 | SZ | Queens Quay? | 27 | | Downpatrick |
|-----|------|-----|--------------|----|---|-------------|

*Remarks:* Sold Dec'59. P'85

| 182 | 1923 | TZ | Queens Quay | 28 | | Whitehead |
|-----|------|-----|-------------|----|---|-----------|

*Remarks:* Sold Jun'56 to Ballyclare farmer, grounded as henhouse. Body P'85 by RPSI for restoration by Limestone Youth Training Project

*Others:*
Body of Clerestory TO P'86 at Downpatrick (59 or 72, former 50ft Railmotor) & placed on u/f from GSWR 802 in '91
At least 2 bodies (ex 6-wheel) by B&CDR Trust, one a Family Saloon (probably No 53), the other a First
Another body (probably SZ) at Whitehead

## CORAS IOMPAIR EIREANN

| 1377 | 1956 | TK | Inchicore | | | Tuam |
|------|------|-----|-----------|---|---|------|

*Remarks:* P'85 by GSRPS, at Mallow & Tralee till loaned to Westrail

| Numbers | Year | Type | Built | Diag | Lot | Location |
|---------|------|------|-------|------|-----|----------|
| 1378 | 1956 | TK | Inchicore | | | Tralee |

Remarks: P'85 by GSRPS at Mallow (now derelict)

| Numbers | Year | Type | Built | Diag | Lot | Location |
|---------|------|------|-------|------|-----|----------|
| 1434 | 1956 | TO | Inchicore | | | Mullingar |

Remarks: P'86 by RPSI

| Numbers | Year | Type | Built | Diag | Lot | Location |
|---------|------|------|-------|------|-----|----------|
| 1445 | 1958 | TO | Inchicore | | | Mullingar |

Remarks: P'85? by RPSI

| Numbers | Year | Type | Built | Diag | Lot | Location |
|---------|------|------|-------|------|-----|----------|
| 1463 | 1958 | TO | Inchicore | | | Mullingar |

Remarks: W'84, P'85? by RPSI

| Numbers | Year | Type | Built | Diag | Lot | Location |
|---------|------|------|-------|------|-----|----------|
| 1467 | 1958 | TO | Inchicore | | | Tralee |

Remarks: P'?? by GSRPS

| Numbers | Year | Type | Built | Diag | Lot | Location |
|---------|------|------|-------|------|-----|----------|
| 1468 | 1958 | TO | Inchicore | | | Tuam |

Remarks: P'?? by Westrail

| Numbers | Year | Type | Built | Diag | Lot | Location |
|---------|------|------|-------|------|-----|----------|
| 1469 | 1958 | TO | Inchicore | | | Mullingar |

Remarks: P'85? by RPSI

| Numbers | Year | Type | Built | Diag | Lot | Location |
|---------|------|------|-------|------|-----|----------|
| 1470 | 1958 | TO | Inchicore | | | Mullingar |

Remarks: P'86 by RPSI

| Numbers | Year | Type | Built | Diag | Lot | Location |
|---------|------|------|-------|------|-----|----------|
| 1483 | 1958 | TO | Inchicore | | | Mullingar |

Remarks: P'85? by RPSI

| Numbers | Year | Type | Built | Diag | Lot | Location |
|---------|------|------|-------|------|-----|----------|
| 1934 | 1956 | BTK | Inchicore | | | Tuam |

Remarks: P'85 by GSRPS, but loaned to Westrail

| Numbers | Year | Type | Built | Diag | Lot | Location |
|---------|------|------|-------|------|-----|----------|
| 2144 | 1954 | CK | Inchicore | | | Downpatrick |
| 1611 | 1971 | | | | | |
| 2572 | 1973 | BG | | | | |
| 3223 | 1980 | Spec | | | | |

Remarks: Latterly Steam Gen Van. P'87 by D&ARC

| Numbers | Year | Type | Built | Diag | Lot | Location |
|---------|------|------|-------|------|-----|----------|
| 2159 | 1956 | SK | Inchicore | | | Tuam |
| 1633 | 1980 | | | | | |

Remarks: P'85 by GSRPS, at Mallow & Tralee till loaned to Westrail

| Numbers | Year | Type | Built | Diag | Lot | Location |
|---------|------|------|-------|------|-----|----------|
| 2163 | 1958 | BCK | Inchicore | | | Mullingar |
| 1915 | 1970 | BTO | | | | |

Remarks: P'85? by RPSI

| Numbers | Year | Type | Built | Diag | Lot | Location |
|---------|------|------|-------|------|-----|----------|
| 2164 | 1958 | BCK | Inchicore | | | Mullingar |
| 1916 | 1970 | BTO | | | | |

Remarks: P'86 by RPSI

| 2166 | 1959 | BCK | Inchicore | | | Downpatrick |
| 1918 | 1970 | BSO | | | | |

Remarks: P'87 by D&ARC

| 2171 | 1959 | BCK | Inchicore | | | - |
| 1923 | 1970 | BSO | | | | |
| | 1989 | RBO | | | | |

Remarks: P'87? by Westrail, damaged by fire in GSR 3205 (qv) & scrapped at Tuam Jul'90.

| 2419 | 1956 | RB | Inchicore | | | Downpatrick |

Remarks: P'87 by D&ARS

| 2422 | 1956 | RB | Inchicore | | | Mullingar |

Remarks: P'87? by RPSI

## DUBLIN & KINGSTOWN RAILWAY (4'8½" gauge)

| ? | c1844 | TY | | | | Belfast Museum |
| 48 | 1860 | | | | | |

Remarks: Railway re-gauged to 5'3" in 1855, then became Dublin, Wicklow & Wexford in 1860

## DUNDALK, NEWRY & GREENORE RAILWAY

| 1 | 1901 | CZ | Wolverton | | | Belfast Museum |

Remarks: Line wholly owned by LNWR till 1933, then some stock taken over by NCC & remainder (incl this one) operated by GNR(I) till final closure in 1951. P'52?

## GREAT NORTHERN RAILWAY

| E | 1934 | R'bus | | | | Belfast Museum |

Remarks: W'66

| 9 | 1954 | TO | Dundalk | K31 | | Whitehead |
| 586 | 1959 | DTTO | | | | |

Remarks: The last coach built at Dundalk, a rebuild from unidentified post-war K23 vehicle. P'75 by RPSI

| 50 | 1911 | Spec | Dundalk? | A3 | | Whitehead |
| 150 | 1959 | | | | | |

Remarks: Directors' Saloon; P'73 by RPSI

| Numbers | Year | Type | Built | Diag | Lot | Location |
|---------|------|------|-------|------|-----|----------|
| 88 | 1938 | RC | | B6 | | Whitehead |
| | 1958 | TRB | | | | |
| 552 | 1959 | | | | | |

Remarks: P'74 by RPSI

| Numbers | Year | Type | Built | Diag | Lot | Location |
|---------|------|------|-------|------|-----|----------|
| 98 | 1941 | TO | | K15 | | Whitehead |
| | 1951 | TTO | | | | |
| 581 | 1959 | | | | | |

Remarks: P'75 by RPSI, now derelict

| Numbers | Year | Type | Built | Diag | Lot | Location |
|---------|------|------|-------|------|-----|----------|
| 114 | 1940 | BTO | | L13 | | Whitehead |
| | 1957 | TBTO | | | | |

Remarks: P' ? by RPSI, now the Support coach for Railtours, complete with workshop

| Numbers | Year | Type | Built | Diag | Lot | Location |
|---------|------|------|-------|------|-----|----------|
| 127 | 1951 | RB | | K23 | | Whitehead |
| 187 | | | | | | |
| 557 | 1958 | | | | | |
| 727 | 1969 | | | | | |

Remarks: Orig K23 workmen's coach. The last GNR(I) coach in traffic, latterly Class 70 DEMU trailer. P'?? by RPSI, now very decrepit

| Numbers | Year | Type | Built | Diag | Lot | Location |
|---------|------|------|-------|------|-----|----------|
| 176 | 1947 | TO | | K15 | | - |
| | 1957 | TTO | | | | |
| 583 | 1959 | | | | | |

Remarks: P'75 by RPSI, but set on fire by vandals at Whitehead on 23/3/78. Though body was destroyed its u/f was retained & currently carries body of NCC 304 (qv)

| Numbers | Year | Type | Built | Diag | Lot | Location |
|---------|------|------|-------|------|-----|----------|
| 189 | 1946 | BTK | | L14 | | Whitehead |
| 595 | 1959 | | | | | |

Remarks: Orig K23 workmen's coach (175?) P'83 by RPSI, now derelict

| Numbers | Year | Type | Built | Diag | Lot | Location |
|---------|------|------|-------|------|-----|----------|
| 227 | 1949 | FK | | C2 | | Whitehead |
| | 1957 | TFK | | | | |
| 561 | 1959 | | | | | |

Remarks: P'75 by RPSI

| Numbers | Year | Type | Built | Diag | Lot | Location |
|---------|------|------|-------|------|-----|----------|
| 231 | 1948 | BFO | | D5 | | Whitehead |
| | 1957 | TBFO | | | | |
| 562 | 1959 | | | | | |

Remarks: P'75 by RPSI

| Numbers | Year | Type | Built | Diag | Lot | Location |
|---------|------|------|-------|------|-----|----------|
| 381 | 1893 | Tram | | | | Belfast Museum |

Remarks: 4-wheel Fintona horse-drawn Tram! P'57

| Numbers | Year | Type | Built | Diag | Lot | Location |
|---------|------|------|-------|------|-----|----------|
| 396 | | | | D3 | | Mallow |
| 508A | | | | | | |

Remarks: P'86 by GSRPS

| Numbers | Year | Type | Built | Diag | Lot | Location |
|---------|------|------|-------|------|-----|----------|
| 788 | 1934 | PMV | | P2 | | Whitehead |

*Remarks:* P'?? by RPSI

# GREAT SOUTHERN & WESTERN RAILWAY

| 247 531A | 1899 | POS | | ˗ | | |
|---|---|---|---|---|---|---|

*Remarks:* P'84? by WISRA; scrapped Jun'89, u'frame retained for Foyle Valley Rly & bogies for 890 (qv).

| 802 525A | 1900 | T | | ˗ | | |
|---|---|---|---|---|---|---|

*Remarks:* P'85? by WISRA; scrapped Jun'89, u'frame & bogies sold to Downpatrick for B&CDR Railmotor (qv).

| 836 463A | 1902 | TO | Ashbury | | | Downpatrick |
|---|---|---|---|---|---|---|

*Remarks:* P'87 by D&ARC

| 838 ? | 1902 | TO | Ashbury | | | Mullingar |
|---|---|---|---|---|---|---|

*Remarks:* P'?? by RPSI as dormitory

| 861 484A | 1906 196x | BCK | Inchicore | | | Whitehead |
|---|---|---|---|---|---|---|

*Remarks:* 12-wheel Clerestory, 'Rosslare Express' stock. P'72 by RPSI

| 890 507A | 1907 | T | Inchicore | | | Limerick |
|---|---|---|---|---|---|---|

*Remarks:* P'90 by Westrail, stored with Steam Crane

| 892 464A | 1907 | T | Inchicore | | | Tuam |
|---|---|---|---|---|---|---|

*Remarks:* P'85? by WISRA

| 907 234A | | CZ | | | | Mallow? |
|---|---|---|---|---|---|---|

*Remarks:* Pc'85 by GSRPS, conv for dormitory use

| 1097 605A AM12 | 1924 | C Ambu | Inchicore | ˗ | | Whitehead |
|---|---|---|---|---|---|---|

*Remarks:* P'85 by RPSI, ex Inchicore breakdown train

| 1110 380A | 1912 | C | Inchicore | | | Mullingar |
|---|---|---|---|---|---|---|

| Numbers | Year | Type | Built | Diag | Lot | Location |
|---------|------|------|-------|------|-----|----------|
| 1142 | 1921 | FK | Inchicore | | | Whitehead |
| 4012 | 1959 | | | | | |

Remarks: P'73 by RPSI

| | | | | | | |
|---------|------|------|-------|------|-----|----------|
| 1297 | 1915 | T | Inchicore | | | |
| 521A | | | | | | |

Remarks: P'85? by WISRA; scrapped at Tuam Jul'90 by mistake (supposed to go to Downpatrick)

# GREAT SOUTHERN RAILWAY

| | | | | | | |
|---------|------|------|-------|------|-----|----------|
| 5 | 1927 | Insp | Drewry | | | Mallow? |

Remarks: 4-wheel petrol. P' ? at Stradbally, Co Laois, till removal by GSRPS in '85

| | | | | | | |
|---------|------|------|-------|------|-----|----------|
| 1287 | 1924 | FK | Inchicore | | | Whitehead |

Remarks: P'?? by RPSI

| | | | | | | |
|---------|------|------|-------|------|-----|----------|
| 1325 | 1935 | TK | Inchicore | | | Mallow? |

Remarks: P'84? by GSRPS

| | | | | | | |
|---------|------|------|-------|------|-----|----------|
| 1327 | 1935 | TK | Inchicore | | | Whitehead |

Remarks: P'73 by RPSI

| | | | | | | |
|---------|------|------|-------|------|-----|----------|
| 1328 | 1935 | TK | Inchicore | | | Whitehead |

Remarks: P'73 by RPSI, slightly damaged by fire Mar'78

| | | | | | | |
|---------|------|------|-------|------|-----|----------|
| 1333 | 1936 | TO | Inchicore | | | Whitehead |

Remarks: Originally non-gangwayed; P'73 by RPSI

| | | | | | | |
|---------|------|------|-------|------|-----|----------|
| 1335 | 1937 | TK | Inchicore | | | Whitehead |

Remarks: P'73 by RPSI

Others:
Former Presidential coach (CIE 351) stored by CIE for preservation
Coach No 3205 at Tuam, burnt out by vandals '90
1 BZ by B&CDR Trust

# MIDLAND GREAT WESTERN RAILWAY

| | | | | | | |
|---------|------|------|-------|------|-----|----------|
| 47 | c1844 | Priv | Dawson, Phibsborough | | | Belfast Museum |
| | 1851 | Spec | | | | |
| | 1904 | CLZ | | | | |
| | 1924 | FLZ | | | | |

Remarks: William Dargan's 6-wheel Saloon, presented to the Railway in 1851, given new u'frame 1886 & used as the State Saloon till 1903; roof raised & lavatory fitted 1904. Presented to Museum by CIE in '64

| Numbers | Year | Type | Built | Diag | Lot | Location |
|---------|------|------|-------|------|-----|----------|
| 13M 467A | | TZ | | | | Mallow? |

*Remarks:* Pc'85 by GSRPS

| | | | | | | |
|---------|------|------|-------|------|-----|----------|
| 39M 479A | | SZ | | | | Mallow? |

*Remarks:* Pc'85 by GSRPS

| | | | | | | |
|---------|------|------|-------|------|-----|----------|
| 47M 383A | | BZ | | | | Mallow |

*Remarks:* 'Birdcage' P'87 from Claremorris by GSRPS

| | | | | | | |
|---------|------|------|-------|------|-----|----------|
| 53M 478A | | SZ | | | | Mallow? |

*Remarks:* Pc'85 by GSRPS

| | | | | | | |
|---------|------|------|-------|------|-----|----------|
| 62M 468A | 1892 | TZ | Ashbury | | | Whitehead |

*Remarks:* P'81 by RPSI

| | | | | | | |
|---------|------|------|-------|------|-----|----------|
| ? 466A | 1893 | TZ | Broadstone | | | Mullingar |

*Remarks:* Pc'79 by RPSI

# NORTHERN COUNTIES COMMITTEE

| | | | | | | |
|---------|------|------|-------|------|-----|----------|
| 1 | 1932 | R'car | | | | Whitehead |

*Remarks:* W'65. P'?? by Ulster Folk Museum but stored by RPSI pending move to Craigavad

| | | | | | | |
|---------|------|------|-------|------|-----|----------|
| 66 278 713 | 1924 1959 1968 1977 | CK DTBCK DTBSO | Derby | F2 | | Downpatrick |

*Remarks:* Converted to 70 Class DMU vehicle '68, rebuilt '77 & W'84. P'91 by DARS as Santa's grotto

68/274 – see MR 3421 (LMS Group Section)

| | | | | | | |
|---------|------|------|-------|------|-----|----------|
| 87 550 | 1950 1959 | RC | Dunmurry | B5 | | Whitehead |

*Remarks:* P'79 by RPSI

| | | | | | | |
|---------|------|------|-------|------|-----|----------|
| 91 472 | 1934 1959 | BTK | | K3 | | Whitehead |

*Remarks:* 'North Atlantic' stock. P'75 by RPSI

238/340 – see MR (LMS Group Section) ?

241/342 – see MR (LMS Group Section) ?

| Numbers | Year | Type | Built | Diag | Lot | Location |
|---------|------|------|-------|------|-----|----------|
| 243<br>358 | 1924 | TK | York Road | J6 | | Whitehead |

*Remarks:* P'75 by RPSI

| 255<br>526 | 1929 | TO | | J5 | | Whitehead |

*Remarks:* P'79? by RPSI

| 304<br>532 | 1951 | T | | J16 | | Whitehead |

*Remarks:* Body P'75? by RPSI, currently sitting on underframe from GNR 176 (qv)

| 404<br>613 | 1936 | BG | | V14 | | Whitehead |

*Remarks:* P'83? by RPSI

| 411<br>616 | 1937 | BG | | V14 | | Whitehead |

*Remarks:* P'83? by RPSI

*Others:*
2 parcel vans at Downpatrick (667 & 674), plus 2 u'frames, 1 van at Whitehead & 2 in care of B&CDR Trust

## SLIGO, LEITRIM & NORTHERN COUNTIES RAILWAY

| B<br>2509 | 1947<br>1958 | R'car | Walker Bros | | | Mallow? |

*Remarks:* Sold to CIE in '58. P'86 by GSRPS having stood derelict at Limerick Jn for about 15 years

## ULSTER TRANSPORT AUTHORITY

87 – see NCC above

| 306<br>534<br>728 | 1951<br>1959<br>1976<br>1979 | TK<br>DTTK<br>TSK<br>TBSO | | 316 | | Downpatrick |

*Remarks:* Converted to MPD DMU vehicle '59 (involving exchange of u'frames with 266) & 70 Class DMU vehicle '76; damaged by firebomb at York Rd '77 & rebuilt '79. W'86 due to vandalism at Larne. P'91 by DARS

## WATERFORD, LIMERICK & WESTERN RAILWAY

| ?<br>900<br>465A | | FOZ | | | | Mallow? |

*Remarks:* Family Saloon. Pc'85 by GSRPS

| Numbers | Year | Type | Built | Diag | Lot | Location |
|---------|------|------|-------|------|-----|----------|
| ?<br>934 | 1896 | C | Limerick | | | Mullingar |

*Remarks:* P'?? by RPSI & in store

| | | | | | | |
|---------|------|------|-------|------|-----|----------|
| ?<br>935 | 1896 | B?O | Limerick | | | Mullingar |

*Remarks:* P'?? by RPSI & in store

# REPLICAS

Gauge shown in Column 5 is either Broad (7'0¼"), Intermediate (5'3") or Standard (4'8½")
Status shown in Column 6 is either Static Display or Runnable

| Numbers | Year | Type | Built | Gauge | Status | Location |
|---------|------|------|-------|-------|--------|----------|

## LIVERPOOL & MANCHESTER RAILWAY

All 6 kept at Derby after WW2, but one of each type displayed at Clapham

| Numbers | Year | Type | Built | Gauge | Status | Location |
|---------|------|------|-------|-------|--------|----------|
| - 'Huskisson' | 1930 | FY | | S | SD | * NRM |

*Remarks:* Loaned to Tyseley 19?-?

| | | | | | | |
|---------|------|------|-------|-------|--------|----------|
| - 'Traveller' | 1930 | FY | | S | R | * NRM |
| - 'Experience' | 1930 | FY | | S | SD | * Liverpool Mus |
| - | 1930 | SY | | S | SD | * NRM |
| - | 1930 | SY | | S | R | * NRM |
| - | 1930 | SY | | S | SD | * Liverpool Mus |

## GRAND JUNCTION RAILWAY

| | | | | | | |
|---------|------|------|-------|-------|--------|----------|
| - | 1938 | POSY | | S | SD | * NRM |

*Remarks:* Built on wagon frame for TPO Centenary, stored at Wolverton till ' ? then displayed at Clapham till ' ?

## GREAT WESTERN RAILWAY

| | | | | | | |
|---------|------|------|-------|-------|--------|----------|
| - | 1984 | SZ | Cathays | B | R | * NRM |
| - | 1984 | TZ | Cathays | B | R | * NRM |
| 9001 | 1982 | ROY | Resco | S | SD | Windsor |

*Remarks:* Built around the underframe and the bulk of the framework of an LMS parcels van

# PRESERVED DEPARTMENTAL STOCK

| Number | Origin | Number | Origin | Number | Origin |
|--------|--------|--------|--------|--------|--------|

**Western Region** – DW (incl GWR Mess, Riding & Tool Vans not shown in preserved stock list)

| Number | Origin | Number | Origin | Number | Origin |
|--------|--------|--------|--------|--------|--------|
| 1 | 4-wh Tool (Didcot) | 150027 | GWR Siphon.G 2790 | 150294 | GWR BG 1159 |
| 4 | 4-wh Tool (Blunsdon) | 150028 | GWR Siphon.G 2775 | 150301 | GWR TK 5043 |
| 9 | 4-wh Riding (SVR) | 150029 | GWR TK 5848 | 150304 | GWR BTK 5804 |
| 29 | GWR CY 290 | 150030 | GWR TK 5929 | 150309 | GWR Fruit.C 2851 |
| 47 | 4-wh Mess & Tool | 150031 | GWR TK 5856 | 150312 | GWR Fruit.C 2826 |
|  | (Didcot) | 150032 | GWR RTO 9653 | 150313 | GWR Auto 174 |
| 55 | 4-wh Riding (SVR) | 150035 | GWR Fruit.B 2356 | 150315 | GWR Auto 163 |
| 56 | 4-wh Riding (Didcot) | 150038 | GWR TK 2434 | 150318 | GWR Fruit.D 2902 |
| 66 | 4-wh Tool (SVR) | 150063 | GWR Fruit.B 2303 | 150319 | GWR Fruit.D 2910 |
| 89 | 4-wh Riding (SVR) | 150066 | GWR Mink.A 101961 | 150322 | GWR Siphon.G 1199 |
| 92 | 4-wh Tool (Bluebell) | 150111 | GWR Bloater 2115 | 150324 | GWR TK 5813 |
| 108 | GWR TY 975 | 150127 | GWR BUO 9055 | 150325 | GWR TK 5863 |
| 109 | 6-wh Tool (Didcot) | 150128 | GWR BUO 9369 | 150326 | GWR RTO 9654 |
| 112 | 6-wh Tool (SVR) | 150160 | GWR Bloater 2671 | 150328 | GWR BT 5539 |
| 118 | 4-wh Riding (SVR) | 150169 | GWR Bloater 2660 | 150330 | GWR RC 9605 |
| 135 | 4-wh Mess & Tool | 150192 | GWR TK 796 | 150336 | GWR RF 9615 |
|  | (Didcot) | 150200 | GWR TK 5085 | 150341 | GWR BTK 5796 |
| 139 | GWR BTK 2360 | 150201 | GWR TK 4886 | 150342 | GWR Auto 160 |
| 141 | 4-wh Tool (SVR) | 150205 | GWR TK 4546 | 150343 | GWR Fruit.C 2815 |
| 143 | 4-wh Tool (SVR) | 150206 | GWR TK 4777 | 150346 | GWR Fruit.C 2823 |
| 146 | 4-wh Tool (DVR) | 150207 | GWR TK 4553 | 150351 | GWR Fruit.D 2887 |
| 161 | 4-wh Tool (DFR) | 150208 | GWR TK 4786 | 150353 | BR RSO 1012 |
| 162 | 4-wh Riding (SVR) | 150209 | GWR TK 4872 | 150354 | GWR BG 297 |
| 174 | 8-wh Riding & Tool | 150210 | GWR Bloater 2240 | 150356 | GWR Fruit.C 2862 |
|  | (Tyseley) | 150234 | GWR BTK 5102 | 150363 | GWR Fruit.D 2913 |
| 215 | GWR CY 8 | 150236 | GWR Bloater 2625 | 150385 | SR BTK 4227 |
| 263 | ?-wh Mess & Tool | 150241 | GWR BG 1150 | 150386 | SR BCK 6601 |
|  | (Didcot) | 150246 | GWR BTK 5131 | 150391 | GWR BTK 2242 |
| 309 | GWR BTK 2370 | 150265 | GWR CCT 565 | 150392 | GWR BTK 2225 |
| 317 | GWR CK 7740 | 150266 | GWR RCO 9580 | 150393 | GWR BTK 2214 |
| 416 | GWR BTY 416 | 150267 | GWR Bloater 2617 | 150397 | GWR BTK 2232 |
| 14198 | GWR T 1941 | 150270 | GWR BCK 6515 | 150400 | GWR BTK 2218 |
| 150011 | GWR TK 3930 | 150272 | GWR BTK 5240 | 150401 | GWR BTK 2233 |
| 150019 | GWR TK 2447 | 150289 | GWR Bloater 2661 | 150402 | GWR BTK 2216 |
| 150020 | GWR BCK 7538 | 150293 | GWR CK 6045 | 150403 | GWR BTK 2148 |

| Number | Origin | Number | Origin | Number | Origin |
|--------|--------|--------|--------|--------|--------|
| 150405 | GWR BTK 2180 | 150420 | GWR SCVZ 752 | 150430 | Pullman 102 |
| 150407 | GWR BTK 2249 | 150424 | GWR HBY 709 | 150431 | Pullman 99 |

## Southern Region – DS

| Number | Origin | Number | Origin | Number | Origin |
|--------|--------|--------|--------|--------|--------|
| 8 | SR PMVY 1168 | 1309 | LSWR PMVY ? | 70155 | SR CK 5600 |
| 11 | SR PMVY 2188 | 1450 | SECR CCTY 267 | 70156 | SR PMVY 2225 |
| 22 | SECR BCL 1084 | 1525 | LBSCR PMVZ 270 | 70160 | SR BTK 3687 |
| 27 | SECR BS 950 | 1601 | SECR BZ 719 | 70163 | SR BTK 3690 |
| 33 | SECR BT 1170 | 1686 | LSWR PMVY 5498 | 70168 | SR BTK 3719 |
| 93 | SR PMVY 2196 | 3065 | SR PMVY 1234 | 70172 | SR BTK 2768 |
| 149 | SR PMVY 1162 | 3104 | U/f of LSWR ? | 70175 | SR TO 1381 |
| 150 | SR PMVY 2186 | 3141 | U/f of SECR C 2351 | 70200 | BR S 1000 |
| 154 | SR PMVY 1240 | 3208 | SECR BC 1061 | 70201 | SR TO 1346 |
| 161 | SR PMVY 1248 | 70003 | U/f of LSWR CK 4668 | 70202 | SR CCTY 2276 |
| 164 | SR PMVY 1184 | 70004 | SR PMVY 1174 | 70217 | SR PMVY 1145 |
| 179 | LSWR BTK 1282 | 70006 | SR PMVY 1213 | 70244 | LMS BCK 6839 |
| 226 | LSWR TK 773 | 70011 | LSWR TK 74 | 70248 | SR BTK 4279 |
| 227 | SR FK 7200 | 70014 | SR TK 752 | 70256 | SR PMVY 1134 |
| 228 | SR TK 730 | 70016 | LSWR BTK 3190 | 70257 | SR PMVY 1720 |
| 229 | SR TK 748 | 70031 | SECR PMVY 153 | 70262 | SR TO 1457 |
| 291 | LBSCR Saloon 60 | 70056 | SR PMVY 1176 | 70266 | SR TO 1323 |
| 625 | LSWR RT 4151 | 70076 | SR PMVG 2339 | 70285 | SR TO 1456 |
| 747 | SECR PMVY 152 | 70085 | SR BTK 3204 | 70313 | SR TO 1336 |
| 792 | SECR PMVY 154 | 70109 | SR SO 7798 | 70314 | SR TO 1482 |
| 800 | SR PMVY 1228 | 70133 | SR BTK 3193 | 70319 | SR BTK 4211 |
| 873 | LCDR BSZ 48 | 70134 | SR TK 1020 | 70324 | SR CCTY 2439 |
| 1035 | SECR PMVY 177 | 70141 | SR PMVG 2462 | | |
| 1119 | LSWR BTL 1520 | 70154 | SR PMVY 2213 | | |

## Midland Region – DM

| Number | Origin | Number | Origin | Number | Origin |
|--------|--------|--------|--------|--------|--------|
| 7243 | MR BTZ 253 | 395149 | LNWR CCTZ 11433 | 395584 | LMS TK 16782 |
| 01836 | LNWR BG ? | 395205 | LMS sRFO 15412 | 395645 | LMS T 15486 |
| 168822 | LYR Saloon 1 | 395209 | LNWR BT 7340 | 395663 | U/f of LMS IMVZ 3826 |
| 195955 | MR TK 634 | 395222 | LMS sRFO 10257 | 395680 | LMS TO 7878 |
| 198512 | LNWR SLF 112 | 395223 | LMS RK 3286 | 395754 | LMS BCK 16411 |
| 198587 | MR BZ 3xxx | 395273 | LNWR CCTZ 12220 | 395758 | LMS BCK 18017 |
| 198614 | WCJS TK 2xx | 395279 | LMS RK 30088 | 395776 | LMS CK 9229 |
| 198715 | MR BTK 435 | 395344 | LMS TO 5913 | 395777 | LMS SLT 14241 |
| 198829 | MR BCK 2944 | 395345 | LMS TO 16122 | 395778 | LMS SLT 14425 |
| 279982 | LNWR BGZ ? | 395346 | LMS TO 16553 | 395780 | U/f of LMS MTZ 6093 |
| 284290 | GSWR BZ 122 | 395347 | LMS TO 16696 | 395798 | LMS TK 14256 |
| 284677 | MR CZ ? | 395358 | LNWR CCTZ 12196 | 395799 | LMS TK 14281 |
| 297290 | MR BZ 3xxx (483) | 395455 | LNWR BG 8898 | 395801 | LMS TK 3030 |
| 395001 | LYR FO 50 | 395470 | LMS CK 8761 | 395812 | LMS TK 16243 |
| 395017 | LNWR SLF 112 | 395476 | LMS BCK 9884 | 395815 | LMS CK 15509 |
| 395031 | MR TL 375 | 395489 | LMS CCTZ 8188 | 395832 | LMS TK 1535 |
| 395080 | LNWR CCTZ 11388 | 395492 | LMS CCTZ 5622 | 395845 | LMS BCK 9864 |
| 395081 | LNWR CCTZ 11010 | 395498 | LMS TK 1371 | 395887 | LMS T 11937 |
| 395092 | MR BZ 184 | 395519 | LMS TO 5861 | 395892 | LMS TO 9125 |
| 395106 | MR CCTY 8272 | 395525 | MR BT 1250 | 395898 | LMS BTK 5734 |
| 395136 | LNWR CK 2997 | 395562 | MR TO 1805 | 395903 | LMS BTK 5793 |

| Number | Origin | Number | Origin | Number | Origin |
|--------|--------|--------|--------|--------|--------|
| 395911 | LMS TK 1782 | 395923 | LMS TO 9205 | 395979 | LMS BTK 26680 |
| 395918 | LMS T 12059 | 395928 | LMS T 12244 | 396003 | LMS CCTY 37103 |
| 395922 | LMS SLT 592 | 395939 | LMS TO 56xx? (44415) | | |

## Eastern Region – DE

| Number | Origin | Number | Origin | Number | Origin |
|--------|--------|--------|--------|--------|--------|
| 320010 | GNSR BZ 68 | 320797 | LNER BFK 4163 | 321089 | LNER TK 22255 |
| 320042 | GNR Saloon 3087 | 320803 | LNER T 61684 | 321099 | BR HBY 96336 |
| 320051 | GNR BCL 2856 | 320832 | LNER T 22219 | 321101 | BR HBY 96347 |
| 320145 | GNR BTK 1798 | 320874 | LNER TK 10023 | 321108 | LNER TO 56856 |
| 320154 | GNR TK 2440 | 320877 | LNER TK 3395 | 321120 | LNER BTK 1866 |
| 320179 | GCR F 957 | 320894 | LNER TK 3374 ? | 321133 | LNER TK 1623 |
| 320180 | NER T 3453 | 320897 | LNER RTO 6118 | 773090 | NBR TZ ? |
| 320206 | GNR FO 397 | 320904 | LNER TK 61634 | 900178 | GNR TZ -459 |
| 320256 | MSLR TZ 1076 | 320907 | LNER RF 1222 | 900192 | NER CZ 1111 |
| 320292 | HBR BT 2 | 320921 | LNER RF 51773 | 900269 | NER Saloon 41 |
| 320325 | GER BTK 295 | 320927 | LNER TOP 42972 | 900270 | NER FOY 1173 |
| 320362 | HBR BTL 5 | 320931 | LNER SLT 1299 | 900271 | GER Saloon 63 |
| 320401 | NBR TK 565 | 320942 | LNER BTO 23834 | 900580 | LNER Saloon (1998) |
| 320405 | NBR BT 467 | 320947 | LNER RF 42969 | 900730 | NER DMB 3267 |
| 320427 | LNER BCK 10178 | 320956 | LNER TO 24109 | 901622 | H&BR Tool Van 2 |
| 320528 | GCR BTO 695 | 320957 | LNER TO 24105 | 902177 | NER Saloon 305 |
| 320540 | GCR TO 664 | 320959 | LNER TK 23890 | 902179 | NER Saloon 1661 |
| 320577 | NBR Saloon 461 | 320960 | LNER TO 43600 | 902260 | LNER FK 1531 |
| 320603 | GCR T 652 | 320984 | LNER BTK 3669 | 902502 | NER Dynamometer 3591 |
| 320610 | GER BTK 1019 | 320995 | LNER BTO 43571 | 903004 | NER Stores Van 5523 |
| 320651 | GNR BFK 3178 | 321001 | LNER TO 43654 | 940281 | GNR BTZ ? |
| 320679 | LNER TO 21772 | 321002 | LNER TO 52256 | 940400 | GNR BZ ? |
| 320680 | LNER BTK 62515 | 321005 | LNER TO 52255 | 940460 | GNR BTZ 1472 |
| 320700 | GNR BCK 229 | 321006 | LNER TO 43632 | 942090 | GNR Saloon 706 |
| 320709 | GCR TO 666 | 321007 | LNER TK 3291 | 950249 | LDECR TZ 28 |
| 320716 | NER TO 945 | 321008 | LNER TK 23896 | 953003 | MSLR CY 103 |
| 320725 | GER ? ? | 321011 | GWR BFO 9004 | 960820 | Pullman 119 |
| 320731 | GER TK 2155 | 321015 | LNER CL 32455 | 960900 | GER ROY 5 |
| 320741 | LNER CK 1065 | 321021 | LNER RC 7960 | 960903 | GER Saloon 14 |
| 320744 | LNER TK 1052 | 321048 | LNER TTO 60505 | 962450 | GER Saloon 1 |
| 320746 | LNER BTK 62565 | 321058 | LNER BTK 41384 | 970012 | NBR TL 1748 |
| 320759 | LNER BT 3107 | 321073 | BR Train Heating Van, | 970204 | GNSR CZ 34 |
| 320779 | LNER BT 3641 | | u/f of LNER wagon | 982002 | GNSR FO 1 |

## Internal Users

| LMR | | 041305 | LNER TO 12134 | 041760? | BR CCTY 94536 |
|--------|--------|--------|--------|--------|--------|
| 022261 | Pullman 135 | 041332 | BR BSO 9269 | 041838 | BR CCTY 94109 |
| 022262 | Pullman 137 | 041366 | LNER BGP 70754 | 041869 | BR CCTY 94286 |
| 024610 | BR CCTY 94605 | 041402 | LNER BG 145 | 041870 | BR CCTY 94709 |
| | | 041403 | LNER BG 6866 | 041896 | LMS BG 31225 |
| ER | | 041418 | GER TK 2155 | 041975 | GNR TK 2440 |
| 040451 | GCR ? 793 | 041435 | LNER BG 5283 | 042197 | LNER TO 43612 |
| 040877 | NER RFO 2118 | 041468 | SR PMVY 1323 | | |
| 040923 | LNER BY 772 | 041469 | LNER BCK 10178 | WR | |
| 041255 | LNER FVY 75169 | 041501 | LNER BGP 5280 | 060903 | GWR TK 4546 |
| 041273 | NER bogie van ? | 041593 | LNER TK 22255 | 060904 | GWR TK 3951 |

| Number | Origin | Number | Origin | Number | Origin |
|--------|--------|--------|--------|--------|--------|
| 060905 | GWR TK 3950 | 079076 | GWR BCK 7545 | 082232 | SR TO 1323 |
| 060907 | GWR TK 4777 | 079112 | GWR RTO 9627 | 082444 | SR BUO 4441 |
| 060972 | GWR Fruit.D 2391 | 079124 | GWR BTO 9103 | 082756 | SR PMVY 1283 |
| 061057 | GWR Siphon.G 2994 | 079133 | GWR BCK 6912 | 082949 | SR CCTY 2400 |
| 064749 | GWR Auto 169 | 079134 | GWR BCK 6913 | 082962 | LNER CL 32480 |
| 064809 | U/f of LNER CCTY ? | 079144 | GWR BTK 5136 | 082975 | SR PMVY 1692 |
| 068724 | GWR Fruit.D 3436 | 079170 | GWR BTK 1645 | 083161 | SR PMVY ? |
| 070843 | GWR Fruit.C 2815 | | | 083180 | SECR BT 1170 |
| 070888 | BR PMVY 92060 | **SR** | | 083181 | SR TO 1346 |
| 071343 | GWR BT 5500 | 081315 | SR TK 2356 | 083409 | SR BTK 3687 |
| 079002 | GWR TK 3299 | 081621 | SR FK 7400 | 083569 | LT tube 3045 |
| 079050 | GWR Auto 16 | 081642 | SR TO 1309 | 083571 | SR B 205 |
| 079052 | GWR Auto 190 | 081901 | SR TO 1336 | | |
| 079060 | GWR Siphon.G 1257 | 082055 | SR PMVY 1134 | **ScR** | |
| 079062 | GWR BY 1399 | 082056 | SR PMVY 1720 | 095001 | LMS BG 31036 |

**British Rail – DB**

| Number | Origin | Number | Origin | Number | Origin |
|--------|--------|--------|--------|--------|--------|
| 975003 | BR DMBS 79998 | 975314 | BR FO 3060 | 975882 | LNER RB 1706 |
| 975004 | BR DMCL 79999 | 975315 | BR FO 3079 | 975944 | LMS BG 31370 |
| 975005 | BR DMBS 50416 | 975316 | LNER BG 14 | 975948 | BR RU 1963 |
| 975006 | BR DTCL 56171 | 975318 | LNER BGP 4238 | 975957 | BR FVY 87948 |
| 975047 | BR BSK 34769 | 975323 | BR RSO 1013 | 975960 | SR PMVY 1323 |
| 975056 | BR HBY 96300 | 975345 | GWR Fruit.D 2391 | 975967 | SR CCT 4605 |
| 975079 | LNER RB 642 | 975347 | BR PMVY 92060 | 975986 | LMS BG 31359 |
| 975084 | BR BSK 34756 | 975381 | BR PMVY 92110 | 977024 | LMS BG 31385 |
| 975137 | BR DMBS 50397 | 975383 | BR PMVY 92069 | 977031 | LMS BG 31361 |
| 975149 | BR BSK 34634 | 975399 | LNER BGP 4268 | 977032 | LMS BG 31384 |
| 975154 | LYR BTK 1856 | 975400 | LNER BG 70592 | 977034 | LMS BG 31387 |
| 975156 | GWR BPOT 814 | 975401 | LNER BG 70630 | 977037 | LMS BG 31407 |
| 975157 | GWR BG 184 | 975406 | SR BUO 4449 | 977065 | SR B 232 |
| 975158 | GWR BG 185 | 975475 | BR BSK 34369 | 977072 | BR CCTY 94502 |
| 975177 | GWR Fruit.D 3461 | 975560 | LMS CCT 37909 | 977073 | BR CCTY 94518 |
| 975181 | LMS SLF 378 | 975562 | LMS BG 30976 | 977076 | BR CCTY 94713 |
| 975182 | LMS SLF 379 | 975584 | Pullman 335 | 977091 | Leyland TSO |
| 975183 | LMS SLF 380 | 975606 | BR FO 3068 | 977097 | BR CCTY 94501 |
| 975184 | LMS SLF 381 | 975607 | BR FO 3064 | 977098 | BR RMB 1829 |
| 975188 | LMS SLF 398 | 975608 | Pullman 316 | 977132 | BR FK 13231 |
| 975212 | GWR Fruit.D 3450 | 975609 | Pullman 320 | 977134 | BR BSO 9208 |
| 975228 | BR DTCL 56160 | 975640 | GWR BG 276 | 977135 | BR BSO 9225 |
| 975229 | LMS CCT 37817 | 975642 | BR FVY 87247 | 977175 | BR TSO 4440 |
| 975242 | LNER BGP 4237 | 975650 | BR FO 3016 | 977176 | BR BSO 9300 |
| 975249 | LMS BGZ 32998 | 975658 | BR FO 3014 | 977186 | BR RMB 1835 |
| 975265 | GWR Fruit.D 3462 | 975660 | BR BSK 35006 | 977189 | BR SK 24576 |
| 975269 | BR BSO 9269 | 975662 | BR BSK 35215 | 977303 | BR CCTY 94338 |
| 975279 | SR BUO 4438 | 975783 | GWR Siphon.G 2983 | 977311 | BR BSK 34540 |
| 975288 | BR CK 15296 | 975789 | GWR Siphon.G 2988 | 977330 | BR BSK 35188 |
| 975289 | BR BSK 34620 | 975832 | GWR Siphon.G 1025 | 977357 | BR CCTY 94264 |
| 975291 | GWR Fruit.C 2424 | 975834 | GWR Siphon.G 1043 | 977358 | BR CCTY 94691 |
| 975300 | GWR Fruit.D 3436 | 975841 | GWR Siphon.G 2943 | 977410 | BR BSK 34531 |
| 975306 | BR FVY 87937 | 975843 | GWR Siphon.G 2994 | 977412 | BR TSO 4355 |
| 975307 | BR PMVY 92067 | 975874 | Leyland R'bus LEV1 | 977413 | BR TSO 4449 |
| 975313 | BR FO 3058 | 975878 | BR RF 302 | 977420 | BR SK 25807 |

| Number | Origin | Number | Origin | Number | Origin |
|--------|--------|--------|--------|--------|--------|
| 977426 | BR BSK 35129 | 977513 | BR SK 25607 | 977719 | BR BDTSO 75808 |
| 977487 | BR FK 13480 | 977518 | BR SK 25891 | 977720 | BR MBSO 61824 |
| 977492 | BR FO 3051 | 977623 | BR TSO 3749 | 977721 | BR DTSO 75758 |
| 977495 | BR BSK 34641 | 977627 | BR TSO 3991 | 999502 | LMS Insp Saloon |
| 977500 | BR BSK 34675 | 977629 | BR TSO 4058 | | |

# BR PLATED NUMBERS OF PRESERVED COACHES

| Number | Company | Orig No | Remarks | Number | Company | Orig No | Remarks |
|--------|---------|---------|---------|--------|---------|---------|---------|
| 95401 | LNWR | 310 | | 99127 | BR | 3117 | 'Cheryl' & 'Carol' |
| 95402 | Pullman | 326 | 'Emerald' | 99128 | BR | 3130 | 'Beryl' |
| 95403 | Pullman | 311 | 'Eagle' | 99129 | BR | 21272 | |
| 95404 | BR | 1100 | | 99130 | BR | 14013 | |
| 95408 | BR | 21236 | see 99120 | 99131 | LNER | 1531 | |
| 99007 | SR | 3724 | | 99132 | BR | 1861 | |
| 99008 | SR | 5644 | | 99140 | GWR | 796 | |
| 99009 | SR | 6699 | | 99141 | BR | 14041 | |
| 99010 | SR | 4035 | | 99160 | BR | 25856 | |
| 99011 | SR | 6697 | | 99161 | BR | 25871 | |
| 99012 | SR | 4036 | | 99162 | BR | 25795 | |
| 99013 | SR | 2850 | | 99163 | BR | 25994 | |
| 99030 | BR | 34666 | | 99164 | BR | 25853 | |
| 99040 | BR | 21232 | | 99165 | BR | 5034 | |
| 99041 | BR | 35476 | | 99166 | BR | 25776 | |
| 99045 | BR | 34625 | | 99167 | BR | 21238 | |
| 99050 | GER | 1 | | 99168 | BR | 25778 | |
| 99051 | NER | 305 | | 99169 | BR | 4941 | |
| 99052 | WCJS | 484 | | 99170 | BR | 4957 | |
| 99053 | GWR | 9004 | | 99171 | BR | 4921 | |
| 99054 | LNER | 24287 | | 99180 | BR | 35333 | |
| 99055 | LMS | 395 | | 99200 | Pullman | 305 | 'Aquila' |
| 99056 | BR | 34612 | | 99201 | Pullman | 219 | 'Christine' |
| 99064 | LMS | 45005 | | 99202 | Pullman | 229 | 'Eve' |
| 99065 | LNER | DE900580 | 'Loch Eil' | 99203 | Pullman | 261 | 'Prinia' |
| 99070 | BR | 35123 | | 99204 | Pullman | 194 | 'Morella' |
| 99080 | BR | 21096 | | 99205 | BR | 15879 | |
| 99090 | BR | 35131 | | 99230 | GWR | | |
| 99103 | GWR | 80972 | | 99231 | GWR | | |
| 99106 | GWR | 9001 | | 99232 | GWR | | |
| 99108 | BR | 14018 | | 99233 | GWR | | |
| 99120 | BR | 21236 | ex 95408 | 99234 | GWR | 1086 | |
| 99121 | BR | 3105 | 'Julia' | 99235 | GWR | 1087? | |
| 99122 | BR | 3106 | 'Helen' | 99236 | GWR | 9615? | |
| 99123 | BR | 3109 | 'Grace' | 99237 | GWR | 9627 | |
| 99124 | BR | 3110 | 'Frances' | 99238 | GWR | 6562 | |
| 99125 | BR | 3113 | 'Eileen' | 99240 | GWR | 6913 | |
| 99126 | BR | 3116 | 'Diane', ex 99358 | 99241 | BR | 35449 | |

| Number | Company | Orig No | Remarks | Number | Company | Orig No | Remarks |
|--------|---------|---------|---------|--------|---------|---------|---------|
| 99242 | BR | 35467 | | 99600 | BR | 3081 | |
| 99300 | LNER | 1866 | | 99601 | BR | 3084 | |
| 99302 | BR | 13323 | | 99602 | BR | 4317 | |
| 99303 | BR | 13317 | | 99604 | BR | 4046 | |
| 99304 | BR | 21256 | | 99606 | BR | 4256 | |
| 99305 | BR | 1862 | | 99609 | BR | 4507 | |
| 99312 | BR | 35463 | | 99629 | BR | 25972 | |
| 99313 | BR | 35451 | | 99630-40 Duplicated numbers of Exhibition | | | |
| 99314 | BR | 18729 | | vans so renumbered 99530-40 in 1986 | | | |
| 99315 | BR | 18955 | | 99670 | BR | 546 | 'City of Manchester' |
| 99316 | BR | 13320 | | 99671 | BR | 548 | 'Elizabethan' |
| 99317 | BR | 3766 | | 99672 | BR | 549 | 'Prince Rupert' |
| 99335 | Pullman | 335 | | 99673 | BR | 550 | 'Golden Arrow' |
| 99347 | Pullman | 347 | | 99674 | BR | 551 | 'Caledonian' |
| 99348 | Pullman | 348 | | 99675 | BR | 552 | 'Southern Belle' |
| 99349 | Pullman | 349 | | 99676 | BR | 553 | 'King Arthur' |
| 99350 | Pullman | 350 | | 99677 | BR | 586 | 'Talisman' |
| 99351 | Pullman | 351 | | 99710 | BR | 25767 | |
| 99352 | Pullman | 352 | | 99711 | BR | 25857 | |
| 99353 | Pullman | 353 | | 99712 | BR | 25893 | |
| 99354 | Pullman | 354 | 'Hadrian Bar' | 99713 | BR | 26013 | |
| 99355 | BR | 21249 | | 99714 | BR | 16187 | |
| 99356 | BR | 21245 | | 99715 | BR | 35337 | |
| 99357 | BR | 3112 | | 99716 | BR | 25808 | |
| 99358 | BR | 3116 | 1982-4, see 99126 | 99717 | BR | 25837 | |
| 99358 | BR | 3108 | 1984- | 99718 | BR | 25862 | |
| 99360 | BR | 2127 | see 99887 | 99719 | BR | 16191 | |
| 99370 | BR | 9400 | | 99720 | BR | 35461 | |
| 99371 | BR | 3128 | | 99722 | BR | 25756 | |
| 99405 | BR | 35486 | | 99723 | BR | 35459 | |
| 99420 | BR | 21214 | | 99750 | NER | 1661 | |
| 99421 | BR | 14021 | | 99760 | BR | 34557 | |
| 99422 | BR | 15644 | | 99781 | BR | 21034 | |
| 99423 | BR | 4828 | | 99782 | BR | 14007 | |
| 99424 | BR | 4823 | | 99783 | BR | 81025 | |
| 99425 | BR | 4822 | | 99792 | BR | 14019 | |
| 99426 | BR | 4786 | | 99800 | NBR | 461 | |
| 99450 | BR | 9241 | | 99801 | GNoSR | 1 | |
| 99512 | BR | 34671 | | 99802 | CR | 464 | |
| 99530 | Pullman | 301 | 'Perseus' | 99803 | CR | 1375 | |
| 99531 | Pullman | 302 | 'Phoenix' | 99804 | LMS | 24725 | |
| 99532 | Pullman | 308 | 'Cygnus' | 99805 | LMS | 27407 | |
| 99533 | LNER | 957 | 'B C No.7' | 99806 | LNER | 644 | |
| 99534 | Pullman | 245 | 'Ibis' | 99807 | LNER | 80417 | |
| 99535 | Pullman | 213 | 'Minerva' | 99808 | LMS | 27389 | |
| 99536 | Pullman | 254 | 'Zena' | 99810 | BR | 4215 | |
| 99537 | Pullman | 280 | 'Audrey' | 99811 | BR | 1866 | |
| 99538 | BR | 34991 | 'B C No.9' | 99812 | BR | 1513 | |
| 99539 | Pullman | 255 | 'Ione' | 99813 | BR | 4224 | |
| 99540 | BR | 3069 | | 99814 | BR | 15834 | |
| 99541 | Pullman | 243 | 'Lucille' | 99815 | BR | 35405 | |
| 99542 | BR | Ferry van | 'B C No.8' | 99816 | BR | 4466 | |
| 99543 | Pullman | 284 | 'Vera' | 99817 | BR | 4529 | |

| Number | Company | Orig No | Remarks | Number | Company | Orig No | Remarks |
|--------|---------|---------|---------|--------|---------|---------|---------|
| 99818 | BR | 1730 | | 99884 | BR | 26208 | |
| 99819 | BR | 4844 | | 99885 | BR | 2110 | |
| 99820 | BR | 4871 | | 99886 | BR | 35407 | |
| 99821 | BR | 9227 | | 99887 | BR | 2127 | ex 99360 |
| 99822 | BR | 1859 | | 99888 | BR | 2442 | |
| 99823 | BR | 4832 | | 99950 | BR | 35362 | |
| 99824 | BR | 4831 | | 99951 | SR | 10656 | |
| 99825 | BR | 13228 | | 99952 | SR | 12123 | |
| 99826 | BR | 13229 | | 99953 | BR | 35468 | |
| 99827 | BR | 3096 | | 99960 | LNER | 23890 | |
| 99850 | BR | 35219 | | 99961 | Pullman | 324 | |
| 99851 | BR | 15xxx | | 99962 | Pullman | 329 | |
| 99880 | LNWR | 159 | | 99963 | Pullman | 331 | |
| 99881 | GNR | 807 | | 99964 | Pullman | 313 | |
| 99882 | BR | 26169 | | 99965 | Pullman | 319 | |
| 99883 | BR | 2108 | | 99966 | BR | 34525 | |

# CARRIAGE BIBLIOGRAPHY

## A LIST OF REFERENCE WORKS FOR THE ENTHUSIAST

The Ottley* number is appended, where applicable, so that out-of-print books may be ordered more accurately through second-hand book dealers.

### General                                                                                    Ottley

| | Ottley |
|---|---|
| *Railway Carriages & Wagons: Their design & construction* Part 1 S Stone (Publishers of 'Railway Engineer', 1903) (Part 2 never publ) | 3154 |
| *Nineteenth Century Railway Carriages in the British Isles* C Hamilton Ellis (Modern Transport Publishing, 1949) | 3186 |
| *Railway Carriages 1839-1939* 'Veteran & Vintage Series' G M Kichenside (Ian Allan, 1964) | 10660 |
| *Railway Carriages in the British Isles: From 1830 to 1914* C Hamilton Ellis (George Allen & Unwin, 1965) | 10661 |
| *Britain's Joint Lines* H C Casserley (Ian Allan, 1968) | 10804/11697 |
| *Historic Carriage Drawings in 4mm scale* Vol 1 LMS & LNER D Jenkinson & N Campling (Ian Allan, 1969) | 10663 |
| *British Steam Railcars* R W Rush (Oakwood, 1970) | 10458 |
| *Preserved Railway Coaches* M Harris (Ian Allan, 1976) | 10666 |
| *Carriage Stock of Minor Standard Gauge Railways* R W Kidner (Oakwood, 1978, with 1980 Addenda) | 10036/10668 |
| *Railway Carriage Album* G M Kichenside (Ian Allan, 1980) | 10662 |
| *150 Years of Railway Carriages* 'Railway History in Pictures' G M Kichenside (David & Charles, 1981) | |
| *British Railcar* R M Tufnell (David & Charles, 1984) | |
| *British Travelling Post Office* P Johnson (Ian Allan, 1985) | |
| *British Railway Carriages of the 20th century* Vol 1: 1901-22 D Jenkinson (Patrick Stephens, 1988) | |

* *A Bibliography of British Railway History* compiled by George Ottley (HMSO, 2nd ed 1983, Supplement 1988)

*British Railway Carriages of the 20th century* Vol 2: 1923-53 D Jenkinson (Patrick Stephens, 1990)
*Clayton Wagons Ltd* J Ruddock & R Pearson (J Ruddock Ltd, 1989)

*Royal Journey: A Retrospect of Royal Trains in the British Isles* C Hamilton Ellis (British            2749
  Transport Commission, 1953)
*Royal Trains* C J Allen (Ian Allan, 1953)                                                              2743
*Royal Trains of the British Isles* (Railway Magazine Special, 1974)                                     –
*Palaces on Wheels: Royal Carriages at the National Railway Museum* D Jenkinson &
  G Townend (HMSO, 1981)
*Royal Trains* P Kingston (Guild Publishing, 1985)

*History of Trains de Luxe* G Behrend (Transport Publishing Co, 1977)                                    –
*Venice Simplon Orient Express* S Sherwood (Weidenfeld & Nicolson, 1983)

*BR General Parcels Rolling Stock* D Larkin (Bradford Barton, 1978)                                     8263
*BR Departmental Rolling Stock* D Larkin (Bradford Barton, 1979)                                        8264
*Departmental Coaching Stock* (Lineside/Platform 5, from 1982)
*Rolling Stock Recognition 3: Dept'l Stock* C Marsden (Ian Allan, 1984)
*Derby Railway Technical Centre* 'Modern Railways' Special C J Marsden (Ian Allan, 1989)

*'Steam' Yearbook* R Crombleholme & T Kirtland (6 editions, 1977-85)                                   12815

## Individual Companies

### Great Western Railway Group
*Barry Railway: Diagrams & Photographs of Locomotives, Coaches & Wagons* Compiled by
  E R Mountford (Oakwood, 1987)
*Register of GWR Absorbed Coaching Stock: 1922/3* E R Mountford (Oakwood, 1978)                        12027
*Great Western Coaches from 1890* M Harris (David & Charles, 1972 & 1985)                              12019
*Great Western Coaches: A pictorial record* Part 1, 1838-1913 J H Russell (Oxford Publishing           12021
  Co, 1979)
*Great Western Coaches: A pictorial record* Part 2, 1903-1948 J H Russell (Oxford Publishing           12021
  Co, 1978)
*Great Western Coaches: Appendix* Volume 1 J H Russell (Oxford Publishing Co, 1981)
*Great Western Coaches: Appendix* Volume 2 J H Russell (Oxford Publishing Co, 1984)
*Great Western Railway Travelling Post Offices* J G Hosegood (Wild Swan, 1983)
*Great Western Diesel Railcars: An Illustrated History* J H Russell (Wild Swan, 1985)
*Great Western Diesel Railcars* Supplement to the above P Karau & J Copsey (Wild Swan, 1985)
*Western Dynamometer Car* T D Allen Civil (Author, 1985)
*Great Western Siphons* J N Slinn & B K Clarke (HMRS, 1986)

### Southern Railway Group
*Carriage Stock of the London, Brighton & South Coast Railway* P J Newbury (Oakwood, 1976)             12264
  Amendments, J D Abson (Brighton Circle Historical Soc, 1987)
*LBSCR Stock Book* P Cooper (Runpast, 1990)
*LSWR Stock Book* P Cooper (Kingfisher, 1986)
*Carriage Stock of the SE&CR: including LC&DR & SER* D Gould (Oakwood, 1976)                            12486
*Bygone South Eastern Steam* Vol 2: Passenger Rolling Stock A R L Ratcliffe (Rochester
  Press, 198?)
*Notes on Southern Railway Rolling Stock* R W Kidner (Oakwood, 1974)                                   12521
*3142: Portsmouth to Peterborough* G D Beecroft (S Electric Grp, 1977)                                 8370
*Maunsell's SR Steam Passenger Stock: 1923 to 1939* D Gould (Oakwood, 1978 & 1990)                     12541
*Service Stock of the Southern Railway, its constituents and BR(S)* R W Kidner (Oakwood, 1980)         12487
*Bulleid's SR Steam Passenger Stock* D Gould (Oakwood, 1980)                                           12548

*Bulleid Coaches in 4mm scale* Model Railway Constructor Planbook 1 S W Stevens-Stratten
  (Ian Allan, 1983)
*Southern Electric Multiple-Units: 1898-1948* C J Marsden (Ian Allan, 1983)
*'4-Sub' Story* B Rayner & D Brown (Southern Electric Grp, 1983)
*Southern Railway Branch Line Trains* R W Kidner (Oakwood, 1984)

## London, Midland & Scottish Railway Group

| | |
|---|---:|
| *Furness Railway Locos & Rolling Stock* R W Rush (Oakwood, 1973 & 1987) | 11707 |
| *Carriages & Wagons of the Highland Railway* D L G Hunter (Turntable, 1971) | 9595 |
| *Electric Lines of the L&Y Railway* Electric Rly Soc Monograph, Forbes, Felton & Rush (Eltrac, 1976) | 12079 |
| *Lancashire & Yorkshire Passenger Stock* R W Rush (Oakwood, 1984) Amendments, R W Rush (L&Y Railway Soc, 1985) | |
| *LNWR Coaches: An illustrated History* (Incl West Coast Joint Stock) D Jenkinson (Oxford Publishing Co, 1978) | 12209 |
| *London's North Western Electric: A Jubilee History* Elec Rly Soc Monograph, F Atkinson & B Adams (Eltrac, 1962) | 6391 |
| *Midland Carriages : An Illustrated Review, 1877 onwards* D Jenkinson & R J Essery (Oxford Publishing Co, 1984) | |
| *Midland Railway Carriages* Volume 1 R Lacy & G Dow (Wild Swan, 1984) | |
| *Midland Railway Carriages* Volume 2 R Lacy & G Dow (Wild Swan, 1986) | |
| *North Staffordshire Railway Locomotives and Rolling Stock* R W Rush (Oakwood, 1981) | |
| *Register of West Coast Joint Stock* H C Casserley & P A Millard (Historical Model Railway Soc, 1980) | 10654 |
| *LMS Coach: 1923-1957* R J Essery & D Jenkinson (Ian Allan, 1969) | 12314 |
| *LMS Coaches: 1923-1957: An illustrated History* R J Essery & D Jenkinson (Oxford Publishing Co, 1977) | 12314 |
| *LMS Standard Coaching Stock* Vol 1: Introduction & Non-passenger Vehicles D Jenkinson & R J Essery (Oxford Publishing Co, 1991) | |

## London & North Eastern Railway Group

| | |
|---|---:|
| *The North Eastern Electrics* K Hoole (Oakwood Press, 1987) | |
| *Coronation: Britain's first streamline train* (LNER, 1937) | 6272 |
| *Gresley's Coaches: Built for the GNR, ECJS and LNER, 1905-53* M Harris (David & Charles, 1973) | 12104 |

## British Railways

| | |
|---|---:|
| *BR Coaching Stock* (RCTS/Ian Allan, annually from 1959) | 3191/10655 |
| *Coaching Stock Pocket Book* (Platform 5, annually from 1979) | – |
| *Locomotive hauled Mark 1 Coaching Stock of British Railways* K Parkin (Historical Model Railway Soc, 1982) | |
| *Rolling stock recognition 1: Coaching Stock* C Marsden (Ian Allan, 1983 & 1987) | |
| *Track Machines* (Platform 5, from 1986) | |
| *Hastings Diesels Story* G Beecroft (Southern Electric Grp, 1986) | |
| *DMU Disposal* A Butlin (Coorlea, 1987) | |

## Pullman Car Company

| | |
|---|---:|
| *Pullman and Perfection* F Burtt & W Beckerlegge (Ian Allan, 1948) | 3855 |
| *Pullman in Europe* G Behrend (Ian Allan, 1962) | 3863 |
| *The Brighton Belle* N Owen (Southern Electric Grp, 1972) | 12509 |
| *'Orion' and the Golden Arrow: the Story of a Pullman Car* G M Kichenside (Peco, 1978) | 10667 |
| *Pullman: The Pullman Car Company, its services, cars, and traditions* J Morel (David & Charles, 1983) | |
| *American Pullman Cars of the Midland Railway* J B Radford (Ian Allan, 1984) | |
| *Pullman Cars on the 'Southern': 1875-1972* R W Kidner (Oakwood, 1987) | |
| *Pullman: Travelling in Style* B Haresnape (Ian Allan, 1987) | |

**Minor Companies**
*London Underground Rolling Stock* B Hardy (Capital, 1988)
*London Underground Surface Stock Planbook: 1863-1959* I Huntley (Ian Allan, 1988)

**Irish Railways**
*Locos & Rolling Stock of CIE & NIR* (Signal Press, 1981)
*Irish Railways Traction & Travel* (Metro Enterprises, 1987)
*Steam's Silver Lining* J Cassells (The Syndicate, 1990)

**Additionally**
*The Trains We Loved* C Hamilton Ellis (George Allen & Unwin, 1947)     2743/7434/7786
*The Beauty of Old Trains* C Hamilton Ellis (George Allen & Unwin, 1952)     127/7796
*British Rail Handbook* B K Cooper (Ian Allan, 1981)
*Great British Trains: An evocation of a memorable age in travel* O S Nock (Guild, 1985)
*Passenger Train Formations 1923-83* 1 LMS/LMR C S Carter (Ian Allan, 1987)

*Hospital Ships & Ambulance Trains* J H Plumridge (Seeley Service, 1975)     11680
*Netley Hospital and its Railways* J R Fairman (Kingfisher, 1984)

*Rother Valley, later Kent & East Sussex Rly* M Lawson Finch (Author, 1949)     6180
*Kent & East Sussex Railway* S Garrett (Oakwood, 1987)

Stockbooks from a wealth of Preserved Railway Societies

The best, but not infallible, sources of data are the Railway Company Official Carriage Register and/or Stock Books. Very occasionally copies of the latter surface via the second-hand book trade, the Locomotive variety being more common than its Coach stablemate. The prices these fetch, especially those from the pre-Grouping years, can be astronomical and well out of the reach of the average enthusiast. Fortunately many records have survived in such establishments as the Public Record Office at Kew, the National Railway Museum Library at York, or the various Local Authority Library collections, but the war years did destroy much of worth. Where information cannot be traced, the best lines of investigation are the appropriate Railway Society or the Historical Model Railway Society.